P.S. Sundaram, who took his Master's degree in English Language and Literature from Madras University (1930) and, later, from Oxford (1934), had a long and distinguished career as a professor of English at Lahore, Cuttack, Bareilly and Jaipur. For a short stint in between, he was Member, Public Service Commission, Orissa. He is the author of two books on R.K. Narayan and has translated an impressive array of Tamil classics into English. In addition to the present work, he has translated into English selected poems of Subramania Bharati, Tiruvalluvar's *Kural*, Andal's *Thriuppavai* and *Nachchiyar Thriumozhi*.

N.S. Jagannathan holds a First Class Master's degree in English Language and Literature from Madras University. After a few years of college teaching and a stint in the Civil Service, he became a full-time journalist, working successively in senior positions in the *Hindustan Times*, the Statesman, the *Financial Express* and the *Indian Express*. He retired as Chief Editor, the *Indian Express*, in 1991.

KAMBA RAMAYANA

Translated by
P.S. Sundaram

Edited by
N.S. Jagannathan

PENGUIN BOOKS
An imprint of Penguin Random House

PENGUIN BOOKS

USA | Canada | UK | Ireland | Australia
New Zealand | India | South Africa | China | Singapore

Penguin Books is part of the Penguin Random House group of companies
whose addresses can be found at global.penguinrandomhouse.com

Published by Penguin Random House India Pvt. Ltd
4th Floor, Capital Tower 1, MG Road,
Gurugram 122 002, Haryana, India

Penguin
Random House
India

First published by Penguin Books India 2002

10 9 8 7 6 5

ISBN 9780143028154

Typeset in PalmSprings by SÜRYA, New Delhi

Printed at Manipal Technologies Limited, India

www.penguin.co.in

MIX
Paper from
responsible sources
FSC® C043100

CONTENTS

CONTENTS

PREFACE

My acquaintance with Professor P.S. Sundaram (1910–1998) began decades ago when, just out of the university, I appeared before the Orissa Public Service Commission for a job in the English department of the Ravenshaw College, Cuttack. As Professor of English in that college, he was the expert among members on the Selection Board. He put me through the wringer with a certain detached cruelty, dictated no doubt by his anxiety to ensure that his future colleague was not a dud. I got the job and thus began a life-long friendship that has been one of the great blessings of my life.

Ravenshaw College was founded in the nineteenth century and is one of the oldest and among the highly regarded Indian educational institutions. Being the only government college in Orissa at that time, it has been the alma mater of innumerable distinguished sons of Orissa and has had some of the finest teachers of the country. In my time, besides Sundaram, there was in the English department the genial V.V. John, an irrepressible wit who hid a profoundly serious mind behind an apparent air of levity and high spirits.

My own stay in Orissa was a brief one, lasting less than sixteen months. But during this short period, both John and Sundaram exercised a profound influence on me, not only in the shaping of my literary tastes but also in instilling in me the ineffable values of a civilized, intellectual freemasonry.

They were much older than me and I, had I lived in Cuttack instead of Madras during my college years, would have been their student. But in their attitude towards me, there was no trace of condescension or hierarchical snobbery so familiar in Indian academia. In the best traditions of Oxford where both were educated, they treated me, a callow youth though I was, as an equal. To my utter consternation, Sundaram made me teach postgraduate classes in Elizabethan literature of which I, then had only the haziest notions. I had to bone up on much dull and wearying stuff trying to live up to his, if not to my students, expectations.

In the years following, when my own wayward career did not permit me to be in daily contact with Sundaram, we were in regular touch, writing to each other and meeting from time to time. Such meetings were more frequent in his later years when he moved to Madras and always stimulating, our discussions ranging over a wide area. For example, Sundaram was fiercely Anglophile, the consequence of the stereotypes implanted in his mind by his deep love of English literature and the example of some of the great Englishmen that taught him in India and at Oxford. On the other hand, though I shared with him a love for English literature, I was bred on a different perception of the benefits of the Raj. This was one of the perennial themes of our heated exchanges, conducted on his side with exemplary urbanity and generosity to a much younger man.

Sundaram's academic credentials were of the highest. A brilliant student of Presidency College, Madras, he got a first class Master's degree in English literature in 1930. As was the almost settled routine of gifted students of the times with a Tamil Brahmin middle-class background, he went to England to join Oxford and, simultaneously, sit for the ICS examination. He tried twice to get into the ICS but on both occasions narrowly missed being chosen to the service, standing fourth or fifth in the ranking. (Unlike in post-Independence India, when selections for the services by competitive examination were a case of mass recruitment in hundreds, those were parsimonious times, with hardly more than five or six being chosen.) So, Sundaram returned to India in 1934 with a degree in English literature from Oxford and launched on a distinguished career as an academician in DAV College, Lahore, in 1934. He joined the Ravenshaw College, Cuttack, as professor in 1938 when he was barely twenty-eight, perhaps the youngest head of the English department at that time.

Unlike John and I, Sundaram stayed on in Orissa for over twenty years, giving the best years of his life to the state, as professor, principal and, from 1953, a Member of the Orissa Public Service Commission. By one of those quirky Constitutional provisions, when his term with the service commission ended in 1959, he could not go back to the government in any capacity. Then in his mid-forties, Sundaram was obliged to seek non-government employment elsewhere. He left Orissa to become Principal of the Bareilly College, and still later, of the Maharani's College, Jaipur, from where he retired in 1974.

It was only then that he could return to his first love—classical Tamil literature, which he had perforce put on the back-burner because of his teaching and administrative duties. A lifelong engagement with English literature had given him a profound understanding of all aspects of literary imagination. This enabled him to bring to the study of Tamil literary classics a mind uncluttered by the hang-up of traditional Tamil scholarship. As a result, he was able to apply to these works the categories of a wider and universal aesthetics and poetics.

His total command of both the Tamil and English idiom enabled him to embark on a translation enterprise, that, in the retrospect of his actual accomplishment, seems formidable, almost, rash, in its ambition. Obviously, it is a case of one thing leading to another, rather than a premeditated project. Starting with the modern poet, Subramania Bharati, Sundaram took on, successively, Tirukural of Tiruvalluvar and then the mystical poems of Andal and other Aazhwars in the Vaishnavite Bhakti tradition (the last two have been published by Penguin). The last years of his life were taken up with the translation into English verse of the whole corpus of some 12,000-odd verses of the renowned Tamil classic Kamba Ramayana. In itself an awesome feat, considering the hazards of the enterprise, it was, to use the language of the Ramayana, the crest-jewel of his brilliant career in translation.

N.S. Jagannathan

INTRODUCTION

I

THE GENE POOL[1] OF THE RAMAYANA MYTH

'Perhaps no work of world literature, secular in origin, has ever produced so profound an influence on the life and thought of a people as the Ramayana,' wrote A.A. Macdonell in the *Encyclopaedia of Religion and Ethics*. The unbroken continuity of the Ramayana myth to this day is indeed unique. There is no comparable visible or aural evidence of the presence of the Hellenic heritage in the daily lives of Europeans. Of the other, Hebraic, strand of their cultural inheritance, except among those highly educated in the humanities stream, it would be difficult to find anyone who remembers the details of the Old Testament. This is in stark contrast to the way the story of Rama has been burnt into the memory of every Hindu child, and the invisible presence of the myth in the daily lives of the people.

To choose a trivial example, unlike in the West where names may or may not have meanings, children in India, specially in the south, are named directly after Rama or Krishna. The latest issue of the Chennai telephone directory contains over 21,000 entries of Rama and its variants like

Ramswami and this does not include Raghava and its variants like Viraraghava. In addition, you have Lakshmana and Bharata in legion, and less frequently, Satrughna. Likewise, Sita and its variants are a favourite name, at least until recently, for the girl child. It is an indication of total and ultimate assimilation that these names are uttered without a consciousness of the epic story.

(This practice has an interesting reason. There is a famous story of Ajamila, a brahmin turned profligate, who had forgotten his piety and lived a dissolute life. On his deathbed, he called out 'Narayana', his favourite youngest son, for a last embrace, with no thought of the Primal God of that name. And yet, because he uttered the lord's name with his last breath, all his sins were cancelled and the messengers of Yama couldn't claim him for hell.)

Thus has the Rama story become part of the texture of the collective unconscious, half remembered, if at all, but within easy recall of the Indian people. And there is no lack of other reminders of the myths. There is, for example, the pervasive presence of temples in south India, some of which were built as early as the ninth century. Their titular deities are specifically named after Rama and worship is carried out in the prescribed manner to this day. The famous Ramaswami temple at Kumbakonam in the Thanjavur district of Tamil Nadu is one example among many. These towering temples dominating the locale are a constant reminder of Rama, even if you did not visit them. Temple-associated sacred art has produced magnificent paintings of the Rama story (as on the walls of the Ramaswami temple, already mentioned) and bronze sculptures such as the 'Panaiyur Rama' (in the Chennai museum) and others in actual worship at Vaduvur and Tillaivalakam in the Thanjavur district.

Historically, the temple culture grew as part of the Bhakti cult of the personalized God that had its origins in south India and spread northwards in the post-upanishadic period of Hinduism. Vaishnavaite and Saivaite mystics in the centuries after Christ were precursors of the formalized Bhakti element in Hinduism. Vishnu and Siva, until then minor gods in the vedic pantheon, overshadowed other gods like Indra and Agni and attained, gradually, the status of members of the primordial Trinity of Brahma, Vishnu and Siva. Of the three, Brahma was in course of time subsumed by Vishnu and became marginalized. (There are only a few temples for him, one in Ajmer in Rajasthan, and a minor shrine in Tamil Nadu.) It is true that latter-day popular religion had myriad gods and goddesses, but they are not the vedic ones and they derive their authority from their association, one way or another, with Vishnu and Siva.

The emergence of the Bhakti cult, of a mystical personal love of incarnate God, decisively transformed the Hindu faith. It not only demoted the earlier pluralistic pantheon of gods but also radically modified the late vedic, upanishadic philosophic abstraction of the Brahman or the formless Primal God. This was facilitated by the emergence of the concept of the avatar ('coming down'), memorably and authoritatively expressed in the fourth chapter of the *Bhagavad Gita*: 'Whenever Dharma becomes decadent, I incarnate myself to destroy unrighteousness triumphant.'[2]

The ten incarnations of Vishnu form an evolutionary sequence from fish to tortoise to boar to man-lion to dwarf to a fully developed anthropomorphic god like Rama, the sixth incarnation, followed by Krishna, and Kalki (yet to come) who will destroy the universe before the birth of a new cycle of creation. (A fanciful identification of this event by some is the nuclear holocaust to come.)

Arising out of this neo-Hinduism, based on a personal God, and the immense output of devotional literature and associated new theology, there came into being a wider and popular methodology of public discourse that persists to this day. An important aspect of the Bhakti movement was its popular base and egalitarian thrust which considerably eroded the harsher aspects of the caste hierarchy. God became accessible to all by the passionate devotional poetry in the vernacular of inspired mystics, some of whom belonged to the lesser castes, including the untouchable ones. In the south, the tradition of public discourse or *pravachanam* (expounding) had two streams. One was a vehicle of theological disputation and the other of popularization, at least from the days when the Bhakti cult had crystallized into the Srivaishnava doctrine of *prapatti* or total surrender to God. Great commentators like Peria Vachchan Pillai, Manavala Mamuni, Vedanta Desika and their disciples with different sectarian and doctrinal positions regularly used the Ramayana—episodes from it rather than the whole of it—in their, often acrimonious, disputations. The Tenkalai (southern school) and the Vadakalai (northern school) of Ramanuja's theological view of vishistadvaita or 'modified monism' in opposition to Sankara's advaita or 'absolute monism' were often locked in arguments over the subtle nuances of their common faith.

For example, a crucial doctrinal difference between the two was on the concept of *prapatti* or absolute surrender to God mentioned earlier and the nature of 'grace'. If one simplifies it greatly, the Tenkalai doctrine of grace was somewhat similar to the Calvinist concept of 'efficacious grace' of God but without the implication of predestination. God's grace 'bloweth as it pleases' regardless of just deserts: even sinners may be blessed with it, while the virtuous may not. The Vadakalais dispute the randomness of such arbitrary bestowal of grace and insist on deserving it.[3] In these controversies, episodes from the Ramayana, such as that of Bharata ruling with Rama's sandals as a surrogate for Rama's sovereignty, Rama's friendship with Sugriva, Vibhishana's taking refuge with Rama, were subjected to ingenious interpretations in terms of their particular doctrines on the subject.

The second and popular version of the Ramayana discourse is what has come to be known as the Kalakshepam, or Harikatha (the latter an importation from Maharashtra into Tamil Nadu in the late eighteenth century). It was a form of musical discourse, giving ample scope for deconstruction of the Rama legend, in which the several written and oral versions were freely retold and reinterpreted as suited the local value system and body of beliefs. Literacy being low and texts limited in number in palm leaf and its substitutes in pre-print days, the oral tradition was strong. The unlettered had access to the Rama legend only through recitation and listening to kathakars (storytellers). It was a very effective form of adult liberal education. Strong mnemonic traditions were built this way and the Ramayana was quietly internalized by the bulk of the population, with music and narrative skills combining to hold hundreds of listeners in thrall in temple yards and elsewhere. The tradition has been so strongly entrenched in people's consciousness that it has become a part of proverbial folk wisdom. This is tellingly exemplified in the famous Tamil quip about the ignorance of the man who, having heard the Ramayana story all night, asked the next morning whether Rama was Sita's uncle.

Equally important in imprinting the Rama consciousness in the psyche of the people was the role of classical Carnatic music, where episodes from the Ramayana formed a major verbal component of the concerts that are an integral part of the cultural life of elitist Tamils. The moving compositions of Saint Tyagaraja (circa late eighteenth-nineteenth century), the most eminent of Carnatic music composers, draw freely from Ramayana episodes such as, for a random example, Rama's encounter with the tribal woman, Sabari. In addition, they breathe an impassioned personal intimacy with Rama.[4]

Another facet of the pervasive presence of Rama and the Ramayana in the daily life of south Indians is associated with their domesticities and the ambience of their homes. Lithographic prints of the original paintings of the royal painter Ravi Varma on Ramayana themes and other reproductions of kitsch art on the same subject are part of puja rooms and even the more secular space of the living room walls. The intimacy of popular art with Ramayana is also seen in the famous Tanjore paintings with their gemstone-set picturization of Ramayana themes, most notably of the Pattaabhishekam (coronation) of Rama after his triumphant return from exile.

A different aspect of the internalization of the Ramayana in the domestic life of the people in south India is to be seen in the routine teaching of music to girls from middle-class homes. Till about a few decades ago, households used to resound, morning and evening, with the music teacher drilling young girls into the elements of Carnatic music, largely with Tyagaraja's compositions in praise of Rama. Some of this music rubbed off aurally on boys (who were themselves not formally taught music) and formed their musical taste—and Rama consciousness—that they carried well into their adulthood.

The amazing thing about the Ramayana tradition is that unlike certain other aspects of Hinduism, with their distinctively elitist—both intellectual and caste-wise—elements, the Ramayana was the heritage of the whole people, being part of the daily life of the rich and the poor, the high and low castes. This included the untouchables, a section among them tracing their ancestry to Valmiki himself. Another sect in the Chattisgarh region of central India self-consciously call themselves Ramnamis and use as their basic text a highly selective version of Tulsidas's *Ramcharitamanas*.[5]

These and other cultural artefacts and practices, past and present, testify to the total assimilation of mainstream Ramayana into the lives of Indians. In addition, there are folk tellings of the Ramayana story in every conceivable form, from puppetry to oral versions in all Indian languages, street theatre, like the Ramlila of the north and Therukuttu (street drama) in the Tamil country. Many of these are improvisatory efforts with extrapolation of local belief structures.

Though not exactly subversive of the basic assumptions of the received form of the storyline, many of them strongly question individual acts of Rama. The 'Sitayana' versions of the story told from the point of view of Sita, prevalent in Karnataka and Andhra Pradesh, are good examples. There are others in which characters and incidents receive treatment that sound somewhat bizarre to modern ears. Thus, in a well-known essay,[6] A.K. Ramanujan (AKR) quotes a folk narrative in which Sita is not only Ravana's daughter born to Mandodhari—a common enough telling—but to a pregnant

Ravana himself! She was born through his nose when he sneezed! Psychoanalytical ardour will no doubt have a field day with such versions. Less fantastically, there are Ramayana texts and oral tellings in which it is Sita or Lakshmana who kills Ravana.

II

RAMAYANA IN LITERATURE

Literary manifestations of the unbroken Rama consciousness discussed above have been equally prolific. As Tulsidas said, *'Ramakatha kai miti jaga nahi'*—'It is impossible to keep count of the Ramakathas in this world.'[7] In the essay mentioned earlier, AKR asks the question 'How many Ramayanas?' and quotes a scholar's answer of 300. (He also mentions a Kannada professor's estimate of a 1,000 versions, which perhaps includes non-literary ones.) He lists eleven Indian languages (with the curious omission of Malayalam in which was written the great sixteenth century classic *Adhyatma Ramayana*, a transcreation of the Sanskrit work of the same name by the great Tuncattu Ezhutttachan) and ten south and south east Asian languages (Annamese, Balinese, Cambodian, Chinese, Javanese, Khotanese Laotian, Malaysian, Sinhalese, Thai and Tibetan). Of *Valmiki Ramayana* itself, there are several versions, the three best known extant ones being the northern, eastern and southern 'recensions' with significant differences in the storyline.

Though Valmiki is traditionally called the Aadi Kavi or the first poet and his Ramayana, the Adi Kavya, or the first epic, it is certainly not the first version of the Ramayana. The very exordium to the epic makes this clear when it memorably sets out the occasion for its being written. Valmiki asks the all-knowing, peripatetic sage Narada the question: 'Who in this present world is the ideal man (Purushotama), endowed with all the virtues of character and heroism, knows Dharma, and is truthful and steadfast in virtue?'[8] In reply, Narada gives a terse conspectus of the whole Ramayana story in a hundred-odd verses. Brooding on it, Valmiki goes for his ablutions when he sees a hunter kill with an arrow one of two birds in the act of love. The sorrow of the surviving bird releases Valmiki's fount of compassion (*karuna*). It is in this mood of empathetic spontaneity that he sets out to tell the story of Rama as told to him by Narada. This is a high point in the epic and has formed the foundation of Sanskrit aesthetic theory to come.

In the following centuries, there have been many Ramayanas in Sanskrit. The Mahabharata itself has several references to Ramayana episodes and characters and a whole subsection in twenty chapters entitled 'Ramopakhyana' in its third book, the 'Vana Parva'. There are then the *Adhyatma Ramayana* and *Adbuta Ramayana* (in which, as in some Jain and south east Asian versions, Sita is the daughter of Ravana) and many more, most of which have been lost in the mists of time.

Simultaneously, self-consciously literary versions of the myth appeared in vernacular languages. Some of these, like Kamban's in Tamil, openly acknowledge Valmiki as their inspiration and model. But they are far from translations or even transcreations, being independent works drawing on the immemorial myth from different sources and shot through with the religious, philosophical, theological and literary influences of their time and regional culture. The most durable of these vernacular Ramayanas with more than a local spread are two: *Ramcharitamanas* of Tulsidas (circa sixteenth century) in Avadhi Hindi, and *Iramavataram* in Tamil by Kamban (circa twelfth century).

III

DECONSTRUCTING RAMAYANA

AKR felicitously calls these versions of the Ramayana in the innumerable languages of India and Greater India of one time 'crystallisations from an endemic pool of signifiers', comparable to a gene pool from which different patterns of living beings are randomly arranged. Another analogy used in this connection is that of the kaleidoscope, in which the same bits of glasses rearrange themselves into coherent patterns, all of them pleasing. Every telling draws from the millennia-old, inchoate Rama consciousness, modified by successive cultural accretions and acculturations and the evolving teleological, eschatological and theological doctrines and even political ideology of the times. They are very much a product of their times. For example, *Kamba Ramayana* is a product of the second wind of Chola splendour with imperialist attributes unlike Valmiki's, which was, hazarding a guess, one of the infancy of Indian society.

I would myself call these different versions 'readings', preferring it to AKR's 'tellings', because it is not only authors who create their own Ramayanas. Every reader of every Ramayana creates his own Ramayana by 'deconstructing' what he reads. His reading is autonomous and is as valid as those of the original authors who have themselves deconstructed the original myth both in its totality and in particular episodes, characters and relationships. In other words, the 300-odd tellings of the Ramayana in literature and in entrenched folk traditions are nothing but deconstructions of the original myth and earlier texts and all of them are equally legitimate.

Such deconstructions include radical 'oppositional readings', as Paula Richman[9] calls them. In these readings, the assumptions of the mainstream versions are altered, modified, or even stood on their heads. Thus, in some of the Jain versions, Ravana's character is deliberately given an altogether different salience. At a trivial level, it is a fussy correction of perceived absurdities such as Ravana's ten heads. One Jain text gives an ingenious explanation: the abnormal nine are merely the reflection of the real head by the nine gems in a necklace put around infant Ravana by a loving mother.

But there are other substantive variations. For example, neither in Valmiki nor in Kamban is Ravana ever less than a heroic figure. Nevertheless, despite his acknowledged grandeur and piety, he is an evil man, a tyrant and an oppressor and given to all vices. But in the Jain versions mentioned, he is more of a tragic hero with a fatal flaw, his one transgression being his preordained passion for Sita. As AKR, among others, has noted, some of these versions scoff at the 'mainstream' characterization as absurd and unreal. He quotes one such text that begins with pouring scorn on the descriptions of the rakshasas as bloodthirsty cannibals and, in the process, makes Ravana a vegetarian. It makes fun of the improbability of monkeys vanquishing the rakshasas, or Kumbhakarna sleeping through torturous violence on his person in attempts to wake him. 'All this looks fantastic and extreme. They are lies and contrary to reason.' Quoting again from a Jain text, AKR says, 'I will tell you what Jain wise men say. Ravana is not a demon. He is not a cannibal and a flesh eater. Wrong thinking poetasters tell these lies.' Apart from these major differences in characterization, there are minor ones in some readings. Among them is making Hanuman not a celibate but 'quite a lady's man'.

Another notable instance, nearer our times, of subversive deconstruction of the mainstream Ramayana narrative is the highly regarded epic poem in blank verse by Michael Madhusudan Dutt, titled *Meghnadavadha Kavya*, written in Bengali in the mid-nineteenth century. It is a counter-reading of great power and beauty, avowedly sympathetic to Indrajit (also known as Meghnad) and his father Ravana and their hedonistic pursuit of power and love pitted against the crabbed self-righteousness of Rama[10]. Dutt made no secret of his unorthodox preferences, the result of his anglicized revolt against the dominant puritanism of the Bengali ethos of the times. About the time he was writing the poem, he wrote (in English) to a friend, 'People here grumble that the sympathy of the poet in Meghnad is with the rakshasa. And that is the real truth. I despise Rama and his rabble, but the idea of Ravan elevates and kindles my imagination. He was a grand fellow.'

But the remarkable thing about this work is that the received storyline is intact, with none of the incidents distorted. The subversion of the received version is achieved by an ingenious artistic legerdemain. In describing the incidents in the story and the actions of the characters, Madhusudan employs elaborate Homeric similes embodying the imagery of other Indian myths like that of Krishna and the gopis with an altogether different tonal and other reverberation. Thus, unlike Milton, who unconsciously made Satan the hero of *Paradise Lost*, Dutt deliberately enthroned Meghnad and Ravana as heroes in place of Rama. It is a tour de force of conscious artistry that has come off.

Thus, the Ramayana story has been deconstructed in written and spoken word, in works of literature and in the almost daily oral exposition by pandits and kathakars, in innumerable plays, folk-theatre and cinema, and most recently, on television. A notable instance of the last was Ramanand Sagar's immensely popular Hindi serial on Doordarshan during 1987 and the years following.

The cultural and political implications of this version troubled the eminent historian Romila Thapar sufficiently for her to come out with an alarmist newspaper piece about the homogenizing threat it posed to the plurality of the Ramayana tellings. One is not quite able to make out whether it was the cultural threat posed by television as the idiot box with its profound subliminal impact on the psyche of the viewer that troubled her, or the specific orientation of that particular television narrative.

In all candour, the serial was a kitsch affair, hybridized from Valmiki, Tulsi and other extant versions. It was more remarkable for its television gimmickry as spectacle than for its thematic impact. Therefore, it seems somewhat far-fetched to burden a purely commercial venture cashing in on popular taste with a hidden ideological 'Hindutva' agenda. In any case, whatever else the serial was trying to do, it was not trying to homogenize the plurality of Ramayana tellings. This certainly was not its effect. It is not very different from any of the received versions of the Ramayana, including the Tamil *Kamba Ramayana*. Its thrust and impact would be no greater than the widely prevalent practice of daily pietistic recitation from *Tulsi Ramayana* or its opposite numbers in other languages of the country, which are equally 'Hindu-centric'. If these and the *Kamba Ramayana* are universally considered as evidence of the *plurality* and not the homogeneity of the Ramayana myth in Indian life, Sagar's effort should also be viewed as yet another deconstruction, adding to the plurality of the Ramayana.

A passing mention of some deconstructive efforts by contemporary Ramayana scholars may be in order. The Sahitya Akademi held a five-day seminar in December 1975, on the 'Ramayana Tradition in Asia'[11]. That doyen of Ramayana studies, the late Dr V. Raghavan, published with an introduction extremely informative papers presented on the occasion. This is an invaluable conspectus of the Asia-wide deconstructions of the Ramayana narrative over the centuries. More recently, the Oxford University Press brought out a volume of essays titled *Many Ramayanas*, edited by Paula Richman, covering much the same ground, but with a heavy overlay of sociological preoccupations and extrapolations of modern concerns, thus constituting deconstructions of historical deconstructions. For example, in an essay in this volume by Kathleen M. Erndl[12] on 'The Mutilation of Surpanakha', the view is hazarded that (in Richman's words) Surpanakha is an independent spirit 'who moves about the forest, independent of a male protector and boldly articulates her passionate feelings, as a kind of alter ego of Sita, often considered the model of the chaste and submissive wife'. By definition, the legitimacy of such unorthodox deconstructive efforts cannot be questioned. It only goes to prove that every one writes his or her own Ramayana.

IV

KAMBA RAMAYANA

Biographical information about Kamban is meagre, inferential and marred by hagiological distortions. His period itself is a matter of perennial controversy unsettled to this day. Different scholars put this down as anything between ninth and twelfth century. Conscientious research by S. Vyapuri Pillai, perhaps the most objective of twentieth century Tamil scholars after U.V. Swaminatha Iyer, assigns Kamban to the late twelfth century, the height of the later Chola power.[13] Tradition makes him the son of a temple drummer with exceptional opportunities for self-education in Tamil and Sanskrit classics. There is more solid evidence for the fact that he was a friend and protégé of one Sadayappan of Vennainallur in the Thanjavur district of Tamil Nadu, considered with good reason the cradle of Tamil art and culture from immemorial times. Sadayappan was a member of the upper caste of Vellallas, whose main vocation was agriculture. Apart from about ten references in *Kamba Ramayana* itself, there is independent evidence for his wealth, influence at the Chola court, scholarly interests, and above all, his munificence, particularly for artistic endeavours, which earned for him the honorific of Vallal (bestower).

There is ample internal evidence of Kamban's wide reading and total assimilation of all the classics in Sanskrit and Tamil available in his time and his complete mastery of the philosophical and aesthetic theories, both Sanskrit and Tamil, of his time. Of the Ramayana lore, he was a total master, having, as he himself puts it in his exordium, 'lapped up like a cat the milky ocean of Rama's lay'. He mentions three earlier works as extant in his time, of which he specifically chooses for his source Valmiki, 'the earliest master.' But Valmiki was only his source, not a text for translation. As we shall see, there are significant differences between the two in tone, texture, underlying philosophical and aesthetic assumptions and revealing departures in the storyline and salience of characterization.

Between the putative times of Valmiki and Kamban's slightly more authenticated times, there had occurred profound alterations in the dominant Weltanschauung of the Indian people. The major changes, as already mentioned, are four: the rise, specially in the south, of the Bhakti cult with its emphasis on a personal God; associated with it, the doctrine of the avatar or incarnation, of which Rama was one; the temple culture of iconization of these incarnate gods and their worship according to elaborately worked out ritual routines; and the increasing presence of God-intoxicated mystic-poets singing ecstatically about their chosen personal deities and their exploits. In the south, there were two streams of such poet-saints, one of Vaishnavite Aazhwars[12] (the 'immersed'— in God, by implication) and the other of Saivite Nayanmars, traditionally sixty-three in number, singing the praise of the Tiruvilaiyadalkal (sports) of Siva.

Equally important are the literary antecedents of *Kamba Ramayana*. The major Sanskrit ones have already been mentioned, except for Kalidasa's *Raghuvamsa*, the famous narrative poem of nineteen cantos, telling the story of the Raghu dynasty to which Rama belonged thrice removed, being the great-grandson of Raghu. Cantos nine to fifteen tell the story of the Ramayana. It is possible that Kalidasa was one of the two poets mentioned alongside Valmiki by Kamban in his exordium. There is also some evidence of his acquaintance with Kalidasa's work. For example, in a significant departure from the Valmiki version of the Ahalya episode, Kamban makes the accursed Ahalya a stone that comes to life at the touch of Rama's feet. *Raghuvamsa* too has this version. It is not unlikely that Kamban followed Kalidasa.

(However, it is interesting that the southern recension of the *Valmiki Ramayana*, probably post-Kamban, has the Ahalya-turned-stone motif, though the definitive Baroda edition of *Valmiki Ramayana* has the northern version. This may be an instance of 'counter-influence' analogous to 'back-formation' in philology.[14] Interestingly, the same version is to be found in the Thai Ramayana, *Ramakien*, which shows other indications of the influence of the Tamil Ramayana on it. For example, the names of some of the characters in the Thai Ramayana are taken from Kamban, such as Kalaikottu instead of Valmiki's Rsyasrnga.)

Kamba Ramayana's Tamil literary antecedents are equally impressive. Ramayana allusions are to be encountered even in the earliest extant Tamil poetry of the Sangam age, flexibly dated as between first century bc and the fourth century ad. Among such works are *Ettu Thokai* (eight anthologies), *Pattu paattu* (ten poems), the famous epic tragedy *Silapadikaram*, and the mystic poems of Vaishnavaite and Saivaite saints.

One of the verses in *Pura Nanuru*, a collection of heroic poems of war and valour of the Sangam age, refers to the monkeys finding the jewels thrown away by Sita, while she was being abducted; being unfamiliar with such adornments, they try them on, but at the wrong places on their persons. Another verse in *Aka Nanuru*, a collection of love poems, makes a mention of Rama holding a council of his advisers before invading Lanka. One of the celebrated poets of the Sangam age is named Valmiki. A late Sangam collection, *Pari Padaal*, gives a terse summary of the Ahalya story ('This is Indra, the Cat/ She is Ahalya/ He is Gautama, who cursed her to become a stone'). In the subsequent centuries, there are several references to this episode, even some tellings in Tamil, including some by Jains.[15]

In addition, throughout this period, there were the hymns of the twelve Aazhwars (circa seventh–eighth century) already mentioned. These were later compendiously collected by Nadamuni, (circa ninth century) under the title Naalayira Divya Prabandam (4,000 sacred hymns).[16] They have innumerable references to the Ramayana story and characters. Periazhwar, traditionally listed first among the twelve, has a set of ten verses dealing with Hanuman convincing Sita in captivity that he was indeed Rama's messenger. Another Aazhwar, Kulasekhara, a prince turned saint, has a lovely lullaby for the child Rama as sung by Kausalya; Dasaratha's lament when Rama left Ayodhya for the forest; and a terse summary of the whole story in ten verses. Nammalwar, considered the most philosophical of the twelve, has two verses that run like this in Sriram Bharati's translation:

> In the blessed Ayodhya, the land created by Brahma—
> down to the meanest grass and insect without
> exception, he gives an exalted place to all the sentient
> and insentient. So would any scholar study about a
> king other than Rama?

For the sake of humanity, Narayana took birth and walked the earth, suffering countless miseries, then destroyed the plague of Rakshasas. He gave the kingdom to Vibhishana and liberation to all. Knowing this, would mortals be devotees of anyone else?[17]

This continuity of the Rama story that found its fullest expression in Kamban, was but part of the larger intellectual and imaginative heritage of the Tamils which, incidentally, included Krishna and Siva consciousness. This continuity was not only a pietistic phenomenon but had its philosophical, theological, cultural and literary evolutionary progression.

Kamban's literary heritage is equally impressive The Tamils had a literary tradition wholly independent of the Sanskritic one of the north. It had its own aesthetics, poetics and grammar derived from the literary practice of the earliest times, the famous Sangam literature (circa 200 BC to 200 AD). The earliest and the most outstanding of extant Tamil rhetoricians was the author of *Tholkappiyum*, a work as remarkable as the Sanskrit grammar of Panini (probably a contemporary). It is a work of comprehensive grammar in three parts on 'ezhuttu' (phonology), 'chol' (word or syntax) and 'porul' (meaning or poetics). *Tholkappiyum* is a tour de force of taxonomical grammar, giving, for example, thirty-four elements that go into the making of a poem, both form and content. On form and structure, it provides detailed prosodic accounts of about six broad metrical forms and its variations. Content-wise, *Tholkappiyum* mentions two broad categories—'aham' dealing with love and 'puram' (human concerns other than love, such as war and worldly affairs). In 'aham' poetry, there is a rigorous schema of locales with their unique identifying flower, appropriate denizens and activity, kinds of love to be written about, kinds of heroes and heroines. (These last could not be identified by personal names but only generically as he or she, implying universality for the emotions and predicaments.)

There are five such locales (*tinais*)—*mullai* (jungle), *kurinchi* (hill tracks), *marutham* (cultivated land), *neytal* (sandy coastal lands), and *paalai* (arid or desert region). There are two kinds of love—secret or illicit ('kalavu') and married and chaste love ('karpu'). Illicit love is again subdivided into 'kamapunarchi' (first union impelled by uncontrolled libido), 'ida punarchi' (second and later union at the same place, love brought about or facilitated by a male or a female friend and so on). Such love is associated with the hilly region. 'Oodal' (sulking and contrariness) is common to both kinds of love. Married love is associated with stable agricultural society (*marutham*). *Paalai* or the arid region is appropriate for love in separation, patience, endurance and lamentation. There are twelve character types of speakers and ten types of listeners. There are eight kinds of emotional states—laughter, weeping, disgust, wonder, fear, pride, anger and joy. This classification resembles but is not identical with the nine rasas (distilled emotions) of Sanskrit poetics. Most of these poems are in the form of dramatic monologues or dialogues with the generic characters of 'talaivan' and 'talaimakal' (hero and heroine) talking to each other or to a sympathetic friend ('paankan', if male, 'tozhi', if female) or foster mother ('chevili').[18] Nothing could be more modern than these terse love poems told with the utmost economy of words and controlled emotion without any frills whatsoever. They were triumphs of understatement, a virtue that later Tamil poetry (including Kamban's) lost completely.

Kamban was heir to this indigenous aesthetic frame as modified by practice and precept during the subsequent centuries before him. By the time he arrived on the scene, the simple poetry of a simple society of isolated communities (already minimally affected by importations of ideas from elsewhere, including the Sanskritic ones from the north) had transformed itself gradually into an elaborate and ornate poetry of the kavyas in the grand manner. Long poems in the epic manner had succeeded the simpler and shorter lyrics of the Sangam age and of the devotional poetry of the Aazhwars. The great five kavya classics of *Silapadikaram, Manimekali, Jivaka Chintamani Valaiyapati, Kundalalkesi,* (of which only the first three are extant), written by poets of Jain and Buddhist persuasion and *Tirukural* (the famous set of 1,330 gnomic couplets tersely embodying an ethical matrix of enduring relevance) had transformed the Tamil literary scene.

This transition was parallel to developments in the political and societal environment, such as the emergence of great kings and emperors like the Pallavas and the Cholas, some of them with imperialistic and expansionist ambitions. In philosophy and religious theology, as already noted, the Bhakti cult had intervened with all the associated changes in popular religion. Buddhist and Jain ideas too had penetrated into the Tamil country and were combatively engaged with mainstream Hinduism (modified by the Bhakti cult). These had opposing royal patronage, often differing from king to king in the same dynasty. The Jains and the Buddhists were at times accorded royal patronage, and at other times were persecuted. Public debates by adherents of different faiths over the relative superiority of their beliefs were common, as is evident in the devotional hymns of the Aazhwars and Naayanmars. Kamban himself has a simile referring to a naked sect preaching non-violence. In poetry, the Aazhwars were the transitional bridge. There is evidence of the Aazhwars adopting the conventions of the 'aham' poetry. Kamban himself refers to and indeed uses the 'tinai' typology in his descriptive passages.

V

KAMBAN AND VALMIKI

The Ramayana is above all a great human story of love and war, of the constant conflict between good and evil that has been the very stuff of heroic legends in all literatures. The correspondence extends to parallelisms in the storyline and characterization. Ramayana has its thematic analogue in Iliad in the abduction of Helen, wife of Menelaus, by Paris, son of Priam, that resulted in the great war between the Achaean Greeks and the Trojans. Rama's wanderings in search of Sita have their counterpart in the wanderings of Odeysseus, with wife Penelope, chaste and loyal and besieged by suitors, waiting patiently for his return, as Sita waits for Rama in Lanka. There is yet another parallel in the old English poem 'Beowulf', itself based on Norse myths, where the eponymous hero fights Grendel and his mother, both incarnations of evil. Such heroic poetry is to be found in all cultures and literatures and, in that sense, Ramayana is yet another version of the archetype.

The differences between the Ramayanas of Valmiki and Kamban in tone, texture, characterization, in versions of particular episodes and poetical attributes, are striking. Valmiki's work, written nearer the infancy of the Indian society, is in simple and limpid Sanskrit, bare and austere without any verbal or figurative artifices such as those found in latter-day Sanskrit or Kamban's. poetry. Valmiki has the same metrical structure throughout (except for the ending of individual cantos). Kamban, on the other hand, has around 'ninety variations of three kinds of Tamil poetic metres, namely *kali, viruttam* and *turai*'[19] He delights in verbal wit, elaborate Homeric similes and involved poetical conceits, often reminiscent of the English metaphysical poets. His is the grand manner of leisurely narration, lovingly lingering over particular episodes. These are marked by a certain descriptive panache and allusiveness and by a conscious recall of other legends and stories—all of which add to the reading pleasure of the cognoscenti. He has, what Bernard Shaw grudgingly conceded as Shakespeare's only gift— an amazing command over words. Kamban is also easily seduced, as Johnson said Shakespeare was, by 'the fatal Cleopatra of the pun, for which he would willingly lose an empire'. His fertility of invention and exuberance and gusto in narration are in sharp contrast to Valmiki's austere verbal economy.

In characterization, Kamban's portraitures, specially of the principals, are on the grand scale, again in sharp contrast to Valmiki's simplicity and austerity. This is partly because of the changes in poetical fashions, the conventions of heroic epic having become well established by the time Kamban came on the scene. More importantly—and this is a basic distinction between him and Valmiki from which all else flows—Rama was no longer, as he was in Valmiki, just a man, though the best among the species—Purushotama. He has, in fact, become God.

Except for the reference in the first canto of 'Balakanda' to the divine descent of Vishnu, to destroy the rakshasas at the request of Brahma on behalf of the gods, Rama in Valmiki is rarely, if at all, treated as God. As V.V.S. Iyer,[20] whose admiration for Kamban is hardly this side of idolatry, has noted (without irony), in *Kamba Ramayana*, 'If he (Rama) runs after the golden deer, he sets forward the foot that measured the three worlds. Every step that Rama takes is that of the foot that measured the three worlds.' We are hardly ever permitted to forget the fact of 'Rama being Vishnu, Sita being his consort Lakshmi and Lakshmana being his bed Adisesha in human form.' If Rama and Sita love each other at first sight (there is no such incident in Valmiki), 'is it not the meeting again of those that were together in the Ocean of Milk and were separated for a while?'

In addition, details of characterization in various contexts emphasize the exceptionally heroic nature of the major characters, particularly Rama. Except for his lamentations (very much in the epic convention of *pralapa*) for the abducted Sita and the fatally hurt Lakshmana on the battlefield, Rama is never anything less than perfect. Unlike in Valmiki, Kamban's Rama is the *stithapragnya* or the steadfast one. He is not elated when he is offered the crown by Dasaratha or depressed when Kaikeyi tells him the bad news about the cancelled coronation and his exile. In Valmiki, Rama rejoices at the king's offer of the crown and shares his joy ecstatically with Lakshmana.

In Kamban, he just accepts it as a duty and shows no emotion, one way or another. There is not a single occasion in Kamban in which Rama shows any resentment towards Kaikeyi for what she did to him. On the contrary, he takes special care to make Rama most solicitous about containing the resentment of others, particularly Lakshmana's and

Bharata's, towards her. On the other hand, Valmiki makes Rama tell Lakshmana, after Sita has been carried away, the following: 'When I am dead for the sake of Sita, and thou art gone, would not Kaikeyi's heart be full of joy? And would not Kausalya, the mother bereaved of her son, have to wait on Kaikeyi, who has her son living and who has everything he desires in the world?'

Rama's godhood is strewn throughout Kamban not only as casual allusions, salience of characterization or adjectival honorifics, but by special assertions in particular episodes, such as Sita's wedding, Ahalya's emancipation and, most importantly, in the harrowing ordeal by fire imposed by Rama on Sita to prove her chastity after his victory over Ravana.

But there is an important point in this connection that should be noted. *Though the godhood of Rama is pervasively present in Kamban, Rama himself is unconscious of the fact and never makes any reference to it*. All such references are by other characters and the author. There is thus a 'conspiratorial' relationship—a familiar enough situation in literature—between the reader and the author, with both having knowledge of the hero's history or nature that he himself does not possess. This ignorance of Rama is not just a matter of inference but the subject matter of the important episode of the *agni pariksha* (ordeal by fire) of Sita. After the (happy) conclusion of that harrowing episode in which Rama had shown himself as all too human and a surrogate of Othello as a jealous husband, he is given a stern lecture by Brahma telling him who he and Sita were.

There are many such departures from Valmiki in Kamban which make Kamban's Ramayana sui generis, despite his acknowledged indebtedness to the master. A few of them are, the Surpanakha episode, the encounter on the battlefield between Vibhishana and Kumbhakarna, the Ahalya episode, Sita's wedding, and so on. In Valmiki, true to his general tenor of 'realism', Surpanakha appears as she is in her ugly rakshasi form whereas in Kamban (and Tulsi) she transforms herself into a beauty, making Rama uncharacteristically susceptible to female beauty other than Sita's. The Vibhishana-Kumbhakarna encounter on the battlefield in which the younger brother unavailingly tries to make the elder change sides is entirely Kamban's invention and typical of his sense of drama. It is one of the finest passages in Kamban. While the two love each other dearly, their notions of ethical conduct and loyalty are totally different. They agree that Ravana's conduct was inexcusable, but while Kumbhakarna (unlike Indrajit in his encounter with Vibhishana on the battlefield), approves of Vibhishana going over to Rama, he himself firmly refuses to desert Ravana at his hour of peril. In these exchanges, Kumbhakarna has certainly the better of the argument.

In the telling of the Ahalya episode, there are two significant variations. First, in Valmiki, Ahalya knows from the beginning that it was Indra who was seducing her and she more than willingly acquiesces in it. This is in consonance with Valmiki's generally more 'earthy' tone and approach to his characters. In Kamban, on the other hand, Ahalya's guilty knowledge of the forbidden pleasure occurs only half way through after Indra deceives her in Gautama's form. But inebriated with unaccustomed pleasure, she does not protest and cease. This is a halfway house towards later deconstructions, particularly by squeamish kathakars, who make Ahalya totally innocent of Indra's deception.

The second variation has already been briefly mentioned. In Valmiki, the enraged Gautama curses sneaking Indra with the loss of his testicles (which the gods replace with those of a ram). Then, it is the turn of Ahalya to be condemned to an agonizing invisible life for a thousand years living on air, and with ash as her bed, until Rama's arrival makes her pure again and allows her to resume her former self.[21] In Kamban, terrified Indra slinks away like a cat and is cursed to be covered with a thousand vaginas (bowdlerized in later tellings to a thousand eyes). Then, for her uncontrolled libido, Ahalya is cursed to become an unfeeling stone. On her pleading (absent in Valmiki), he mitigates the curse, saying that she will become her former self, when Rama, 'with garlands humming with bees, comes and the dust of his feet falls on her'. (As already mentioned, this version is to be found in other tellings, including the southern recension of *Valmiki Ramayana*, *Raghuvamsa* and the Thai Ramayana, probably influenced by Kamban, and later in *Ramcharitamanas*.) Interestingly, the 'stone-curse motif' provides Kamban the occasion for a memorable utterance by Viswamitra. Recalling Rama's earlier killing of Tataka, he says, 'I then saw the "colour" (virtue) of your hand, and now I see the hue of your feet.'

In this, as in many other things, Kamban is midway in the progressive deification of Rama, from the merely exalted human hero he was in Valmiki, to God-incarnate. By the time Tulsidas came to write his *Manas* in the sixteenth century, the transformation was complete. Any suggestion of defects of character in Rama, Sita or Lakshmana was unacceptable. Thus, the all too human responses to Lakshmana (which makes his basic idealism shine forth all the brighter), that one finds in Valmiki and Kamban, are muted or even absent. Thus, *Tulsi Ramayana* omits Lakshmana's outburst against his father when he hears of Rama's banishment. Other omissions include Sita's snide remarks about his intentions when he shows some reluctance to go in search of Rama (in Valmiki, more offensive than in Kamban) and Rama's unconvincing justification of his dubious conduct in killing Vali from a hidden place. (Rama says that Vali is only a monkey and a beast and therefore fair game for human hunters!)

Even more significant of the changing mores of Indian society over the centuries is the way details of Ravana's abduction of Sita are treated. Consonant with his 'realism' in the treatment of his characters, Valmiki makes no bones about Ravana physically seizing Sita and carrying her off. Kamban, on the other hand, cannot bear the idea of such a physical contact. He therefore invokes (more than once) the curse on Ravana that would blow his head off if he touched an unwilling woman. For this reason, Ravana digs out the ground beneath the hermitage before carrying Sita off. By the time Tulsidas came to write, even this was unthinkable. A maya (unreal) Sita had to be invented to be carried away. So, before Rama goes chasing the mirage of a golden deer, Tulsi's Rama conjures up a Maya Sita who it is that Ravana carries away and who resides in Lanka. (In Valmiki and Kamban, Rama never performs miracles. Only rakshasas and, to some extent, the monkeys have magical powers of transforming themselves and performing improbable feats.) During the ordeal by fire, it is the unreal Sita that enters the fire and disappears and the real Sita, in hiding so far, emerges unscathed from the same fire.[22]

From the artistic point of view, there are striking instances of differences between Kamban and Valmiki in the narrative mode and details of characterization. Kamban is altogether more self-consciously poetic, full of a descriptive passion of natural scenes and emotions. In consonance with Tamil epic traditions, Kamban begins his work with an elaborate description of the splendours of the locale—the river, the land, the city and the king before getting down to the story. Sights and sounds that Valmiki dismisses in a few verses, Kamban lingers on, as much in love with nature as with words. Valmiki dismisses the journey of Dasaratha to Mithila for Rama's wedding in a couple of slokas. The same is rendered by Kamban in 300-odd verses spread over four cantos, describing the idyllic countryside, the rivers, mountains and the plains that he and his entourage pass through. There are long and vivid descriptions in these passages of young men and women disporting themselves in amorous abandon. Kamban's poetic credo is the Keatsian one of pleasing by a 'fine excess'.

Kamban's diction is conventionally poetic, full of stock phrases, extended similes and metaphors, repetitive allusiveness, pathetic fallacies and poetic conceits. Unlike Valmiki, Kamban has a sense of the drama of particular episodes, and exploits every occasion that has a theatrical potentiality, often by the use of the dialogic mode. In contrast, Valmiki is almost deadpan in his narration, his diction sparse and cut to the bone, the explosive emotional content of a situation in total control, inferential rather than explicit, as in the Tamil Sangam poetry. In western terms, Kamban is a romantic poet and Valmiki a classical one.

This is easy to illustrate from particular episodes. In the episode of Rama's wedding to Sita, Valmiki dismisses the run-up to it in a few verses with no mention whatever of Rama and Sita having seen each other before the actual wedding. But Kamban (and the Thai Ramayana, probably following Kamban and Tulsi) invent an elaborate love at first sight situation and the related agonies of uncertainties over identities. In some famous and well-loved verses, Kamban expatiates on the stunning effect that Rama, walking the streets of Mithila, had on the women there, particularly on Sita, and the similar impact of Sita on Rama. Having fallen in love, the two are racked not only by love but by doubts: in Rama's case, it is whether the maiden he saw was the princess for whom he broke the bow. In Sita's case, it is whether the ravishing young man she saw and fell instantly in love with was the one that broke the bow. She goes to the extent of saying that she will kill herself if it turned out to be different.

The actual wedding is a glittering occasion in Kamban with the presence of gods, sages and kings, whereas in Valmiki, it is simplicity itself. The whole occasion is dismissed in forty-six verses, whereas in Kamban it runs to 103 verses with elaborate descriptions of Rama and Sita arriving with trepidation and with their divine antecedents specially recalled. The giving away benediction too is different. In Kamban, it is a single verse:

Janaka pouring the cool water/ says, 'firm with my daughter may your union be / Like Vishnu's with his consort Lakshmi' And gave her into his lotus hand.'

In Valmiki, it is a touchingly human occasion with Janaka's tear-choked words:

This my daughter Sita is all yours, to be your companion in dharma./ Please accept her and clasp

her hand in yours. And let all blessings attend you./
Totally devoted to her husband, she, like a shadow,
will for ever go with you.

To this day, Hindu weddings in the south have these two
verses as part of the ritual of *Kannika dhana*, or the gift of the
bride.

VI

MORAL AMBIGUITIES

All epics, indeed, all great literature, have almost as their
hallmark a rich texture of ambiguities that provide the
essential tension in the enjoyment of literature. In his famous
book, *Seven Types of Ambiguity*, William Empson explores
this theme in all its ramifications. He applies the term to
'any verbal nuance, however slight, which gives room for
alternative reactions to the same piece of language,' and
identifies seven such categories of more than one meaning.
First, a simple metaphor, 'a word or grammatical construction
effective in several ways at once;' second, the double entendre,
'where two or more meanings are resolved in one'; the third,
'two apparently disconnected meanings co-existing as in a
pun, and by extension, allegories where there is more than
one universe of discourse'; the fourth where 'alternative
meanings combine to make clear a complicated state of mind
in the author'; the fifth is 'fortunate confusion' in the minds
of the author, where the ambiguity is really an infirmity and
the author is less than at his best and has muddled his own
meaning, but which, nevertheless, is productive of much
speculative pleasure for the reader; the sixth where the text is,
deliberately or otherwise, meaningless or contradictory and
offers alternative interpretations; and the seventh, the most
important of them all, the ambiguity arising from a 'division
in the author's own mind' about his characterization and
where, he 'buildeth better than he knew', as in the case of
Milton's Satan.

Kamban and Valmiki offer happy hunting for all these kinds of ambiguities, but we are concerned here only with the last two. Very often, heroes and heroines in literature have a streak of character or temperament that is discordant with the totality of their personality as intended. In such cases, literary pleasure consists in unravelling this discordance. This is particularly applicable to epics, where unlike in novels, heroes and heroines are larger than life rather than complex, with their mould set and static, with hardly any evolution as the story unfolds. The problem of reconciliation of these flaws with the totality of the personality of the characters and the dominant world view of the author is particularly difficult when, as in Kamban, these characters are presented as men of exceptional and heroic virtues, indeed, as gods in human form.

But this is precisely where opportunities for deconstruction and writing one's own Ramayana have presented themselves for exegetists of all kinds, from traditional kathakars and upanyasakas to more ambitious literary critics. Indeed, successive Ramayana versions have added, subtracted, glossed over or expurgated uncomfortable moral ambiguities in the characters. Two episodes have proved particularly indigestible to universal moral sensibility and unamenable to easy rationalization even in terms of the mores of the times in which the different Ramayanas were written. Indeed, they are in flat contradiction to the ethical superstructure assiduously presented by example and precept in the works themselves. These are Rama's killing of Vali and his treatment of Sita after his victory over her abductor Ravana.

How deliberate are these ambiguities? If ambiguities are the essence of epic literature, we may have to take them as intended and even worked in. Orthodox commentators have expended much ingenuity on these texts. Indeed, an elaborate rehearsal of the rival arguments is the staple of the expositions that are avidly listened to by bemused audiences. Both in Valmiki and in Kamban, Vali clearly comes out better than Rama in the exchanges. His arguments against Rama's behaviour are devastatingly logical and unanswerable. In contrast, Rama's defence is pitifully inadequate, ungenerous and damaging to his reputation as God-incarnate. In particular, he has no answer to Vali's coup de grace on fighting from a hidden place and therefore lets Lakshmana speak in his defence.

Lakshmana gives an ingenious reason for Rama's apparently unheroic behaviour: he had to hide himself from Vali because if he had seen Rama, he too would have solicited his help and this would have put Rama in a dilemma of choice between the brothers. Some plausibility attaches to this plea, since a major motif in Ramayana, specially Kamban's, is Rama as *saranagata vatsala*, or a protector who can never say 'no' to anyone seeking him in distress. This is repeatedly shown in his adoption of Guhan, Sugriva and Vibhishana as friend and even brother.

Rama's treatment of Sita after her rescue is even more problematic. Ending his work with the coronation, Kamban has spared himself the agonies of having to explain King Rama's exile of Sita on the basis of slanderous rumours about her chastity. But the details of the retained ordeal by fire are harrowing enough. Rama deliberately sends Vibhishana (significantly, not Hanuman) to Sita with the order that she should come resplendently adorned. When she so appears reluctantly and after an unavailing protest—Vibhishana throws Rama's order at her—Rama berates her cruelly for her frivolity and worse in captivity. He then makes several insinuations about her and tells her to be gone from his sight or kill herself. And then follows her ordeal, vindication and his ungracious acceptance (in a single verse, in sharp contrast to the hundreds of lines of his earlier *vipralamba* or lamentation in separation). Even then, Dasaratha has to come down from heaven to convince him and Brahma has to tell him of his forgotten past.

How deliberate are these contradictions? On the basis of the centrality of ambiguity in literature, they are indeed intended. Unravelling the mystery of this ambiguity is a major element in the enjoyment of the epic and the livelihood of kathakars. The episode has provided hundreds of occasions for deconstruction by later writers, many of them very perceptive and moving. I shall refer only to a very ingenious modern one in a Tamil short story, 'Shapa Vimochanam' (Release From the Curse), by Puthumai Piththan, a brilliant writer of the 1930s and '40s. It is cast in the form of a conversation between Sita while in exile at Valmiki's hermitage and Ahalya, years after her emancipation. They discuss the ethics of Rama's conduct, with Ahalya indignantly berating Rama, and Sita defending him. In the last sentence of the story, Ahalya says, her eyes blazing, 'I don't want the life given me by a man of this kind', and wills herself back into a stone. It is difficult to think of a greater oppositional deconstruction.

Notes and References

1. A.K. Ramanujan's 'Three Hundred Ramayanas' in *Many Ramayanas*, edited by Paula Richman, OUP, 1992.

2. Bhagavad Gita, Chapter IV, verses 7 and 8. Says Krishna:

   'Yadaayadaa hi Dharmasya, glaanir bhavati Bhaarata/ Abhyuthaanam adharmasya, thadaatmaanam, srijaamyaham.' (Whenever there is decay of righteousness, O Bharata! And there is exaltation of unrighteousness, I incarnate myself.)

   'Parithraanaaya saadhunaam, vinaachaayacha dushkritaam/ Dharma Samsthaapanaarthaaya Sambhavaami yuge yuge.' (For the protection of the good, for the destruction of the evil-doers and for the sake of firmly establishing righteousness, I am born from age to age.)

3. Patricia Y. Mumme, *Srivaishnava Theological Dispute: Manavaalamaamuni and Vedaanta Desika* (New Era Publications, Madras, 1988). Also, 'Ramayana Exegesis in Tenkalai Srivaishnavism' by the same author in *Many Ramayanas*, edited by Paula Richman, OUP, op.cit.

4. Dr V. Raghavan's introductory essay to *The Spiritual Heritage of Tyagaraja*, published by the Ramakrishna Mission Students' Home, Madras, 1957.

5. Ramdas Lamb, 'Personalising the Ramayana: Ramnamis and Their Use of the *Ramcharitamanas'* in *Many Ramayanas*, op.cit.

6. A.K. Ramanujan, 'Three Hundred Ramayanas', op.cit.

7. *Ramcharitamanas* 1. 32.3

8. '*Kaunvasmin saampratham loke, gunavaan, kashcha veeryavaan?' Dharmakyachak, krithakgyascha, satyavaakyo dhridavrathaha. Chaarithrena cha ko yuktaha, sarvabhutheshu ko hitaha? Vidwaan kaha, ka samarthashcha kaschaika priya darshanaha?'*

'Who, in the present world, is a man of character and an incomparable warrior?

'Versed in Dharma and gratitude, of truthful speech, and firm of purpose?

'Appropriate in action, kind to all living things, learned and able, and of genial appearance?'

9. See Paula Richman, *Many Ramayanas*, op.cit.

10. See 'The Raja's New Clothes: Redressing Ravana in *Meghnadabvada Kavya*', by Clinton Seely in *Many Ramayanas*, op.cit.

11. *The Ramayana Tradition in Asia*, edited by Dr V. Raghavan, Sahitya Akademi, 1980.

12. Kathleen M. Erndl, 'The Mutilation of Surpanakha', in *Many Ramayanas*, op.cit.

13. S. Vyapuri Pillai, 'Kamban Kaaviyam' (Tamil) in the fifth collection of the writings of S. Vyapuri Pillai (1891–1956), published by the S. Vyapuri Pillai Commemoration Society, 1993.

14. Dr A.A. Manavalan, 'Counter-influence, A Strange Literary Phenomenon', *Journal of Tamil Studies*, no. 47 and 48 (1995), published by the International Institute of Tamil Studies, Chennai.

15. See essays in the *Ramayana Tradition in Asia*, published by the Sahitya Akademi (dop.cit.) in particular, 1. Dr R. Nagaswami, 'Sri Ramayana Tradition in Art, Thought and Literature'. 2. R. Singaravelu, 'Tulsidasa's *Ramcharitamanas* in Hindi and its

Relationship to the Sanskrit version of Valmiki, the Tamil version of Kamban and the Thai version of King Rama'. 3. S. Shankar Raju Naidu, 'Recreations of the Ramayana in Tamil and Hindi.'

16. See Srirrama Bharati, *The Sacred Book* (Divya Prabandham), published by the Sri Satagopan Tirunarayanaswami Divya Prabandha Pathasala, Chennai (2000).

17. Ibid, pages 143, 146 and 149.

18. See 'Poetics in Tamil: A Diachronic Survey' by S. Muthiah. Also another article with the same title by A. Pitchai (pages 133–148) in the *Encyclopaedia of Tamil Literature*, Volume One, published by the Institute of Asian Studies, Chennai (1990).

19. Dr J. Parthasarathi's *'Akam Poetry'*, ibid.

20. V.V.S. Iyer, *Kamba Ramayana: A Study*, published by Bharatiya Vidya Bhavan (third revised edition, 1987).

21. See 'Tulsidas's *Ramcharitamanas* in Hindi and its Relationship to the Sanskrit Version of Valmiki, the Tamil version of Kamban and the Thai Version of King Rama', by S. Singaravelu, in the *Ramayana Tradition in Asia*, op.cit.

22. *'Vaayubakshya niraahara tapyanti bhasmasayani.'* But in the southern recession, this reads, *'Vaayubakshya silaabhutva tapyanti bhasmasayani.'*

A NOTE ON TRANSLATION

Both Valmiki and Kamban have been translated innumerable times into English. All of them are unsatisfactory, if one were looking for 'faithful renderings' of the originals. Robert Frost once defined poetry as that which is lost in translation. In his study on *Kamba Ramayana*, V.V.S. Iyer puts it succinctly. He begins by quoting Coleridge who said, 'The translation of poetry into poetry is difficult, because the translator must give a brilliancy to his language without the warmth of the original conception from which such brilliancy would follow of its own accord.' Iyer then goes on: 'The mind of the (translating) poet is weighted with the thoughts and images of the original which he has to render closely into another language. His mind loses its natural flow and has to substitute for it a simulacrum by all sorts of subterfuges. And the result is a travesty of the original and even below the quality of the works of the translator himself, as one can see by comparing, for instance, Pope's Iliad and Odyssey with his other works.'

The same idea has been expressed by George Steiner thus: 'There are no total translations: because languages differ, because each language represents a complex historically and collectively determined aggregates of values, proceedings, social conduct, conjectures on life. There can be no exhaustive transfer from language A to language B, no meshing of nets so precise that there is identity of conceptual content, unison of undertones, absolute symmetry of aural and visual association.' And the examples he gives are of translations from English to French, with such common words as the French 'pain' and the English 'bread'.

These difficulties are multiplied and become well-nigh insurmountable when it comes to cross-cultural transferences from Sanskrit or Tamil to English. On first encounter, lotus feet, carp eyes and mountainous shoulders that an Indian reader would not even try to visualize because they are dead metaphors for him, would make the non-Indian reader wince with shock and embarrassment.

A.K. Ramanujan distinguishes three kinds of translations: the iconic one, that attempts to faithfully reproduce the original by 'not only preserving the basic textual features such as characters, imagery and order of incidents', but also tries to reproduce even the metrical features of the original. The second kind he calls indexical which transfers the original text to the translator's own locale and cultural ambience, with details of local beliefs, folklore, imagery and poetic traditions. If the language of translation has, as Tamil does, a rich tradition of its own of aesthetic theory and metrical complexity, it ceases to be a translation but becomes an original work with the same material. The third kind is the symbolic translation, in which the original text is only a starting point for an altogether different, often subversive, telling of the original story to represent a different collectivity of beliefs and ethical assumptions.

Fortunately, deconstruction theorists have liberated the reader and the translator from the tyranny of the original. The text is only a *vyaja* or excuse for you to invent your own Ramayana. The best way to read Kamban even in an English translation is to treat it not as a written text to be read but as one meant for recitation, importing into the reading the cadences, alliterative assonances and internal rhymes, to the extent possible. (If this translation looks 'over-punctuated' by modern English standards, it is to aid this process.) This was indeed the way original Kamban was 'read' in the preprint era of oral traditions and mass illiteracy. Written texts in palm leaf duplications were all too few, meant only for the learned who used them as aids to their explications and exegesis for the benefit of listeners. Even today, most people know their Kamban only by hearsay, with their memory garbled by extrapolations from other sources.

As one who has had a lifetime love affair with both English and Tamil, P.S. Sundaram has overcome with remarkable success the hazards of transferring a great work rooted in a particularly enduring civilizational soil to a language with a very different cultural, literary and linguistic grounding. No doubt the underlying universality of the theme of heroic epics in all languages makes for a ready response from an eager reader. Even so, it does require of a non-Indian reader a great leap of the imagination to fully savour the original's unique beauty. But Sundaram's command of the idiom of both languages makes his rendering both faithful and felicitous.

A word about the abridgement of Sundaram's translation of the complete work: both Valmiki and Kamban are eminently abridgeable without great loss except for scholars. There are in both too many digressions from the main story in the form of other legends and elaborate genealogies that a common reader can well do without. There is a surplus of descriptive detail and a surfeit of repetitive conventional similes and metaphors and poetic conceits. Even the most conscientious reader routinely skips much of this, the full text itself being read over days and months. Hopefully, this leaner and tighter abridgement has omitted nothing of value in Kamban, though it is possible that in the excised passages some stray gems of the purest ray serene may have been lost.

Note for the reader: In the rendering that follows, the italicized passages within brackets are 'link narratives', mostly in the poet's own words.

BALA KANDAM

PROLOGUE

He alone is our head,
Our sole refuge, who, by himself,
Creates, preserves and puts an end
To all the worlds in ceaseless sport.

A milky ocean is Rama's lay
Which I, a lowly cat, would fain lap up—
Its huge waves, refulgent, roaring,
I, a feeble wit, try to take on, led by a fond hope of success.

How strange that, with the poorest of words,
I should tell again that arrow's tale
Which pierced seven trees like a Rishi's curse—
a great story by a great sage.

So doing, I dare the scorn of learned men,
But my aim is noble. 'Tis to show the world,
That spotless writer's splendid work,
In all its majesty.

My tawdry verse might offend those,
Used to the sweetness of various modes,
As a loud drum will the sensitive ears
Of an *asunam* used to a honeyed lute.

One thing I would say to those expert
In trinal Tamil—verse, song and play—
A critic's ear is ill-attuned
To the words of a madcap or a devotee.

Will children's sketches of rooms and halls
Scratched on a floor annoy an artist?
Should my poor and foolish poem
Irk those well-trained in making verse?

Of the three that in the sacred tongue
Told this story, I shall take
The earliest master for my source
To render into Tamil song.

In the Vennainallur of Sadaiyan
Was this lay made which sets at length
The spotless Rama's mighty deeds—
Great models left by his descent.

THE RIVER

Let us talk now of the Kosala land where arrows never strayed, be they shafts from the five senses of its men or the sharp ones discharged from the eyes of women, their breasts bedecked with jewels.

Clouds, ashen-hued like Siva, grazed and drank their fill of the sea only to return dark-hued, like the Lord who has goddess Lakshmi on his chest.

They rose and spread over Himavaan, as if the sea said to itself, 'The sun once taxed Siva's father-in-law; it is but fitting that we cool him now with our waters.'

Eyeing the gold of the hills, the sky dug it up with its silver torrents. The clouds, generous souls that they were, gave it back in the form of rain!

Like a woman of the town, the river in flood was given to depriving the hills of all they had! Clasping men's bodies only for a moment to denude them of all their possessions!

Like merchants and tradesmen, it bore on its back pearls, gold and peacock plumes, white tusks of elephants, *akhil* and rare sandalwood.

Pastures turned into ploughlands, hills into dales, barren and saline soil into fertile fields; the river, changing form and function at will, was like fate, ceaselessly working the cycle of birth and death.

THE LAND

With his immutable four-foot verse, Valmiki once regaled the gods. I, a garrulous mute, drunk on words, will now describe the land he praised.

Pearls on the border, conches in moats, red gold in channels, scarlet blooms in pools, corals on plains, swans in rich fields, canes oozing honey and groves with drunken bees.

The sound of water and of cane-presses at work, oysters, buffaloes and fighting bulls symbolized its arable lands. With lotuses for lamps, peacocks danced in groves. Clanging clouds provided the drumbeats, blue lilies the unblinking eyes. The waves of the river acted as curtains and humming bees provided sweeter music than lutes. And presiding over it all, the great King Marudam.

The wealth of this gleaming land was the green of its paddy fields and the gold turned up by ploughshares. Add to this the pearls that oysters shed, the heaped gems from levelled farms, fishes and sugarcane in plenty, and bees that were forever hoarding honey.

Juice from fruits, sugarcane, toddy from fronded palms, and honey were to be had for the asking.

Mouths dripping toddy, farmers seemed to have nothing to do all day and simply walked around waving rice stalks, daydreaming of the eyes, hands, legs, mouths and faces of the farm girls they fancied. When love to the lowly comes from above, can they ever wake from it?

Who can count the numbers of sword-eyed maids who awoke men's love with their sweet prattle? Or the red-lipped ones with lightning waists who stole innumerable hearts when they went bathing in the freshes the river brought, spreading all over the fragrance of flowers and the saffron they had applied on their breasts.

(It was a happy and contented community.)

Many married their mates. Others mated music to words, one a flying bird and the other its shadow. Still others listened raptly to learned talks, sweeter than ambrosia. And many there were who merely enjoyed the sight of guests and the prospect of feasting them.

Some engaged in cockfights, setting bird against bird, not out of enmity but for love of fight. Hearts black, crests redder than eyes, sharp knives attached to toes, these cocks enjoyed the fight and scorned to run away.

Yet others engaged in bullfights. Red-eyed, fierce and dark, as if the whole world's blackness had been divided into two, and one half set against the other, they were a thrilling sight. Spectators watching them in furious combat, shook their heads and shouted out curses and plaudits, marvelling, 'These are no amateurs but experts in the game.'

They tilled the land, sowing and harvesting. Whipped their oxen and drove them till their plough-ends broke the stems of lotuses and dug up pearls, gold and gems that lay carelessly scattered on the ground. Fish in furrows leapt, turtles drew in their limbs and the *varals* hid themselves in sluices as the ploughshares dug in deep.

Paddy was cut and heaped to the sky, got trodden on by oxen which knew their minds. The grain thus separated from the chaff was first given to the poor and only then taken for oneself and the guests. Carts that carried the huge harvest bent the land and rutted the roads with their weight.

Scratching dust heaps, cocks, red-hued and crested, brought out gems that sparrows mistook for glow-worms and bore off to their nests to eat. Dark-eyed little girls, sifting through mounds of arecanut to build castles of sand, found pearls instead and promptly discarded them as trash!

Elsewhere on the river banks ships coming from distant lands, bringing exotic goods in return for rare merchandise, rested awhile after unburdening themselves, looking as if Mother Earth herself had put down her load to relax for a bit under the umbrella of a benign king who ruled by the code, angry when he should be, gentle otherwise.

No evil, hence no death untimely. No unclean thoughts and hence no wrath; since virtue was their sole pursuit, they could only rise, and never knew a fall.

Bounds were broken only by flood, for men respected each other's land. The only small things in this kingdom were the waists of the irrepressible maidens.

Women of this land were experts at mockery! Their spear-eyes laughed at Fate, their gaits at the elephants, their tight breasts at lotuses, and their faces at the moon.

Koels learnt the prattle of girls, treacle-sweet; peacocks to dance from their lively steps, and oysters to produce pearls by imitating their teeth.

The toddy-seller's house had its toddy; the ploughman's house its plough; the drummer's house never lacked its drums and the lute player's its lutes.

None were generous in that land as none was needy; none seemed brave as none defied; with no liars around,

Truth never needed to speak up. No learning stood out as all were learned.

Their beauty had its root in goodness, their justice in the absence of lies. Their women's virtue sprang from their love and their chastity brought on the seasonal rains.

THE CITY

Great Sanskrit poets, subtle and winsome, have sung the praise of that great city, Ayodhya. Their descriptions roused even in the hearts of those who had gone to heaven, the desire to come and dwell here.

How should I describe that city? As the face of that goddess born of Earth? The beauty spot on her brow? Or was it her eye? Mayhaps, it was her auspicious marriage thread?

The gem-studded necklace that nestled on her breast? Her beloved lotus flower? Vaikuntham, that supreme heaven? Was it perhaps Vishnu's chest, the ultimate refuge when the entire world is dissolved?

Neither he, whose half is Uma, nor the one with two wives, nor patient Brahma on his lotus could ever discover its equal. Hence it is that, their eyes unwinking, the sun and the moon circled the heavens, in the hope that *they* may succeed in that hopeless task!

Indra's dwelling and Kubera's, were but the handiwork of an amateur. On seeing this city with its tall towers, divine architects like Maya and others gave up their craft, crestfallen.

Like the vedas infinite, like the gods that haunt the sky, like secretive sages, self-contained and self-controlled, like Durga on her antlered deer, the city protected its people. Like fierce Kali, it held a trident to keep lightning at bay. Its greatness, like all things great, cannot be described or put into words.

The moat that surrounded that fortress was low as a prostitute's mind, turbid like bad poetry, inaccessible as a virgin, and full of alligators, like the rebellious senses that lead men astray.

The brightness of that virgin town shone like the sun that gives the sky its golden sheen. He who lit the sky was himself but the shadow of Queen Ayodhya, with her gem-set jewels.

What drove darkness away from the houses of this city that Lakshmi chose as hers? Rows and rows of ghee-fed lamps? Or chandeliers that shone like brilliant jewels? Neither! It was the golden limbs of its women.

The women of this bright city spent their time in diverse pleasures. Some spent hours admiring the fragrant flowers in their gardens. Some sported, fawn-like, with young men. Others bathed in the beautiful river, sipped toddy, their red lips pallid with drink. Many spent their time writing love notes.

Drums that beat all day shamed the rain-clouds and the sea. There were no guards because there were no thieves. None ever gave for none ever took. Since no one in that city ever stopped learning, none was ignorant and none fully learned. Since everyone had as much as they needed, none was poor and none rich.

THE KING

The ruler of that famous city was Dasaratha, scion of the solar race. A king of kings, his righteous sceptre held sole sway over all seven worlds. Virtue incarnate, he was the father of this story's peerless hero, Rama, beautiful and strong.

Sense, grace, virtue, calm, valour, generosity, rectitude—traits other kings might have had but in half, in him alone were found in full.

On this ancient sea-girt earth, no hand was found unwetted by his gifts. Neither was there a *yaga* fit for a king he had not performed.

A loving mother, a fruitful penance, a balm in disease, a sharp intellect—the king was all this and more. With no foes to attack him, he ruled his kingdom with the ease with which a poor man runs his farm.

THE DIVINE DESCENT

One day, the king bowed to that sage pure as Brahma and said, 'You are father, mother, boons, God and all else to my ancient family. My ancestors ruled over this earth undimmed, brighter than the sun and, by your grace, I too have enjoyed this long reign.

'For 60,000 years I have ruled this earth. I lack nothing. But I'm worried what'll happen to it when I am gone. This pain wrings my heart.'

(When the emperor spoke these words, Vasishta suddenly remembered an old incident. The gods in heaven, much harassed by the rakshasas, had approached Siva for help. He directed them to four-faced Brahma. The creator, in turn, took them to Vishnu.)

Hands folded, they said, 'O Lord of Lakshmi, the brutal strength of the ten-headed Ravana, his brothers and other rakshasas has deprived earth and heaven of peace. We are utterly lost.'

He, an ocean of grace with fragrant basil decked, said, 'Grieve not. I shall in due time cut off his heads and relieve the earth. Meanwhile, all those who are here in heaven should descend to the earth as monkeys and inhabit its forests, groves and hills.

'I myself shall alight on earth as Dasaratha's son and pulverize with my deadly shafts the mirage of boons that so misleads that rakshasa. Adishesha, my capacious bed, my conch and my discus too will come to earth as brothers for me to command.'

Recalling this now, Vasishta said, 'Don't grieve, O doughty king! Perform with a pure heart the *putra kameshti yaga*, the sacrifice that will beget you sons and your anxieties will end. Your sons will guard our own seven worlds and the seven above.'

Filled with joy, Dasaratha asked how he should go about the sacrifice. Vasishta felt that Rishyasringa, the deer-horned son of Sage Kashyapa, was the best person to officiate as the priest and related the interesting story of that incomparable ascetic.

'It so happened,' Vasishta said, 'that once the land of Romapada, descended from Manu, was afflicted by a drought of the worst kind. With the sky holding back its gift of rain there was distress unrelieved.

'Wise men told the king that only the dust from the feet of Rishyasringa, a young and guileless ascetic of immaculate virtue, could bring relief to the land. But the boy-ascetic was so innocent of the ways of the world that he did not know the difference between man and beast, or even man and woman. So wholly given to penance was he.

'Then it was that some women of easy virtue, of dazzling brows, red lips, pearly teeth, timid eyes and silk-soft breasts, offered to meet the challenge. Assuming the form of ascetics, they went to the innocent boy-hermit when his father was away. Thinking they were rishis, he showed them utmost courtesy.

'After several days, they asked him to grace their abodes and he readily set off with them. Filled with trepidation but still set upon their aim, they walked on till they reached the capital city of the Anga kingdom.

'Even as he set foot on its soil, the sky above grew dark as Siva's neck, and rain poured down in torrents, filling all tanks and rivers. Wilting crops revived, everyone rejoiced. Heart full of gratitude, nonetheless anxious, the king fell at the young sage's feet.

'It was then that young Rishyasringa realized that he had been tricked. The gods trembled with fear but the generous sage forgave the king. The happy king gave his flower-lipped daughter, Shanta, in marriage to the ascetic and they have been living happily in the Anga kingdom ever since.'

(*Dasaratha at once set off on a bejewelled chariot driven by the ever-faithful Sumantra to fetch the young sage. When he arrived at the Anga capital, Romapada, delighted with the rare honour of having the emperor himself visit him, went forth to receive him. Informed of the purpose of the visit, Romapada lost no time in persuading young Rishyasringa to proceed to Ayodhya to preside over the sacrifice. Soon Dasaratha, with the sage beside him, reached Ayodhya.*)

He descended from his chariot and fell at the flower-like feet of his companion. The sage with the stag horns, the very trellis for the vedas, blessed him in pregnant words.

'King, don't grieve,' he said, 'you shall have sons to rule with skill not only this world but all the fourteen. Start here and now the great *yaga*.'

Quickly were brought the plough and the tools and other essentials for the sacrifice. Three fires were lit and kept aflame by sacred offerings for twice six months. The serene skies were thick with gods, no space unfilled.

Lotus-faces warm with love, the gods showered fragrant *karpaka* flowers on the king. That eminent stag-horned sage poured in the fire the son-blessing oblation.

There quickly arose from that fire a red-eyed god with flaming hair, carrying on a plate of gold a ball of rice, sweet as ambrosia. Placing it on the sacrificial ground, he went his way. The sage told the king, 'Give this to your wives in proper order as is fit.'

As conches blew, the king of kings gave a part to Kausalya, the bright and comely, soft-curved and fragrant, with lips red as the *kovvai* flower. Next the emperor of Kosala placed a portion in the hands of Kaikeyi, the daughter of Kekaya.

He then placed the third part in the hands of Sumitra, his second wife. Carefully picking up what he had spilt, he gave that, too, to Sumitra. And Indra, the king of gods, shouted with joy, 'Finished is my foe!'

After some days, the three matrons felt the sickness of pregnancy. Not just their lovely faces, but their entire bodies grew wan like the moon.

Then arrived the day, hour and second, when the star *punarpusam* was in precise conjunction with the sign of Cancer. To the great delight of Goddess Earth and the acclamation of all heavenly folk, the great Kausalya gave birth to that dazzling splendour, that inscrutable rain-cloud who had once hidden in his stomach all the worlds in the cosmos. Dharma was at peace at last.

Indra and the other gods shouted jubilantly as Kekaya's daughter bore her child, when *pusa* conjoined with the Fish.

It was then the turn of Sumitra to delight the gods. At the moment Cancer joined the Serpent star, she with venom-dark eyes brought forth the younger hero. She yielded again, at the precise moment *makam* joined Leo, another son. Earth, borne on the head of the many-headed snake, danced with joy.

'No taxes for seven and seven more years!' announced the delirious king. 'Proclaim that our treasuries are unbolted. The needy shall take what they want, how they will.

'All wars shall cease and vassal kings shall go back, each to his land. Let priests perform their duties, and fairs and feasts be held everywhere.

'Renovate temples, set aside plots for *yagas* at all points where street meets street and worship the gods with flowers and incense morning and night.'

Thus ordered, the drummers proclaimed the news from atop elephants. Young men and women with lightning waists drowned in a sea of joy. Crowds of people, friends and playmates, ran amuck on the streets in delirious happiness, scattering sandal-paste, and saffron all around.

(Thus, for twice six days, people knew not themselves.)

Sage Vasishta, the royal preceptor, gave thought to the names he should give the newborn princes. To that True Being the elephant invoked in his weary struggle with the crocodile, he gave the name Rama.

He who was born knowing the essence of the vedas was given the name Bharata.

Said the sage, 'Crooks shall perish, gods revive, and Goddess Earth lose her grief. The might immovable born to Sumitra shall bear the name Lakshmana. And this other splendour of hers, a pearl incarnate, shall be known as Satrughna.'

With every passing day, their lisps ambrosial, and walk unsteady, delighted everyone. Their presence dispelled gloom like the sun that destroys darkness. It seemed to the people that the vedas had found their voice in the childish prattle of these four.

As they grew, sagacious Vasishta arranged for their tonsure and initiation into knowledge fit for kings. With his infinite learning and wisdom, he taught them the vedas pure. Divine Rama, with his brothers, also learnt the art of warfare.

Though the brothers loved one another deeply, by a mysterious chemistry at work, the four became two twosomes—Rama and Lakshmana and Bharata and Satrughna.

Like a shuttle and thread inseparable, Rama and Lakshmana roamed the dark groves, rivers, and sacred tanks. Likewise, Bharata and Satrughna never parted for a single second, whether on horses or chariots, or engaged in the study of the sacred vedas.

THE HANDING OVER

To Dasaratha, king of all he surveyed, sitting in council, came one day Viswamitra, the irate, who had once vowed to create a new world and a new Brahma.

The king received him exactly as heaven's king, Indra, would have welcomed the creator, Brahma. He led him to a seat of gold set with gems, and worshipped his lotus feet saying, 'Great sage, that you should have come here thus and given me the opportunity to worship you is a fruit of the good deeds of my ancestors.'

Replied the sage, 'O victorious king, when gods and sages are beset with trouble, where can they seek refuge, if not at the snowy range that scorns all others, or the sea of milk, or Brahma's land, or Indra's town, or your own Ayodhya, with its golden terraces?

'When Indra lost his capacious heaven and took refuge under *your* umbrella, did you not, out of pity for him, kill doughty Sambaran, kith and kin, and restore to him the realm he rules?'

His heart flooded with joy, the king, at whose gate the drums beat forever, said, 'I've reaped the fruit of my kingship. Be pleased to tell me what I should do.'

The sage replied, 'Like the lust and rage that ascetics shun, the rakshasas are hindering my *yaga*. So lend me that dark and handsome prince out of your four to guard my *yaga* site.'

Hearing this, the king's heart was pierced as if Death himself had demanded his life. He felt his life swing on a thread and was like one who, born blind, had gained his sight only to lose it again!

Recovering his poise, he said, 'Great sage, he is but a boy untrained. If you so desire, let me offer myself. Should Siva with Ganga in his matted hair, Indra, and the four-faced Brahma themselves hinder your *yaga*, I will stop them. So please, let us leave at once.'

The sage who had once created a whole new world rose in wrath. 'Is this the end?' wondered the gods. The sun grew dark and all things fixed, whirled madly. His beetle brows rising, he laughed in derision. His eyes grew red and the world darkened.

Sensing his anger, Vasishta begged him forbear and turned to the king, 'Will you stand in the way of your son getting gifts else not attained? Noble king! The time has come for rare and arcane knowledge to come to your son, in the manner that floods released by unceasing rain reach the sea.'

Obeying his guru's advice, the king ordered, 'Bring the prince here.' The wise one came at once. Presenting him and his younger brother to that vedic sage, Dasaratha said, 'You, O great sage, are their father and mother. Take charge of them and do as you deem fit.'

His anger gone in a trice, Viswamitra accepted the boys, blessed the king, and started on his journey.

Rama girded on his sword and placed on his hill-like shoulders two quivers of arrows which, like Truth, never failed. He then took his bow, bearing it as he bore the world! With his brother armed likewise, they left that golden city, following the sage like his shadow. The king's own life was left dangling on a thread.

THE KILLING OF TATAKA

They passed that night with pious folk who welcomed them with open arms and warm hearts. Next morning, when the sun arose from behind the hill, they approached a desert.

That place lacked every season except summer, when, bent on sucking the world dry, the sun goes on parade with his victory flag. By merely thinking of that heat, even the fire god got his innards burnt, and upon daring to look, got his eyes burnt.

That desert land was scattered with branches of *akhil* trees, as if they had been split and strewn by demons. Also scattered on the ground were white pearls, spilt from leafless bamboos and red gems spat out by venomous snakes.

The earth being earth, couldn't flee that heat. The desert deities couldn't walk, only run. Neither the sun nor the clouds, nor the wind dared pass directly over it.

Like those stern ascetics who wage incessant war against the triad of lust, rage and ineradicable delusion, the desert was completely free of compassion. It was also a stranger to tenderness, like women who sell their love for a price.

On reaching this burning desert, the great ascetic thought to himself: however strong, these flower-like princes will wilt and droop under this intolerable heat.

He, therefore, taught them the two mantras given by Brahma. These they took at once to their minds and hearts, and uttered them reverently. All at once the heat, fiercer than the flames of Dissolution, became cool as crystal water.

Rama bowed to the sage: 'Tell me this, O all-knowing one. Was it a look from Siva that burnt this land, or is there some other cause for it? Why is it more barren than a land cursed with a cruel tyrant?'

'Dear child,' replied Viswamitra, 'this is the doing of that wicked woman of whom you must now know more. Looking like Death, she roams about spreading devastation and she has the strength of a thousand elephants in musth.

'Should she wish to uproot the earth, to drink up the sea, or pierce the sky, she has the might and energy for it. Evils unnumbered have taken the form of a woman and wander about in the form of this demoness.

'If you can conceive of a combination of two mountains rolled into one, innate venom, a voice like thunder, the final fire, two crescents rising out of the sea, you can see them all in her terrible form! This forest dweller, with a snake-like spear, bears the name of Tataka.

'What more can I say? Like clinging greed that by itself can destroy unnumbered virtues, this cruel demoness has made this fertile land a desert. My child, she thinks that all creation is there only to serve as food for her. Within a few days she gobbled up everything. And under the orders of Lanka's king, she is now hindering my *yaga*.'

On hearing all this, Rama asked, 'Revered sage, where dwells this evil creature?' Even before the sage could speak, she herself appeared from nowhere like a smoking volcano.

Her anklets made of hillocks made the level earth sink, and the sea came rushing in to fill the holes thus made. Fearless Death itself cowed down and fled to take refuge in the caves that mountains hid.

Wide open in a snarl, her mouth itself resembled a cave out of which issued two crescent-like fangs. The sinful demoness glared, eyebrows quivering and fiery eyes spouting venom. Around her waist was a band made of the trunks of elephants, and she made a clamour that set the heaven and the far quarters tremble.

Verily a thundercloud, she looked at the three of them and laughed. Triple-headed spear held aloft, she gnashed her teeth and opened the cavern of her mouth, letting fall the following words of jeer and rage:

'This entire place is in my keep. All things in it I have destroyed, seed, root and branch; is it out of pity for me with nothing left to eat, that you have come to offer your sweet flesh? Or is it that you are in love with easeful Death and Fate has given you a push from behind?'

Her glare undid and scattered the clouds and her kick broke huge hills to pieces. She ground her fangs and aimed her spear at their hearts with intent to kill.

Though Rama knew the sage's wish, he held back his deadly shaft. His large heart wouldn't permit him to kill a woman, though her frightful threat was to his own life. Well-versed in the four vedas, the sage knew what the benign prince was thinking.

So he spoke: 'Guilty as she is of every sinful act that has ever been devised, O beauteous prince, is this demon a woman? To think of her as a dainty woman is folly and cowardice.

'To kill a woman pure at heart is, I grant, a shame. But this is no such woman. Her name will unman a man, reduce to impotence his strength and sword. Who is a man then, who a woman?

'Not out of anger do I say all this against this woman. I am but obeying the codes in urging you to kill her, evil all-compact. To be patient with her any longer is no virtue, my son. Kill her.'

The hero replied, 'Noble sage, my qualms are stilled. Your command is god's own, and obeying you is a virtue in itself.'

Her eyes darting fire, she sensed the thoughts of the prince and flung at him the spear she held. The three-pronged weapon came down on him like the serpent Rahu eclipsing the moon.

No one saw his bow bent or arrow fixed. They only saw broken into two the deadly spear the demoness had flung. Before a word could emerge from anyone, she, dark as a rain cloud at dead of night, sent down a shower of stones, enough to fill a sea. The hero met them with a torrent of arrows.

Swift as a sage's curse, the burning shaft aimed at that night-dark woman did its work. Her heart of stone could no more be held in her body than a dolt's mind could retain a wise man's words.

Hit sharp by that shaft from that mountain of gold, down she collapsed like a cloud from the sky, like a storm of stones unloosed by the whirlwind of Dissolution. Her blood flooded the forest that had been covered with dust. Her fall symbolized the collapse of the flagstaff of the many-headed Ravana.

The deluge of blood the sharp arrow released from her hard heart made that forest a sea of red. It looked as though the crimson of the evening sky had descended on the jungle.

'Our places restored and your obstacles removed,' said the gods to the sage in joy, 'now is the time to invest the prince with missiles divine.' They drenched the hero with a rain of flowers and went their way.

THE YAGA

The gods departed and the great sage gave Rama mantras for many a sovereign missile. Their utterance raised powerful spirits who rushed to Rama. 'We have come to you, hero,' they said, 'never more to part from you. We'll do your bidding as a younger brother would.' And from then on they became his devoted friends.

(Proceeding further, the three reached a grove and the two princes wished to know its history. Then the sage told them the story of Mahabali.)

'He whose mystery none can plumb, once did penance here for a hundred years, for what purpose we do not know. About that time, Mahabali, the asura king, too, started a *yaga*, at the end of which, he had vowed, he would give away to the brahmins the earth and all else he possessed.

'Coming to know of this, the gods sought Vishnu's help and begged that he end this ambitious penance that threatened their absolute hegemony. Vishnu agreed to do so.

'The blue-hued one then took birth as the son of Aditi and the all-knowing Kashyapa in the form of a diminutive dwarf, no larger than the seed of a fig tree.

'Wearing a brahmachari's three-stringed sacred thread and around his waist a cord of grass, God in dwarf's form confronted Mahabali, intent on his mysterious task.

'Mahabali was puzzled but welcomed his short guest. "O omnipresent one, there is no brahmin like you; and I am most blest."

'The all-knowing dwarf said to that symbol of manliness,

"Blessed are they who come to you who, liberal-handed, give more than asked. The rest, for not asking, are poor indeed."

'Delighted, Bali asked, "What do you want?" "O doughty one", the brahmin replied, "If you wish to be gracious, I want but three pieces of earth." "Done," said Mahabali, even before he could finish! But Sukra, the royal preceptor, intervened.

"This, O king, is a piece of trickery. Don't think that this is just an ugly cloud-hued dwarf. Know him for the one who once swallowed world on world without end!"

"If this is indeed the hand of Vishnu, dark as a raincloud, needing nothing but now held low with my hand above, what greater glory can I have? How is it you don't realize this?

"Those who know the codes don't talk of friend and foe. If great are those who deserve to be given, then who greater than this?

"Too simple in your simplicity, don't you know that the great have ordained that gifts should be boundless and one should give even one's precious life if asked for? To ask is mean, to give great.

"My father! the dead are not those who stretched their hands to live. Lifeless indeed are they who lived, but never gave when prayed to. Those who give what they have when they have it, gain fame here and bliss hereafter. He who counsels sticking to greed is the enemy within.

"Unworthy Sukra, does it become you to prevent a man from giving something even as he gets ready to give it? For this cruel act, you and your kin will go without food or clothes forever and ever."

'Convinced that his counsellor was an evil man, he thus dismissed his words. Addressing the supplicant dwarf, he said, "Take your three feet." And the lord immense, stretched his short palm for the water of donation. The moment it touched his palm, the dwarf shot up, to the amazement and fear of all beholders.

'Wonder of wonders! What was happening! One fixed

foot measured all the earth and spread no further: the world was too small for the stride. And the other foot measured all the sky and, lacking more space, came back.

'Two paces measuring the earth and the sky, none was left for the third. The basil-crowned then found Bali's willing head for the third.

'The gifs thus obtained, he gave away to Indra and went back to his ocean bed. There, the dark feet which had measured the worlds, were then massaged by Lakshmi till they turned red.'

(Sage Viswamitra then began his great yaga. Reaching a lovely grove, he marked a spot for the sacrificial fire. Like the eyelids that guard a man's eyes, for six days the king's sons guarded that yaga meant to please the denizens of heaven.

The elder of the bull-like heroes then asked the omniscient sage, 'Virtuous sage beyond all praise, when will those cruel fiends attack us?' Vowed to silence, the sage was mute. Even as the warrior prince bowed and left, he saw the sky spread with dark clouds and a roar that put thunder to fright!)

The dark army of fiends rose to the sky like a fish-filled sea. They shot and hurled numberless missiles, rained water and fire, tore up mountains and flung them down. They railed and ranted, swung down axes and played, not one, but a thousand wicked feints! They flung in their rage weapons on which were stuck bits of flesh from past exploits, covering the forest like summer clouds.

The bows, swords and thundering drums that filled the sky were like the roaring rain and storm at Dissolution. Looking at those red-haired creatures that had fangs for teeth, Rama said to his brother, 'These must be the cruel demons the sage told us about.'

Like the gods who fled to the crescent-crested one when that terrible poison rose from the sea, the frightened ascetics ran to the one dark as the clouds, seeking refuge from those monsters. Calmly, he held up his palm and said, 'Be not afraid.'

He looked at the sky and then at his bow. 'You will soon

see them cut up and strewn,' he said to the sages and bent his head to the bow. 'Please ensure that the flesh and blood of these smoky fiends do not fall into the *yaga* fire.'

He then drew to his ear the divine bow's string and made a roof of arrows in the sky. The land below became a sea of blood and a hill of rakshasa heads. The fearsome missiles Rama aimed at terrible Tataka's pair of sons, plunged one of them into the sea and sent the other to Death's abode! Those who survived ran helter-skelter.

The thundering arrows hit those who were attempting to flee; their headless corpses danced a jig. Carrion birds from the sky descended from time to time to feast on the strewn corpses.

The gods rained flowers on the twosome. The drumbeats in heaven roared like the sea. Indra and the other gods blessed the handsome bowman. Pious ascetics showered their benedictions.

His *yaga* ended without mishap, the happy sage said to Rama. 'Thanks entirely to you, this *yaga* is now complete. For me, this is a great moment, but to you, who once swallowed entire worlds, saving this *yaga* was child's play, a mere trifle.'

The three stayed with the other sages for a day in that grove full of flowers. Rama asked Viswamitra the next morning, 'What is your pleasure today, great sage?'

'There's nothing I want that's too much of a task for you,' said the sage, 'but great things lie ahead. Let's go to Janaka's fertile land and see the *yaga* that the king of Mithila has proclaimed.'

AHALYA

They reached the river Sone, a lovely damsel, her sand-dune breasts decked with well-washed gems, and sandal and *akhil* brought down from the hills. Her waist was the tender *vanji* creeper and fresh flowers that hummed with bees were her tinkling waistlet; the black sand was her tresses and the hill-encircling channels her anklets.

Dispelling the darkness that resembled Death's own hue, the sun rose out of the blue sea, like Brahma on the full-blown lotus emerging from Vishnu's bejewelled navel. Those three, reminiscent of the triune, rose and saw the great Ganga, so like that river carrying gold, and the *konrai* flower from Siva's locks.

By and by they reached Videha, the land of Janaka, king turned sage. There they saw half-awake storks in lotus ponds that, mistaking the reflections of the lovely eyes of farm maidens for *kayal* fish, pecked at them and, upon realizing their error, drew back abashed.

Walking with pleasure thus in that land of plenty, they reached Mithila's fort with its resplendent flags. On its outskirts, they saw an upright stone, a sage's wife brought low by betrayal.

When the dust from Rama's feet fell on that stone, she turned again into her former self, just as one who, freed of delusion, realizes his true self and reaches the feet of God. The astonished prince turned to the sage, a thousand questions in his lovely eyes.

To the one whose forbears brought Ganga down from the sky, the sage said, 'Prince! That joyous lightning which stands to one side, shy and trembling, is Ahalya, wife of the great Sage Gautama, who gave Indra the sinner a thousand eyes.'

'Alas! Alas! What sort of world is this!' exclaimed the prince, 'Was it fate or chance that caused such havoc to one so holy?'

Replied his sagacious companion, 'Listen, O child of Fortune, once in days gone by, the God of Thunder saw the sage's doe-eyed wife and was smitten. Pierced by her spear-like eyes and Madan's shafts, he sought, his senses lost, a healing balm in her arms. Tricking the sage away, he entered the hut in a guileless guise.

'She knew who he was, but inebriate with unfamiliar feelings induced by his ingress, she didn't desist—so low she'd sunk. When her lofty husband hurried home and saw what he saw, he became a second Siva.

'An arrow might have been thwarted, but not his curse or blessing. She knew this and stood trembling, a figure now of everlasting shame, while the rattled god tried to flee in the guise of a cat.

'Fire darting from his eyes at what had passed in his absence, his words blazed forth, like one of your own shafts: "A thousand *pudenda* shall cover you," he said, and Indra was so covered that very instant!

'Thus, mantled by shame, a laughing stock to the whole world, guilt-laden Indra left. Turning to his soft-limbed wife, the sage thundered, "Whore, you shall harden to a stone!"

"The great are ordained to forgive. O fiery sage, grant an end to my curse!" she pleaded with him. Said he, somewhat mollified, "When dust from the foot of Rama falls on you, you will rise from that stone!"

'That was the past: now, you have shown her the path to salvation for all the world to see. Earlier, I witnessed the prowess of your hand and now I see the grace of your foot!'

Absorbing all that the sage narrated, Rama, ever compassionate, said, 'Don't grieve, mother. Seek that sage's mercy,' and bowed to her golden feet.

When the great Gautama saw these visitors at his hermitage, he was astonished but welcomed them with utmost courtesy. Whereupon Vishwamitra enlightened him about the purpose of their visit: 'The dust from his feet did but touch her and your slim wife regained her form. In her heart she is without guilt, so take her back.'

(*And that Brahma-like sage paid heed to those words. The virtuous prince bowed to Gautama, went around him in a pradakshina and gave that lady, now without stain, into his hand. The three of them then continued their journey to Mithila.*)

APPROACHING MITHILA

That fortressed city with its bejewelled flags seemed to welcome with open arms the prince with the lotus eyes. It was as if it was keen that he should hurry up to meet the goddess who had left the spotless flower to make Mithila her residence—a big boon that kingdom got as a result of rigorous penance.

When the sun set and the sky turned into a red sea, they saw the banners standing close on Mithila's towering mansions. Soon enough, the clouds approached and gave them a loving stroke and they got wet. But the smoke that rose from the burning *akhil* wood with which Mithila's women scented their hair dried those towers once again!

They went through broad and beautiful streets, littered with garlands and golden ornaments, thrown away in reckless abandon by sweet-tongued women, exhausted after sexual combat, wherein the honours were equal!

They saw dance halls where girls with waists too slender to spot, swayed to the tune of lute-strings, honey-sweet vocals and the beat of drums. The eyes of the dancers followed their hands and their minds chased their eyes!

They saw girls on swings that hung from emerald palms with coral fruits and their thoughts swung back and forth with them. The bees that rose from the girls' garlands screamed out of sympathy for their waists!

They saw numerous shops heaped with merchandise—gems and gold, pearls and yak tails, peacock plumes and ivory goods—brought by traders from far off lands. They looked like farmers who had shored up riverbanks with silt brought down by the Caveri.

They saw elephants fighting in sport, eyes reddened with rage and tusks entwined. Clashing inseparably, their passion churned up, they looked like lovers engaged in fierce combat.

They saw harnessed horses going round and round, like vessels on a potter's wheel, unremitting like the friendship of good men, undistracted as a yogi's mind.

At every window of the jewelled terraces they saw a moon, rid at last of the dark spot on its face, equipped with lances and Madan's bow.

They saw girls playing ball. Black as their eyes when first spotted, the balls became red when they reached the hands of the girls. Taking thus the colour of the hands they touched, they then resembled those wanton women, fickle and inconstant, who sell their cobra-middles for money and take the colour of those they allow in!

They saw many tanks wherein girls sported, embracing their own images as nothing else could match them; lotuses and lilies, blue and white, leaves of tendrils spread out wide, red leafed *kitai*, frisky carps and the pregnant *varaal*, made these tanks a sight for the gods.

They saw groves full of women looking like peacocks and flowery stalks, trading sweet words with parrots and putting heavenly nymphs to shame. More graceful than the swans were these maidens; bees applauded their dainty hands, even when they snatched the flowers from their mouths.

As they stood before the maidens' mansion where swans played in joyous abandon, the sheen of gold, the scent of flowers, the taste of honey and melodious music—all assailed their senses and held them in thrall.

Even as they were walking in wide-eyed wonder, they saw in front the golden fortress with a ditch around, fed by the bubbling waters of the Ganga. The sheen of gold, the scent of flowers and the honey-sweet sound of melodious verse assailed them and made them halt before the mansion. And looking up, they saw the wide-eyed Sita!

Poets from Brahma down, seeking hard to define beauty, take Lakshmi who dwells in heaven as a paragon. But with Lakshmi herself now incarnate Sita, who shall we look to for comparison?

Her eyes were more graceful than a gazelle's. They outshone the spear and the sword in dazzling brightness and outstripped the carp in agile movement. Her boundless beauty seemed a rarer nectar than what once rose from the milky ocean.

'Give us another damsel like her,' the gods might beg, but Brahma can't oblige. Even that bountiful milky ocean could yield its nectar only once.

Seeing her beauty, bright-eyed Menaka and all other nymphs, much sought after by the gods above, became sick at heart, their moonlight killed by her perpetual day!

She left her lotus-throne to dwell among us. Whom shall we thank for this great honour? Stern sages on ceaseless fasts? The earth, the sky or the gods up above? Or do we owe it to Dharma's generosity?

Fair beyond thought she stood there. Her eyes met Rama's and, stunned, they feasted upon each other. Their souls, no longer in their own possession, became one.

The hero gazed long and so did she! Into his powerful shoulders her look drove a pair of spears, while his large red eyes, those of a conquering hero's, rested on the charmer's breasts.

Bound by devouring looks, the bowman-hero and the sword-eyed maid seemed to merge into one another, finding their sanctuary in each other's hearts. The spotless pair who were once together on the milky ocean, had been apart a brief while and were now together again. They stood speechless. When separated lovers meet, what need of words?

When the prince had gone beyond the reach of her eyes, she became still as a picture, her gaze endless and unwinking. The love that had entered her eyes went searching in vain for the one who had stolen her heart. Distressed in mind, she pined and stayed mute. Kama, who had shot his arrow, added fuel to the fire.

Her long eyes, that reached her earrings, were distracted; her tresses and clothes loosened, she became a green tendril wilting in a flame. Her golden complexion lost, and firmness of mind gone, she looked like the sea denuded of all its treasures when churned by the gods.

Jewels in disarray, shame gone, beauty lost and breast wounded by love's shafts, she was a stricken deer. Neither her distressed and bewildered maids in attendance nor her surrogate mothers could solve the mystery of her sudden withdrawal. Greatly worried, they performed the protective arati, to ward off the evil eye, swirling before her a plate of red rice and yellow water.

They then took her to a bed, spread with leaves and sprouts, soft and soothing. Her jewels and garlands scorched her, her body burnt in the fire set ablaze by waving fans. The princess looked like a statue of gold melting in a fierce flame.

'Who is this cruel man, barging into me so unceremoniously and melting and destroying my steadfast mind and blameless womanhood? He cannot be the God of Love, for that lucky bow on his rock-like shoulders was not a thing of sugarcane.

'The womanly virtue of bashfulness I was born with has now deserted me. The one who on sore feet walked away, must have entered through my eyes and robbed me of it! Will these eyes of mine ever see that prince again and get to know him before I die?'

Thus in that maidens' mansion she lay on her bed of flowers, her mind aflame with unrequited love. Let us now turn our attention to that hero who had glimpsed a lightning.

The three of them went and met the king who welcomed them with delight and lodged them in a tall mansion in that golden town. The sage and his brother having departed to their sleeping quarters, Rama, that dark hero, was left with the night, the moon and thoughts of that maid.

'Can lightning discharged by a cloud take, I wonder, the shape of a woman? I don't know how else to explain what I see in my mind and my two eyes.

'Though heartlessly she has devoured me with her terrible, venomous eyes, I see in all things moving or still, only her golden image. A jewelled middle, two long sword-eyes, and a pair of arrogant breasts, a smile held back tight in the mouth—does Death need so many missiles?

'If a bow of sugarcane and shafts of flowers can so easily vanquish me, where indeed, I should like to know, is that thing called strength to be found? The moonlight spreading far and wide, as if the milky ocean was boiling over in a flood, seems determined to pierce my innermost being. Can poison be clothed in white?

'Since my mind can never tread a path that is not right, there is no need for further proof that the jewelled maiden, so ravishing, is a girl unwed.'

When that night, seeming an aeon, came somehow to an end, he rose and performed the rites that tradition had prescribed. Then the sage took the two of them to Janaka's *yaga* ground. When the sacrifice was completed to the sound of thunderous drums, Janaka moved to a neighbouring hall of vast proportions.

He then seated the sage, Rama and Lakshmana on high thrones set with precious gems. Struck by the beauty of the princes, the king begged to be introduced to them.

'These guests of yours,' said the sage, 'are sons of the mighty Dasaratha, come to see your *yaga*. They'd like to have a look at your bow too.'

THE BOW

'What!' said the king, astonished, 'My heart quivers in anticipation! If indeed this youth can string it, I shall have crossed the sea of my sorrow and my girl will be truly blessed.'

He then ordered his men to bring out that mountainous bow. Obeying the king's command, four men ran to where it stood, wrapped in bonds of gold. Sixteen thousand men of might, strong as tuskers and with rock-like shoulders, carried it on supporting poles.

To the relief of Earth's broad back and the shame of tall Meru, the bow changed place. Those who saw it were amazed to see it occupy every inch of the space in the hall.

'Where is the one who can string this bow?' they thought. 'To call it a bow,' they exclaimed, 'is a false description. It is a mountain of gold.'

'Brahma didn't create it with his hands but obtained it through the power of his penance,' they said.

'Is this a bow or is it the mighty Meru? Is it the ocean-churner? Is it Ananta, the king of serpents? Or Indra's bow, fallen from the sky?'

'Why did he order this to be brought? Are there other kings as mad as Janaka? Who knows, fate may yet prevail. Has the bride ever looked at this? Will Vishnu, sitting there, string it for sure? Alas, our wretched fate!' Thus the words buzzed around.

The bow that had been pressing down on earth was set before the king. Some vassal kings who had come to see it and try their luck, threw up their hands in despair.

Then Rama rose, like a flame that leaps up when ghee is poured. 'Done for, the bow!' the gods exclaimed, and relieved were the sages. 'Too heavy is that bow,' some opined. 'Too bleak her life, alas,' they said mournfully, doubtfully shaking their heads, 'if her soft hand remains unclasped by this hero here!'

Hands clasped in prayer, they said, 'Dear God, make this man string the bow and gladden our hearts. Else it is meet that Sita and we, the people of Mithila, all court death by fire.'

'How utterly silly of our king,' said some women, 'to ask a mere boy to string Siva's bow? If he was truly bent upon on this match, he should simply have given him his daughter's hand, no strings attached!'

'How shameless of the sage!' said some others; 'How heartless of the king!' they thought. 'If this young man can't bend the bow, what use her breasts? Her life a wreck!'

While matrons and maids thus bemoaned Sita's fate, the sages cheered and the gods in heaven were filled with joy.

Putting to shame bulls and elephants, the hero strode, majestic. Effortlessly he lifted and held aloft that mountainous bow that glittered gold, as if it were a garland with which to wed bejewelled Sita.

They watched with bated breath, eyes unwinking, but didn't see the toe pressed or the string fixed. The lifted bow they saw as a flash and only heard the thunder of its crash!

'Broken now is the great orb Brahma created! Where shall we run for refuge?' the gods in heaven lamented, wilting. With those immortals in such a state, what need to speak of mere earthlings?

Heaven rained flowers and clouds rained gold. Flashing seas and oceans acclaimed the feat and scattered gems. Hordes of sages blessed the hero. Janaka, king of lancers, said in unbearable happiness, 'At long last, my good deeds have borne fruit!'

Their jet-black eyes reddened with the toddy they had drunk, women clasped their mates in wild abandon, their shyness shrugged off like white clouds that sucked the surging waves. The poor and the needy helped themselves freely to the kings's wealth.

'Dasaratha's son,' said some in wonder; 'The lotus-eyed one,' said others in a trance. 'Is this real or are we being tricked? This is no man but the very God of the mighty ocean!' they thought.

'Our lady needs a thousand eyes to take in this lad's beauty. And he will need a thousand eyes each time he looks at her. How blessed is our world! Bless the sage who brought them here!'

Let us now set forth what happened to that golden maiden. When the moon and the night departed, she recovered somewhat in the hope of seeing that prince again. 'If only I can see that chest again, with its bow like mount Meru!

'If I could but glimpse those shoulders, each like a pillar, and the sacred thread that shone white like a moonbeam dancing on the waves, my life will return to me,' she told herself.

'O tireless breasts, forever surging, what good are your leaps towards the phantom memory of his serene face? If you want to find a way to clasp that chest with its mountainous bow, take the steps that will lead to that consummation.

'Like a fool who lets slip from his hand a golden jug full of nectar churned out of the milky ocean, I let slip the chance to clasp those mighty shoulders. What use lamenting now and at such great length?'

(Her heart all sore, she lay there sighing and sobbing in turn, even as a maid came to her. Instead of bowing in the customary fashion, the pert maid, her eyes black and mind cool, she made a racket, sang and danced in exultation. For she had witnessed the breaking of that mountainous bow.)

'Tell me, my beauty, your joy's source,' she was asked by a puzzled Sita, whereupon she bowed and said: 'The son of mighty Dasaratha, handsomer than Madan, Rama by name, has come to our city with his younger brother and a renowned sage.

'The royal youth had come to see great Siva's bow, our king was told, whereupon the bow was duly brought in. And wonder of wonders! he strung it at once, setting heaven and earth atremble!

'Foot pressed, in a second he bent that bow as if it were a long-learnt trick. And to our terror, the bow broke and fell! The gods applauded and rained flowers,' said the maid, excited and exultant.

'It must be he, that has done this, the raincloud I saw yesterday walking with the sage,' Sita thought with mounting excitement. Her tender breasts swelled and grew hard. 'Sure it is the same man she has described or else,' she vowed to herself, 'I'll die.'

Elsewhere, Janaka, in a voice that drowned the crash of that bow Brahma had made, asked of Kausika: 'Answer, my lord, is it your wish that your son should wed forthwith or should I invite with the beat of drums the hero's father and his army?'

'It will be good,' replied the sage, 'if he can come without delay.' Bursting with joy, the king sent his men to Ayodhya to tell Dasaratha all that had happened in Mithila.

JOURNEY TO MITHILA

Swift messengers, running like the wind, reached Ayodhya and touched the feet of that great king and gave him Janaka's message. When he learnt of his eldest son's feat, his heart swelled with pride. 'Was it the breaking of Siva's bow that made that great noise we heard the other day?' he said in wonder.

He then loaded the envoys with lavish gifts and announced at once his departure to Mithila, accompanied by his vassal princes, counsellors, army chiefs and others.

Led by a convoy of mountainous elephants and prancing horses, the king and his three wives got into a chariot and started their joyous journey to Mithila.

It was a grand march through a lovely countryside of forests and groves, hills and rivers, wherein countless young men and women sported with abandon.

The king and his entourage saw with delight innumerable sights that warmed the hearts of the old and made the blood of young men race.

They saw creepers weighed down with fragrant flowers and trees giving prodigally of fruits of every kind. Deer, elephants and snakes roamed as one, unafraid of one another.

Mountain or grove, forest or river, men and women made love, intoxicated as much by passion as by the wine they sipped.

They saw couches of flowers and discarded garlands everywhere. They also saw gobs of red betel, half-chewed and spat out, wine cups left half drunk by red-lipped women, left for bees, beetles and wasps to feed on.

They saw uxorious husbands doting on decorous wives and dissolute roués left sapless by women who sell their gold-decked middles. Fulfilled love and thwarted lust, joyous encounters and disappointed waiting—there was evidence of all the varied moods of love.

Enchanted by the lovely countryside, men and women in the king's train enjoyed themselves thoroughly. Looking at the coconuts on a tree, a chieftain in Dasaratha's entourage exclaimed, 'How like a woman's breasts!' At which his wife fumed, 'Which woman's?'

Upon sighting a flowery pool humming with bees, they plunged into it and sported with reckless abandon. Some women clasped their husbands' chests, some men splashed water on their wives; some others, afraid of the swordfish, clung to each other.

Fragrant powder and garlands of flowers were flung at each other. Pushing their long tresses back, women with waists like lightning and shoulders like bamboos, rose from the water. Some asked the swans to come and play with them, wincing even when flowers hit their tender breasts.

Sweet-tressed women on well-laid beds, all eager for sexual contests, imbibed fresh wine from golden goblets, as if it were nectar churned from the milky ocean! No apsaras from heaven could compare with these earthly women of flesh and blood, from whose lips wine drooled like honey from flowers.

Their tresses fragrant with flowers and myrrh, the wine they drank was like ghee poured into sacred fire, setting ablaze their dormant passion.

A bright-browed one, with killing eyes and words like nectar, saw herself reflected in the wine she held in her hand and said to that image, 'Come, sup with me, you beauty!'

Whether due to toddy or sex, red lips lost their colour and the mouth its saliva. The breast was bare, the garment awry, and loosened hair and words from loosened tongues flew around.

Her arms bedecked, a peacock in looks, she flashed a smile with her pearl-like teeth. But tears rolled down her *kayal* eyes, when her husband called her by her co-wife's name.

Why should it be a matter for wonder when a woman puts away her jewels and clothes or even her shame? Doesn't a true ascetic discard every single thing he owns? Love too is quite capable of giving up its very self!

A young man like Madan, peerless, and a young woman like Sri, engaged in a combat of love, neither yielding to the other; both alike, their life one, their senses identical—who vanquished whom?

A peacock from a *ragi* field, full of wrath at her husband's lies, engaged in a war of love with him. But what triumphed in that war was not the wrath on her face but the love in her heart!

With eyes that pierced like deadly spears and limbs that pierced her clothes, she clasped her husband's rock-like chest. And then she checked his back to see if her breasts had pierced him!

Amidst such frolic, the king himself stood like Mount Mandara surrounded by the divine nymphs that emerged from the sea as nectar was churned.

(It was a sight for the gods.
The night wore on and the moon withdrew. And up the dark sea came the sun, resplendent like the queen·jewel on Vishnu's

chest. The king of kings thereupon resumed his journey towards Mithila, the fabulous capital of Janaka's kingdom.)

THE WELCOME

Dasaratha, wise and just, reached the Ganga with his army. Laden as they were with thousands of weapons, they drank so much of the water that the river shrank and one could see down to the Naga world that lay beneath its white sands. Denied supplies, even the brackish water of the sea thirsted in vain for Ganga's bounty.

Heart pounding at the king's approach, Janaka met him halfway. It was like the moon greeting the sun. Decorated with tassels and peacock plumes, their white umbrellas shut the sky out, eclipsing light and spreading darkness. But this darkness was dispelled by the gold worn by the men of the two armies.

When Dasaratha, the faultless king of kings, and Janaka, the sage among kings and king among sages, drew forward to greet each other, the scented powder sprinkled by onlookers and the pollen from the flowers flung upon them were the only dust on the road!

Saffron mixed with *akhil* and paste of sandal and the musth dripping from elephants were the only mire on the road! The victory flags and white umbrellas of the two kings provided welcome shade for the tired concourse.

When they arrived together into the gracious city of Mithila, the one whose hue was the colour of dark-blue flowers, approached his father. It was a touching sight, as though the wayward soul was returning to its mislaid body.

He fell at his father's feet, and rising, was embraced and the lofty shoulders that broke the bow disappeared into the chest of that second Manu. Dasaratha, whose righteous rule had served as a model to the world, gave leave to his son to proceed ahead of him.

THE BRIDEGROOM'S PARADE

Blessed muse! Inspire me to accomplish the impossible task of describing the thoughts of the swooning women that rushed to see the first of gods as he went down the streets of Mithila paved with gold.

A herd of deer, a flock of peacocks, they were the city's jewels. Hair adrift and wet with flowers, they swarmed around, waistlets slipping, garments loosened and gait unbalanced, saying breathlessly, 'Make way, make way!'

Red-soled girls from mighty mansions whose tops were always capped with clouds, crowded all available space. Bracelets tinkling, tresses unbound, anklets keeping prescribed time, breasts surging, women from five to forty made dance halls of the streets.

Covered with maidens pierced by Madan's flowery arrows, there was not an inch of space to spare on the streets of the city. Sandal paste dripped off perspiring breasts, bangles of conch slid off delicate hands and chaplets of flowers came undone from unbound tresses; yet there they stood, eager to catch a glimpse of that hero of heroes.

Like water rushing into a pit, their dark eyes larger than the sea, they ran, straining their slender waists, as if to overtake their hearts that had gone in pursuit of the hero.

'It is Love in person we see with our eyes. We will reap the benefit of womanhood today,' said they, eager to lap him up with their eyes, like a deer herd that had sighted water on land gone dry with no rain.

Though the chariot drawn by leaping horses moved sedately, it seemed to the women, waiting impatiently for but a glimpse of incomparable Rama, as though it sped faster than their own thoughts. 'The one who caught and held in her eye and the one who'd measured earth and heaven are indeed blessed,' they said fervently.

One there was, whose years should have made her more discreet, who seemed to have thrown to the winds every womanly virtue. Delicacy and innocence, womanly reserve and decorum, family pride and personal reputation, were all abandoned, along with her clothes and bangles. Left with only her life, she stood forlorn.

Whether the maids darkened the rims of their eyes by gazing at Rama, or he it was who got his dark complexion from their eyes, we do not know. There stood one, fair as Lakshmi, the very picture of love ineffable, drawn by a great artist: she felt even her body a burden and threw everything away except the garment on her person.

Then there was that woman, deadly with spear-like eyes, who wondered hopefully if he was alone! Heart weary and brows perspiring, sickly pallor spreading over her limbs, she had eyes only for him!

Another with black hair and red mouth, bright brows and a melting heart, said to her friend, 'I have entrapped the rogue who entered my heart by closing my eyes tight. I'll now tell him, come, let us to bed!'

The racks of dark hair and the ample breasts of those who had managed a place in front hid the view of a generous maiden eager to see him. But she managed to look at him through the empty spaces between those women's narrow waists!

Those who saw his shoulder, his shoulder only saw; those his foot, only his foot; those his arm, only his arm. Which of those sword-like eyes caught his form complete? What single creed grasps God entire?

'Is this a trick or a dream?' said a woman, dark-eyed and bright-browed, 'Instead of coming in a precious carriage he has come alone and stands before me?' A bright-browed, sweet-mouthed one said, 'Come to think of it, such beauty is not human. You will soon discover that this is God himself.'

'Is this man, of purity all compact, capable of love at all?' wondered another, 'He doesn't seem to want a single thing from us women entranced by him. Doesn't he know what mercy is? Is he not of this world or is he a murderer?'

Love-lorn women thus crowding around, the hero, surrounded by kings, reached the hall where Vasishta was waiting with Kausika, expert in the vedas. Lakshmi's lord fell at their feet, his necklace of gems flashing like lightning, like a rainbow in rainy season.

King Dasaratha with his family, looking like the resplendent moon with stars and planets in his train, reached the hall that resembled Vishnu's own throne room. As he bowed to the two sages, a rain of flowers fell from heaven.

The crowned heads of the sixty-four kingdoms under the canopy of heaven came to grace the occasion. Kangas and Kongas, Kalingas and Kulingas and Chola, Chera, Pandiyas of the south; Assamese and Avantikas and Vangas from the north; Malwas, Marathas and heroes from Magadha. Matsya, Mlechcha, Ilada and Vidharba of the middle kingdom; outer Chinese, Dakshinites, Chenchakas, Somakas, Sonakas, Turkis, Kurunadis, Yadavas, Konkanis and the seven-fold Chedis, Telugus and Kannadigas—they all came.

Janaka sat on his throne like a towering tree. Comely maidens stood on either side, waving flywhisks and setting in motion a gentle breeze. Nymph-like maidens with divine voices sang the invocatory benediction, to the accompaniment of lutes and flutes.

What more is there to say than that the happy occasion was marked by ample evidence of Janaka's munificence? In his unbounded joy, he exhausted his treasures, giving everything away in equal measure to all, from the lowliest to Rama himself!

THE ADORNING OF SITA

The royal preceptor Vasishta said to Janaka, 'Please send for the fawn-eyed maid.' Joyous and respectful, the king told his attendant maidens, 'Bring the princess.' Love abounding and heart pounding, those sweet maids went quickly to do the bidding.

This world of ours has never lacked fools who think they can sweeten nectar and beautify beauty. Though the eyelids that shielded her eyes were jewels enough, those charged with adorning her loaded her with more, hiding her charms.

They put a chaplet of flowers on her head, making her face look like the moon in the rain cloud of her dark hair. Her fluttering hair, the colour of her lord, like her thoughts of him, fluttered around like flags in the air.

They decked her ears with dazzling drops that oscillated to and fro like her own heart, which did not know who the breaker of Siva's bow was. Was he the same who had shattered her life and seized all her womanliness? Or was he another—a different one? Were they the same or were they not?

How to describe the pearls on her breast? A galaxy of stars unerring? Pieces of the flashing crescent? One of her own bashful smiles?

They put round her waist a lovely waistband set with gems. Under that they fastened a string of pearls that resembled the stars in heaven. On her brow, a red lotus with two blue lilies, they put a kumkum mark, a beauty spot on one who was herself a beauty spot.

(The dazzling brightness of the bride was enough to blind the eyes of those engaged in her adornment.)

Her vermilion breasts, full and surging, were a burden to her slender waist. Her slender shoulders had no rivals excepting bamboos, and were adorned with blinding pearls and gems.

Her middle was like a cobra's hood and her feet, red even without painting, were softer than the *aniccham*. The anklets fitted to them sighed, 'How delicate, O how delicate!'

Her eyes like rain, benign and cool and a stranger to theft and deceit, looked as if black venom was embedded in nectar white. Was their blackness due to the collyrium that had been applied along their rims? Or was it borrowed from her lord's rain-cloud hue?

To ward off the evil eye, they went round her with a ghee-fed lamp, sprinkling water and scattering flowers. They then whirled before her the arati, ensuring everlasting joy for her, the peacock they had themselves reared.

The dark-haired maidens stood entranced by this full moon with her jewelled breasts. Every woman in our world might boast of one kind of beauty or another. But who can resist all beauties distilled in one?

Like bees sucking honey from a lotus, they fed on her beauty, speechless, transfixed and transformed.

Surrounded by dwarfs and other short women, she entered the great hall like the moon with a host of stars. The sheen of gold and the scent of flowers, the cool of sandal and lightning's flash, all commingled, as she walked with deliberate steps that put swans to shame.

Into the bejewelled hall wherein were gathered kings of fame, she came like a peacock with its plumes spread. Flywhisks fanned her from head to foot; she was like the swans that had come to watch her gait, rising and falling— won't go, won't wait!

She came with dainty steps, the gems in her waistlet scattering light, armed as though with a blazing bow, herself a sword, moving soft and slow. Like the vedas self-created, her pure body and full breasts reduced all the men and women there to unwinking and breathless statues.

Sea-hued Rama saw that ambrosial maid and was straightaway reassured that the goddess before him was the same he had seen in the maidens' mansion.

'This red-lipped koel has brought me down to earth from that high tower,' said the hero to his heart. 'She's the long-churned nectar my virtue has earned; but is all this in my mind or has it an existence in the real world?'

When that sweet-tongued maiden arrived, all except the sages and kings closed their palms above their heads, convinced that she was a goddess. Isn't our body our mind's slave?

She, who had left her lotus-seat to enter a king's palace, bowed to the emperor and sages and took her seat near her father, whose eyes were dewed with tears.

Kausika, the archetype of sages, thought: 'If this is indeed the lotus maiden, won't Rama, that mountain of jade, break for her not just this one bow but all the seven mountains of the world?'

She'd heard the story of the bow, of how it had been bent and broken. And now, she saw the truth for herself and shed her fear. Even so, with a glance from the corner of her eyes, as if to adjust her bangle, she made sure that the youth in front was indeed the one in her heart.

Dasaratha, the king of kings, then asked Vishwamitra, the master of learning: 'What day, great sage, is best for the wedding?' To which he replied: 'Lord of fertile fields, tomorrow is a suitable day.'

This settled, Dasaratha, surrounded by his vassal kings, left for his palace. The swan-girl too, though loath to do so, left. The kings having departed, the sages too exited, and the sun sank behind the Meru.

THE WEDDING

Back in her palace:

'O cruel night,' Sita said, 'who will kill a weakling treacherously? Let the sun but rise and my lord will be gone!

'O mind of mine, eagerly would you go with that dark sun, and with him return. You, who have been so long with me, can't you stay just one day more?

'O moon, why do you wish to torture me, an innocent waning day by day, with your beams, a sharp lance burning like the hot sun?

'O south wind, cool and fragrant, though not to me! Why are you, with your hot breath and moon-beam fangs, prowling for my life like a tiger in a cave?'

'Why does a warrior of rain-cloud hue roam the street night and day, trailing an unwed girl? Does this become a prince well-bred?

'If that cruel man, dark and wicked, won't come to me, would it be proper for me to seek him? Is this night a black sea, shoreless and lasting aeons?

'The songs don't stop, the day doesn't dawn; thoughts don't flee, night doesn't end; heartache lasts, life doesn't leave; and eyes don't close—O what a fate!

'Tell me, Sea, are you too a maiden cowed down by Madan's killing shafts? Your bangles loose, body weary, now up, now down, are you too a stranger to sleep?'

While thus she spoke distracted, tired and distressed but in virtue firm, let us tell what went through the mind of the spotless one that night in his palace.

'I saw her but once and my boundless love drew with my eyes her picture in my heart. I saw her again, but have yet to see the fullness of her beauty. Who can grasp the lightning?

'O moon, love's embryo, manure, seed and fruit, all in one, what have you done? Are you incapable of helping one who is helpless and alone?

'The night has spread like the dark eyes of the one who has taken possession of me, squeezing my very life out of me. It won't grow less, like the shame of a man who deserts his lord in the field of battle to save his life.

'My mind! You who have gone with that gazelle, have you lost all memory of me? Is it that you don't think of me, or is the distance too great for you? Or is it that you will not bid goodbye to one who cares not to ask who you are?

'That poison is only to be found in the fangs of snakes whose eyes spit fire is an ancient story. In my case, it is in the soft glance of one forever embedded in my eyes and heart.

'When there are so many mountains, flowery lakes and groves around, why should a honey-tongued, bright-tressed woman choose my heart for her playground?'

While the divine lord was thinking thus, announcements were being made to the accompaniment of drum beats from atop elephants: Sita's wedding was to be held the next day and the city should be decked with gems and flowers.

Women with the gait of swans and men who strode like bulls erected banana trees and arecanut stems around the hall. Many hung streamers and set jewelled pots on the tops of mansions.

Others sprinkled the streets with sandal-paste water, scattered petals of fragrant flowers and let down from housetops strings of pearls, whose colours put the rainbow to shame.

They placed on crystal *pials* resembling the moon, various kinds of lamps, big and small: huge jewelled ones that burnt like the sun, small ones with lambent wicks and tall ones that burnt like torches. In addition, they prepared pots full of cool and tender sprouts.

Kings arrived, brahmins assembled, as did lovers of music; wandering minstrels, handmaids galore and those appointed to mark time. Groups of courtesans and diverse artists crowded around, jostling against each other, waiting for Janaka.

As the king of kings wended his way to that enormous wedding hall, gold-roofed and tall as a hill, auspicious drums sounded like thunder.

Conches blew and trumpets and tabors raised a din. The vedas chanted by the brahmins were like the roar of the sea at night.

Chariots, elephants and prancing horses followed in large numbers carrying kinsmen and vassal kings, forever bowing in his direction.

Thus he went to that hall and ascended his golden seat set with gems. The sages and kings sat in their order and Janaka, too, took his seat. Kings, sages and gods, and maidens with swan-like gait filled up that matchless hall, making it resemble the golden Meru.

Let us talk now of the one who left his snake-bed for Ayodhya. After a bath in the waters brought from the seven seas and also from Ganga and other holy rivers, he bowed to the Primal Splendour and gave the brahmins the gifts prescribed.

The embodiment of grace eternal, the one who had been born to bring back penance and virtue, appeared resplendent. The sandal paste smeared on his rain-cloud person shone like flashes of lightning.

Flawless earrings, like the sun and the moon, whispered messages in his ears, as if Sita had sent them to acquaint him with her thoughts of love.

An upper garment hung from his neck like a string of pearls, a symbol of his grace. The sacred thread he wore on his chest was unmatched in brightness, proclaiming to all his true identity, beyond the grasp of gods and sages. Shining thus, he who had left his snake-bed in the milky ocean for their sake, revealed his unique self.

The hero stepped down from the chariot with Bharata and his other brothers, bowed to the sages, and touched the feet of the king, his father, and took his seat.

Her face the moon, her brow a bow, her eyes two quivering fish, Sita came in a chariot from the east, her smile bringing to mind a jasmine flower. Born first in the milky ocean, then issuing from the earth, she now seemed to spring from a mountain to reach the marriage hall.

How can I, with my feeble wit, describe her in her wedding attire, her beauty exceeding the beauty of all on earth, in heaven and below? The grateful gods saw the hero and thought, 'How much more beautiful is today than the day on which the winsome maid, churned from the ocean, wedded her lord!'

Janaka, pouring the cool water, said, 'Firm with my daughter may your union be, like Vishnu's with his consort, Lakshmi,' and placed her palm in his lotus hand.

The hero recited all the mantras, poured the ghee into the fire and took the tender hand of the bride in his own big and sturdy one. Walking behind his broad shoulders around the sacred and blazing fire, the gentle girl was the very symbol of a body pursuing its beloved soul in the ceaseless cycle of births and deaths.

They circled the fire, left to right, with the amulet thread around their wrists and finished the rest of the rites. Then she, Arundhati in person, chaste and unwavering, set her foot on the grinding stone and looked at her husband.

The brahmins' blessings, the auspicious songs of married women and felicitations from kings and poets reverberated like the sound of a million conches. The rain of flowers, fresh and bright, by gods, kings and commoners, made the earth look like the sky scattered with stars.

The rest of the rites he performed with joy and crowned his head with the sages' feet, after which he fell before his father in obeisance. Then, taking the braceleted girl by her hand, he went into his own residence.

PARASURAMA

After blessing the newly-wed couple, Kausika went north to the Great Mountain. Rama and Janaka's daughter spent several happy days together. Then,

The mighty king said one day, 'Let the army leave for our city.' He then ascended his peerless chariot as vassal kings bowed. His sons and wives at his feet, the mighty king took the road to Ayodhya. Mithila's citizens were plunged in sorrow, as if their own bodies were parting with their souls.

That king, majestic like an elephant, saw peacocks flying to his right and crows fluttering to his left, impeding movement. He stopped his chariot, sent for an augur and asked him if these omens were good. Well versed in bird-lore, the augur said, 'There will be trouble, but all shall finally end well.'

Just then came one, whose flaming hair pierced the darkness of the sky. Axe in hand, eyes darting fire, he was a walking hill with a thunderous voice! On seeing him, Dasaratha's entire army fled in fright.

For one king's single sin, that axe of his had hacked a thousand shoulders of jewels among kings, like so many branches of a tree. He had then bathed in blood that rose like the sea. He'd thus decimated root and branch twenty-one generations of the Kshatriya race.

In thundering rage, brows beetling, he approached the chariot carrying the prince with the lovely eyes. A bull confronting a lion, he asked, 'Who is this?'

Anxious to placate the irate wielder of the axe, the king placed his chapleted head at his feet. But the rage of the avenger of the race of kings was like a sea that couldn't be crossed. Blazing like the fire of Dissolution, he addressed the hero:

'I know the strength of the bow you broke and will now test the strength of your jewelled shoulders. My shoulders too are itching a little. For no other reason have I come,' he said arrogantly.

On hearing this, the distressed king pleaded: 'You conquered the world and gave it to a sage. Siva, Vishnu and Brahma are nothing to you. Is a poor mortal of any account? You now hold to ransom both his life and mine.

'With your battleaxe belching fire, it is the wicked you should kill. Has he wantonly done any wrong? Why should the strong, whot should engage the strong, expend their strength on the weak?'

'O mighty sage with shoulders like pillars of stone! My son is not your foe. Should he die, I too will die, with my people and kin. Don't destroy me along with my race, I beg of you,' he beseeched.

Ignoring Dasaratha who fell at his feet, the fiery-eyed ascetic went to Rama resplendent. Utterly helpless, the king collapsed like a snake struck by lightning.

Unmindful of the great king's reaction and of his own fate lying in wait in the womb of Time, he said, 'That bow which was Siva's once, was cracked. Listen to its history now,' he confronted Rama.

'My enmity, Manava, is not with you but with your race. A diabolical king killed my guiltless father. With my battle-axe, sharp and joyous, I've killed twenty-one royal descendants and with their blood offered libations to my dead father.'

He paused a while and then added, 'There once were two matchless bows, strong and imperishable like Mount Meru, made by one no earthling can approach.

'One of these Uma's husband liked and the other was taken by the one who measured the world. Which of these is the stronger one, the gods wondered and asked Brahma. To settle the question, Brahma contrived that the two, regarded as the foremost of gods, should fight each other with their bows.

'They strung the bows and the seven worlds trembled, the quarters changed places, fierce fires broke out all over. In the fight that ensued, Siva's bow cracked. Undaunted, he decided to resume the fight. However, the gods separated them.

'Siva then gave his bow to Indra. Proving himself the victor, Vishnu gave his to sage Richika and left. Richika gave it to my father and he, in turn, gave it to me.

'I reside in the mountain over there. I heard with my ears the sound of Siva's bow broken by you and have come here in a rage.

'To break a damaged bow is nothing. Take this bow from me, string it and fight me, if you dare. If you, lad, can bend it, no king will ever rival you and I shall abandon my cause.'

Thus he spoke, and Rama smiled. His face shining, he said, 'Give me that bow, Vishnu's victorious one.' He took it, and to the terror of that sage, bent it.

'You killed all the kings on this earth. But since you are the son of a vedic sage and a tapasvi too, I shall not kill you. But this shaft can't be denied its target. Show one to me quick.'

'O righteous one,' the sage replied, 'do not be angry. I know now that you are the First, the one with garland and discus. How could that bow which Siva wielded not break in your hand?

'That the arrow you aim should not go vain, I concede readily. Let it destroy all my penances,' he said. Rama's hand released the arrow, and it promptly gathered all of the rishi's penances and came back.

'O lord with the hue of the purest gem, garlanded with the basil, you are the refuge of all! May all your wishes be well fulfilled. Grant me leave to go.' So saying, he bowed and left.

The immaculate Rama then restored to his father the life he'd almost lost through fear. His senses regained, his sorrows ended, that great king plunged into an ocean of happiness. He embraced his son, kissed his head, bathed with tears the incomparable prince who had taken from that heartless man his bow and loaded him with shame.

Of the many gods that rained flowers on him, Rama chose Varuna to bestow the bow. 'Guard well this bow that is at once a boon and a bane.'

Filled with unalloyed happiness, Dasaratha left for Ayodhya with his matchless son.

Then, one happy day, the great king sent for Bharata and told him, 'Dear son, your grandfather, king of Kekaya, is most desirous of seeing you. So, my handsome boy, you must go and spend sometime with him.'

Thus bidden, Bharata went to Rama, and with his blessings, reluctantly left, taking only his body to the Kekaya capital, leaving his soul behind. Many things happened thereafter, which shall be told by and by.

AYODHYA KANDAM

MANTARA'S PLOT

(It was as if Ravana's sins had taken the form of a lock of Dasaratha's hair and whispered into his ears: 'The time has come for you to yield this land to your son and depart for the forest.' The emperor sent for his ltearned counsellors headed by Vasishta, the royal preceptor, to consult them on this idea.

'You are my conscience keepers,' he said. 'I have taken an important decision. I can no longer bear the burden of this earth. So I must leave the kingdom to Rama, go to the forest, and start a great penance to end this life of delusion. What do you advise?'

All of them said with one voice that it was a wise decision. Vasishta said approvingly: 'O king! This action of yours becomes you and is truly virtuous.' The assembly of kings nodded, 'Who can ever stand in the way of the village pond filling up or of rain waters flooding a river and its canals?'

Rama was sent for and told of the decision. He was neither happy nor unhappy to hear it, looking on it as a duty to be fulfilled. The people of Ayodhya became delirious with joy upon hearing the news. After consulting the astrologers, the royal preceptor fixed the very next day for Rama's coronation.

When news reached Kausalya, she was thrilled and rewarded the messenger with many gifts. Preparations for the great event began with competitive enthusiasm. And then intervened fate in the form of Mantara, the hunchback servant-companion of Kaikeyi.

With the city in a bustle over preparations for that momentous event, there appeared on the scene Kuni, uniquely evil, as if she were Ravana's sins personified. With unwavering anger in her heart, her mind tortured and eyes belching fire, the crookback was set upon plunging the three worlds in pain.

Still brooding over the balls of mud that Rama, as a boy, had shot at her years ago, mouth twisted with vengeful anger, she went to red-lipped Kaikeyi's palace.)

As if she were a coral creeper or the lovely lotus of the milky ocean, Kaikeyi lay on a resplendent bed, decked with jewels from the four seas, eyes bright and shining.

Kuni, an evil planet, caught hold of Kaikeyi's small golden feet. She, divinely fair, didn't bother to open her long eyes.

Egged on by hostile fate to do its dirty work, Kuni started her tales. 'Lady, they say that even when the fell serpent slithers close, the cool full moon shines on, losing none of its virtue. You too slumber on unconcerned when great disaster threatens you.'

When that venomous woman said this, spear-eyed Kaikeyi said, 'My boys, victorious bowmen, are well, each in his station, wedded to virtue. What danger can threaten me here? All those who have worthy sons are assured of freedom from sorrow. And what sorrow need I fear who has Rama, the vedas in person, for a son?'

When thus she spoke out of her deep love for Rama, the crookback, hovering around like sin, said, 'Fallen your good; fallen your fortune. Kausalya has outsmarted you.'

The exquisite jewel, still unconcerned, replied, 'With the king of kings for my husband, and priceless Bharata for my son, what greater glory can she claim as hers?'

'Rama,' the crookback answered, 'that blot on manhood, the one who deserves the jibes of true warriors for killing Tataka, a woman, against all canons of Dharma, will be crowned tomorrow. That will be Kausalya's glory, not yours.'

The love in her heart roared like the sea, her face grew bright like a moon that would never wane. In her great joy she, a queen among flawless jewels, gave Mantara a necklace in appreciation for the news she had brought her.

The cruel crookback shouted and screamed; her small eyes shed fire; she railed and ranted; sighed hot sighs of frustration; finally, shedding tears, she tore at her clothes and turning down the gift, flung it down so hard it dented the earth.

The ill-boding hunchback glared daggers at Kaikeyi and said, 'You are a fool. For this lofty impartial generosity, you and the son who is born of you will suffer. You may think nothing of it, but I won't serve your co-wife's servants.

'When the red-lipped Sita and that dark one sit pretty on a throne with your son as their despised servitor, what cause is there to rejoice?

'If indeed, Rama with Lakshmana is to rule over the world, it'd be better for displaced Bharata to go with Satrughna to the forest on a long penance. Not numbered among those in the line of succession, Bharata might as well be dead.

'I now see the reason why the king sent luckless Bharata away to a far off place,' Mantara continued with her tirade. 'A father cruel and partial, his own mother unmindful and cruel, alas, Bharata! What will you do? Your beauty, valour, shining youth, boundless energy, rare skill in archery and countless other virtues—what use are they? Nothing but nectar spilt on grassy ground.'

Mantara's words, so cruel and bitter, were ghee poured on a blazing fire. They made Kaikeyi's red-streaked, carp-fish eyes, even redder,

She said: 'Wicked woman, what petty words to damage the name of the solar race, which, even if life and all else fail, will never fail to observe the code. You are doing no good, neither to me nor to my son, Bharata; not even to yourself.

'Thoughtlessly, by fate inspired, you have said what seemed right to you. Go away, idiot, and keep your mouth shut. I have let your mean tongue unslit too long. Should others know, they will hold you guilty of premeditated malice.'

Mantara heard her, unmoved and unafraid. Like poison that cannot be purged, she persisted with her wicked pleas. 'My refuge! I won't cease trying to make you see the truth,' she said and fell at the queen's feet.

'O lovely creeper! Even rishis full of virtue change once they acquire power. Those who may not want to hurt you now might in future cause you unending pain.

'If her son becomes king, jealous Kausalya will claim the whole world for herself. What will remain for you or your son to command except what she chooses to give you?

'When men, impelled by pain or poverty, come begging to you, how will you give them relief? Beg of her? Refuse them succour? Feel ashamed and die? How will you live?

'What holds you back? Think. If your father, mother or any kin of your race come to you in their hour of need, will all the wealth they see belong to your co-wife?

'Sita's father, Rama's father-in-law, has so far spared your father out of fear of your loving husband. Has your father a future?

'Fool! Your father has many enemies; when beset by foes, without help from here, how will he cope? You have ruined your rare son. The great kingdom the emperor has entrusted to his first son will go *to his* son, not another.'

(Because the gods had thus planned it and the penance of the sages had now to bear fruit, these words of sinful Mantara corrupted the pure mind of the queen. She lost her head. But for her fate-driven heartlessness, would we have been given a taste of the nectar of Rama's legendary fame?)

Her mind now changed, Kaikeyi looked fondly at Kuni, Fate's own agent, and said, 'You have saved me, done my son immense good by opening my eyes. Now advise me how he can get the crown.'

Mantara, relieved and victorious, said, 'How clever, my friend and succour! Take my advice and the seven worlds will be yours and your son's.

'O lady of dazzling smiles! Remember the two boons the victorious king granted you when Sambaran was quelled? Ask for them, now,' she said, her mind as crooked as her body.

'Of the two boons, get the kingdom with one. And with the other, get Rama exiled to the forest for twice seven years. This entire kingdom will then be your son's, to be enjoyed by you without let or hindrance.'

Gladdened by such sound advice, Kaikeyi embraced the crookback maid, made a gift of a gem-set necklace and said, 'You who have given the earth to my son are from now on the mother of the earth's king.

'Your advice is good. To crown Bharata and drive Rama to the forest will at one stroke ensure my unalloyed happiness. If I fail to get these boons today, I'll die in the king's presence. Goodbye.'

KAIKEYI'S STRATEGY

(After Kuni left, Kaikeyi descended from her bed of flowers, tore off her chaplet from her hair, plucked her waistlet off, threw down her tinkling bracelets, rubbed off from her dazzling forehead the red kumkum. Thus dishevelled, she rolled on the ground, a sprig denuded of its flowers.

The emperor came after midnight to the palace of the sweet-voiced Kaikeyi and saw her lying on the floor, her bed abandoned. His heart sank and he picked her up, trying to clasp her to his heart. But she leapt out of his hands, saying nothing. When the bewildered king asked what had happened, she said, tears rolling down her eyes and flooding her breasts, 'If you really love me, keep your promise of old.')

Knowing nothing of her dark intentions, the king laughed and said, 'I swear by Rama, your great son, I'll do whatever you desire. Tell me at once what you want and ease my burden.'

'Redeem then the two boons you once gave me,' she said. 'The first, my son, Bharata, shall rule the world; the second, Sita's husband shall go rule the forests.'

The instant the cruel poison from that cobra's tongue entered his body, Dasaratha trembled and fell down, an elephant envenomed.

Who can describe that terrible grief? Tongue dry, his life started to flee, his heart shrank and his eyes shed blood. An elephant wounded, and his own spear the cause! The gods shivered as if doomsday had dawned.

But not Kaikeyi. Her eyes like arrows and her heart relentless, she looked on at her husband's sorrow, unmoved. To call her shameless would make one blush.

The shattered king pleaded, 'Are you bewitched? Has someone treacherously put you up to this? Tell me the truth, on my honour.'

'I am not under a spell,' she said, 'nor has anyone evil set me up. If you but grant these boons, I'll take them. Else, to your everlasting shame and scandal, I'll kill myself.'

The words were like a spear thrust in a wound. The astounded king, whose only life was his elder son, collapsed distraught.

Recovering, he wrung his hands, ground his teeth and said, 'That the entire earth be rid of women, I shall kill them all with a keen sword.'

'To punish her,' thought the righteous king, 'not caring for the truth, would be a sin. It'd be better to beg and coax her out of her folly.'

Bent on avoiding evil and choosing to be patient so that good might yet come of it, the mighty monarch, whose feet many kings had kissed in reverence time and again, now fell at Kaikeyi's feet.

'Your son will not accept the kingdom,' he said. 'Even if he does, the world will frown on such an action. And the praise you wish the world proclaim will never be yours. What use then to bear the terrible blame of this heinous act?

'The gods won't approve and earthlings will sulk in silent fury. With whom then will you rule this land? It was I who convinced Rama to be king. And he himself will give the earth to your son.

'I shall give you my very eyes, if you want them. If you want my life, right now you shall have it. O woman! Daughter of generous Kekaya, take the earth if you must, but forget that other thing.

'I will not go back on my promise. Don't say things that will destroy me. Even fiery-eyed devil will, when beseeched, yield like a mother.'

Thus pleaded the king. But the woman, sinful beyond compare, stood unmoved. 'You promised but will not yield. If you dislike it, king, what then? Who will uphold the truth?' she taunted.

'Your son shall rule. All this land shall be yours to rule. I grant you this. I shall not go back on my word. But, my son, my eye, my life, the son of all living things—don't exile him.

'When I see truth itself cutting me down, I am withered. My tongue is dry. Woman! Should he, my son, the one with the lotus hands disappear from my sight, I will not live—you hold my very life in ransom!' he cried.

Impervious to his piteous pleading, malice unabated, heart wooden, shameless and unmindful of blame, she said, 'Mighty bowman! When you ask me to give up my boon, what prompts you is not right but might.'

'Till now women have won fame by dying before their husbands did, not for killing them. Do you, cruel wretch, covet for yourself that kind of fame?' cried the distracted king.

To the king writhing on the ground covered in dust, she said sternly, 'Do I, mighty one, get my boon? Or should I kill myself?'

Lest the monster should do as she threatened, the king moaned, 'Granted, granted. My son shall rule the forest, and I, dead, shall rule the upper regions, while you and your son wallow forever in the mire of blame.'

Ere these words were out, the stricken king swooned and she, her aim fulfilled, sought her rest in sleep. That gentle damsel, Night, departed as if ashamed to show her face after seeing what bright-browed Kaikeyi, one of her own kind, had done to her stalwart husband.

The rooster, marking the passage of the night, beat its breast and cried aloud. Small birds, their hearts aflame, denounced in whispers Kaikeyi's poisonous meanness.

The Sun in the east grew red with wrath at seeing his dear son Dasaratha's life ebbing away as a result of that sinful woman's obstinacy.

Meanwhile, unaware of the thunderbolt that awaited them, the citizens of Ayodhya were wild with excitement as though the seven seas had come together in a giant surge.

(Preparations for the auspicious occasion had been completed. Pots filled with water from all the sacred rivers from the Ganga to the Tambrabarani as well as the four seas, had been brought in.

The great sage, Vasishta, got the sacred fire ready, set up the throne, and completed other formalities. When the astrologers said it was time, he asked Sumantra to bring the king.

Not finding the monarch in his abode and learning that he was with Kaikeyi, Sumantra repaired to her palace. When informed of Sumantra's errand, Kaikeyi bade him bring Rama to her. Suspecting nothing, he crossed the golden streets to Rama's palace.

Finding him in deep meditation, he bowed low and said that the kings, the sages and the rest of the world were waiting for him, but his stepmother wished to see him at once.

On reaching Kaikeyi's palace, Rama was somewhat puzzled not to find his father there as he had expected. He saw Kaikeyi.)

Like a calf welcoming its mother when she returns in the evening, he greeted her, prostrating full length, his hand covering his coral mouth.

The iron-hearted one, cruel as Death, said, 'There is something I must tell you that your father wanted me to convey to you.'

'My father's order passed on by you? What greater happiness in life than to carry it out? Has anyone luckier been born, can there be greater gain! Command, two parents in one! I obey.'

'This sea-girt earth Bharata shall rule, while you, in a rishi's garb, matted locks and all, shall seek the forest, take holy baths and do penance for twice seven years. Thus says the king,' said she.

How can the likes of me describe that lovely face of virtuous Rama, serene, unchanged! It remained, before and after, bright and tranquil as a lotus, fresh-blossomed.

The burden of the world he had agreed to bear only to obey the king's wishes and he was glad to lay it aside, like an ox unyoked from a wagon.

'Even were you, and not the king, to say so, will I refuse? In my brother's well-being and prosperity lies my happiness. What remains to be said? I will act as you bid. This very day I'll seek the forest. I take my leave.'

Bowing to her yet again, and to his father who still lay stunned on the ground, he left, his shoulders higher than the hills, Goddess Earth bewailing his departure.

THE DEPARTURE

(As he approached Kausalya, she saw from a distance that there were no waving fans and no white umbrella over his head. Heart aflutter, she thought, 'Uncrowned? Hair not wet with waters from the holy streams? What is wrong?' Even as he touched her feet, she asked, 'Did anything impede the process of your glorious coronation?')

The noble one replied gently, 'It is Bharata, your beloved son, my younger brother without stain, who will wear the sacred crown.'

'Oh! Though not quite right, he is a thrice-virtuous soul, faultless, even better than you,' said Kausalya, whose love embraced all four. 'The king's command, though strange, must be obeyed. Well, give the land to your brother and may both of you live long.'

Delighted, Rama spoke, 'My own good mother, his majesty issued a second command.' 'What command?' she was puzzled; and he replied, 'For seven and seven years I must in the deep forests dwell, with those who perform stern austerities.'

Bewildered, she blanched. Feeling as though her very womb had been wrung, she screamed. 'Were those words a lie, that the land was yours to rule, a poison to kill me? Great is the king's kindness!' she sneered.

'When do you plan to depart?' She felt like a luckless beggar, who picks up gold only to let it slip through. Crying out, 'O God, what sins have I committed?' she swooned in despair.

Rama helped her up gently. Choosing his words carefully, he said, 'Would you, Mother, make our gracious king a liar, by this behaviour? What greater blessing can there be than not causing my father to break his word, even unawares? Heaven, earth and all the seas may perish, but I can't disobey my father.

'How can you forget, Mother, that Sagaras, our great ancestors, lost their lives while digging the earth at the command of their father? Or Parasurama, the wielder of the axe, obeyed his father and killed his own mother?'

'Then take me with you,' she begged, 'so that I may bear the life that should have ended with your words.'

'How can you say such a thing, Mother? With my departure, the king of kings is plunged in a sea of sorrow. It is now that he needs you most. Once Bharata is king, my father will to the forest hie and it'd then be proper for you to accompany him.

'Please don't stop me, dear Mother. After all, how long is my term? Seven and seven years will flee swift as that many days.

'In the forest, great sages I shall seek and learn rare skills, glean knowledge without sin and return in no time at all.'

(She heard all this and much more, saw that his will was set on exile and accepted the inevitable. Her thoughts now anxiously turned to her husband.)

'Let Bharata rule the land,' she told herself. 'I must see that my husband does not die. If possible, I must seek his help to prevent my son's exile.' And so to the king she hastened.

Upon reaching Kaikeyi's palace and seeing the king lying on the ground, she fell on him like a lifeless corpse and lamented, 'O king of kings, does it become one who ruled the seven worlds not to ask what ails me?'

His body, static lightning, did not move and no words emerged from that still form. Alarmed, crazed with despair, she cried 'O son, come and see the state the king is in!'

Hearing her cry of panic, kings and sages came rushing in and were struck dumb at what they saw. Examining the prone figure, Vasishta said, 'The king isn't dead, only unconscious. But death may not be far off.'

(Looking around, he saw the unmoved Kaikeyi and the distraught Kausalya and exclaimed: 'What motley world is this, where one grieves and another is unconcerned, in the face of disaster?'

Turning to Kaikeyi, who bowed to him first, he asked, 'What

ails the king, daughter?' And Kaikeyi told him everything. He
lifted the emperor's body from the ground, sprinkled rose water,
fanned him and spoke soothing words till he came around, uttering
only his beloved son's name.)

The sage was relieved and said, 'O king, give up your
sorrow. Kaikeyi is incapable of baseness and will herself give
him the sceptre.'

Dasaratha replied, 'O holy one! Make me crown him
before I die and tell him to forget about the forest, and save
me from forswearing.'

Said the sage to the cruel woman: 'Give the kingdom to
your son Rama and life to all of us including your husband,
and clothe yourself, O golden queen, in sinless glory.'

Even before the sage could complete what he had to say,
Kaikeyi interrupted, sobbing. 'If the king should break his
promise, I don't wish to live. And to keep *my* word, I shall
die this very day.'

Shocked, the sage replied, 'What more can I say to
convince you? That your husband will die and the world scoff
at you mean nothing to you? Are you a woman or a fire or a
demon perpetual?

'Before the king himself, in his own words, could tell
his son to go, you ordered him off to the forest. He being
the spotless man he is, obeyed instantly. You are a cruel and
vengeful fire, destroyer of honour and life alike. Can there be
a greater sinner than you?'

Even as the sage was pleading with her, the king had
completely regained consciousness. He looked at that woman
with the venomous tongue and asked in pain, 'O wretch, did
you yourself ask my life, my son, to go to the woods? Has he
indeed gone away?

'Now at last I see your heart revealed in all its wild
nakedness. Long did I taste your sweet but venomous lips
that have now sucked my life away.

'When I first took you before the fire, you wretch, I
wedded, not a wife but Death.

'You plotted to send to a fearful forest the son whose
sight my eyes crave. Shameless wretch, you have cleft me.

Why say more? Ptull out that string with which I married you and make it now an amulet to guard your son.'

Turning to the sage, he said, 'Sage, I declare today that she is not my wife. I have abandoned her and him, the future king. I no longer regard him as my son and he shall have no right to perform my obsequies.'

(*Distraught Kausalya saw that everything that had happened was the doing of her co-wife. The die cast, she could neither ask Rama to stay nor persuade her husband to change his decision and invite the world's scorn by becoming known as one who broke his pledge.*

Dasaratha learnt from her that his noble son would by no means take the kingdom and would certainly go away to the forest. Distraught with grief the delirious king spoke as though Rama was around.

He recalled his valorous deeds and declared that he would rather die than see his son clad in bark. Prattling thus, he fainted once again. With her fair hands the alarmed Kausalya massaged his feet and hands by turn till the king revived enough to ask again, 'Will the sage fetch our son?'

It was then that he recalled the curse laid on him a long time ago when he had gone on a hunting expedition.)

Hiding, bow in hand, some distance from a stream and looking for a prey, he had heard suddenly the sound of agitated water. Thinking it to be an elephant, he shot an arrow towards the direction of the noise.

On hearing a human scream, he rushed to the spot only to find that it was no elephant he had hit, but the son of a blind rishi couple. The young man had come to the stream to collect some water for his thirsty parents. Dasaratha was horrified at what he had done.

The dying young man forgave the king, beseeching him to take the water to his waiting parents. Anguished, he carried his body to that blind couple. The father said, 'What a time you have been, my son. We were worried. Come and be embraced.'

(The shattered king told them who he was and related the details of the accident. Begging forgiveness, he placed his head at their sacred feet. The heartbroken parents were torn with grief. Dasaratha consoled them as best he could, promising to be a son to them and always do their bidding.

But the rishi, inconsolable, had no use for the offer, wishing rather to go to the heaven their son had gone to, than be father to King Dasaratha.

He said, 'O king, we invoke no dreadful curse on you, realizing that what happened was a mistake. But, parted from an obedient son, you too in sorrow shall one day heavenward go.')

'I was hardly distressed by this half-curse, for issueless as I then was, it seemed a blessing rather than a curse. But today, that sage's words will prevail. My son will indeed leave and I will die.'

The king may be dying, but duty was duty. Vasishta hastened to the emperor's palace where the kings and sages had gathered for the coronation of Rama. To their puzzled and anxious queries, Vasishta replied,

'Kaikeyi has obtained two boons from the upright king. She has asked that Rama be exiled, but there is no cause for worry. By the king's command, her son, Bharata, will now become the ruler of this world while stalwart Rama, fortune's beloved, against convention, will go to the forest.'

Before the ever-truthful sage's words reached their ears, the kings, sages and all others assembled there fell on the earth like Dasaratha had upon hearing Kaikeyi's demands. As though a red-hot brand had been thrust into a wound, they rolled on the ground, their tears copious enough to fill the sea.

Like stalks of flowers broken by a storm, women crashed to the ground, hair loosened, eyes bloodshot, and feet sore. Frightened at what these developments portended, they shed their ornaments and marriage strings.

When news of that great prince's banishment had reduced birds, animals, and innocent children to tears, why speak of grown-ups?

Crows wept; calves wept; fresh blown flowers wept;

birds wept, and groves oozing with honey wept. Elephants and horses yoked to chariots shed tears.

Except Kaikeyi, unmindful of the fact that even sages couldn't live without Rama, and Kuni, the cruel crookback, was there anyone in that kingdom whose body had not turned to water?

'Bharata will not reign,' they said. 'O cursed fate, that a coronation should prove so dire! Who could be harder-hearted than we, who are still alive despite all this?' they moaned.

'Infatuated with Kaikeyi, the senile king seems to have lost all reason,' they said angrily. 'Let us all go to the forest with Rama, or else enter fire.

'This banishment has been demanded to gain the kingdom for her son. It's a shameful sin—a red-lipped harlot and seductress, this woman knows no true love.

'Let us leave her to the dirt she has been smeared with, and clinging to the one who was born heir to this earth, go with him to the wilderness, which will be paradise for us.

'What kind of king is this? To first give the world to the peerless one and then, against the rules, snatch from him and hand it over to his younger brother—isn't this standing truth on its head?'

When Lakshmana heard that Kaikeyi, his sharp-eyed stepmother, had used her boons to take the entire kingdom and given his elder brother only the forest, his rage shot forth and he became the terminal blaze.

Eyebrows lifted and eyes darting a fire that raged more fiercely than the flame in the sky, his breath a tempest, he resembled Adisesha himself.

'The meat meant for a lion's cub, she would happily feed a cur. How clever! How clever!' he laughed and jeered.

'I stand here,' he said, 'to unburden Mother Earth of those who think they can oppose my will to crown my brother this very day. With their corpses I'll raise a hill to fill the world. Let those who dare try to stop me!

'Whoever comes, gods or men, Vidyadharas, Nagas or anyone else from the eight quarters, be they the Creator,

Preserver and Destroyer united—I won't let a woman rule the world.'

Rama, who had gone to Sumitra's palace to take sorrowful leave of his other mother, heard the twang of Lakshmana's bow and rushing to his side said,

'Dear brother! You who ne'er lose your temper, why do you stand now with bow in hand?' Furious Lakshmana replied, 'Against that black-hearted woman who will kill truth and deny your right have I hefted my bow.

'I am determined to make you king and burn like cotton in fire those who oppose me, be they the gods themselves.'

Rama reasoned with him, 'How come you who ne'er swerve from the path of right, allow anger to rise in your heart and become privy to the drying up of eternal Dharma?'

Lakshmana laughed in anger. 'This wide world, our father said, shall be yours, and you accepted it. If you now yield to the enemy and go to the forest, when, if not now, should I lose my temper?

'When those ill-disposed towards you send you away on a long exile, should I cling to my vile body like the heartless king who gave you the kingdom in front of my eyes and then reneged on his word?'

Said Rama: 'How's the valorous king at fault? The river is not at fault when it runs dry. Nor is the king, nor she who bred us, nor her son. Fate it is that is to blame. My child, abandon this wrath.'

'My heart is like the fire in a forge. Set ablaze by the bellows, it is hard to quench. My mind shall quell her mind and my bow prove wrong the fate of that Fate that the primal gods obey.'

To those anguished words, his brother replied, 'Does your mouth speak or your moral sense? What you have said, no right-minded man would approve. How can anyone hate one's parents?'

'You are my father and sole lord and the mother who bore me. I have none else. You have learnt to give away what is yours, but you will see today what you will see,' said Laskhmana, who, in his anger, looked like crescent-crested Siva himself.

Said gracious Rama to his fuming brother: 'Will you, in order to quench your wrath, fight and defeat your good brother? Or your unique and much-praised father? Or win the glory of defeating your mother?

'It is not for me,' said Rama, who had crossed the ocean of Tamil and knew in full the Sanskrit culture, 'to disobey my father who taught me what was right and what was wrong and fostered me with such great care. But you are free to disobey me.'

To that expert speaker, Lakshmana had this to say, 'I have borne the praise of enemies, and now, bear the burden of my useless shoulders; bear too in vain my bow and quiver. How impotent is my indignation!'

But he gave up his wrath, and his opposing stance. He, who had never been known to retreat, calmed down like the four seas, which, like the four vedas, never presume to cross the mark set by Him.

(*The two of them then went together to Sumitra's palace and Rama consoled as best as he could his disconsolate stepmother. While he was still, there, Kaikeyi's maids came to him with the bark-clothes she had sent for Rama to wear on his journey. He gladly donned them and then, surprised, saw Lakshmana similarly attired.*)

'Our mothers and the emperor are plunged in sorrow; they too are about to lose me. For my sake, stay with them in my stead and try to lessen their grief.'

On hearing these words, Lakshmana, his shoulders trembling, sobbed like one no longer sure of his life: 'What is my offence?

'Great bowman!' he said, 'Consider this: can fish and blue lilies live without water? This is crueller than your stern command asking me to give up my wrath. Must you not only forego your right but also wash your hands of me?'

Rama could say nothing to counter this heart-rending plea. His eyes clouded with tears, and he could only gaze fondly at his incomparable brother and accept the inevitable.

(Then came forth kings and sages from the now dispersed assembly led by the great Vasishta himself, their eyes glistening with sorrow and despair. Vasishta looked at the two princes, took in their appearance in the new garb and read their resolute minds, What more remained to be said? In his sorrow, even the eloquent all-knowing sage couldn't find a thing to say.)

'On an auspicious day, the inauspicious arrives to clothe you in bark. Though Brahma himself may seek to prevent it, fate will have its way.

'The queen's wickedness did not cause it. How then did it happen? Who plotted it? Some day all will be revealed.'

Approaching that mighty bowman, he said, 'If you, my son, go to the hills, the emperor will cease to live.' But the one who had quit his serpent bed to fulfil a promise made to the gods said, 'It is my duty to carry out reverently the king's command and yours to remove his sorrows. That is the only right thing to do.'

'He did not ask you to go to the forest. The king promised those two boons unthinkingly to one whose words have proved as sharp as an enemy's lance,' said the sage.

'My father gave the boons; my mother the orders—I bear her command. Will you who witnessed it all forbid me from doing my duty?' said the one who had descended on earth to uphold Truth. The sage had nothing to say to this.

Clad in bark, his brother following him, Rama set forth on his fateful journey, face radiant as a lotus without blemish.

Ayodhya was plunged in the deepest sorrow. Some fell to the ground in shock; some sobbed inconsolably. Others were too stunned even to react to the loss of such great treasure.

'Must we, who stood waiting here to see him crowned, now see him off to the dreadful forest instead? How despicable to be born in a country where one sees such cruelty wrought by a woman,' they thought.

They derided their foolish king! 'You who have always prided yourself on never departing from the path of virtue, how are you any different from the one who has wished for the exile of the raincloud-hued prince?'

Some rushed madly for axes to break their hearts hard as stone but slid and fell in the mire caused by the tears they were shedding. Mothers forgot their offspring. Children wailed, not knowing where their mothers had gone. They wilted, they melted, they drooped, their senses robbed by a sorrow that would not go away.

Kitchens went smokeless, *akhil* fumes were missing from palace tops and parrots missed their milk. Red-lipped mothers forgot to suckle their babes and children in cradles screamed for their mothers.

Sacrificial fires had no ghee; moralists forgot their philosophy; and vedas ceased to be chanted. Crowds of dancers wept and the masters of the seven swaras wept. Flirts wept and so did lovers locked in embrace.

Elephants refused to dip their trunks in water and horses spurned grass. Birds sought no food for their young and cows didn't suckle their calves. Even yogis, who take in their stride grief and joy, were desolate. What then of lesser mortals?

(While the entire city was thus plunged in sorrow, Rama, the man with the steadfast mind, went to Sita's palace to bid her goodbye. Seeing him clad in wretched bark and surrounded by weeping mothers, ascetics, brahmins and kings, all covered in dust, Sita rose in alarm.)

Her large eyes brimming, she asked anxiously, 'O hero with the golden anklet, what has happened to the renowned king to cause all this distress?' Her body trembled like a flash of lightning.

'My matchless brother will rule the world,' said he, 'and obeying the wishes of my parents, I leave today for the forests and will get back soon. Do not grieve.'

She did not sorrow because her husband was losing the kingdom and going to the forest. What made her cry were those cruel words that burnt her ears—'Do not grieve. I am going.'

He'd left his bed in the milky ocean to be born in Ayodhya and prevent Dharma from perishing. Unable to bear that separation, she had joined him here on earth. How then could she reconcile to those words, 'I am going'?

'It is right indeed that you do what your father and mother bade you do. But why are you asking me to stay behind?' said she, nearly lifeless.

'Your painted feet,' he said fondly, 'will be unable to bear the cruel heat of the rocky forests with mountains dark as demons.'

'You strive against love and can with ease renounce the ties that bind. Where will that terrible sun burn with greater intensity—there or here? What wild forest can scorch me more than separation from you?'

She, who had once placed her hand in his, walked calmly into the inner apartments and came back soon clad in bark and stood beside her thoughtful lord.

'O princess, whose smile will put to shame the jasmine and the pearl, you don't seem to realize the endless trouble your wish to come with me will cause.'

'Could it be,' she hissed in anger, 'that the real reason is that with me left behind, you'll be free to enjoy yourself in the forest?' Silenced thus by adamant Sita, and led by her and followed by his brother, Rama set forth for the forest.

(On the way, he stopped at his father's palace where he bowed to his mothers and bade them console the emperor who was oppressed by grief. Accepting what had been ordained by fate, they blessed their sons and Sita in tear-choked voices.

Parting with some difficulty, they then bowed to Sage Vasishta. Rama then got into a chariot with his dear brother and dazzling wife, and the three of them set off on their journey.)

THE EMBALMING OF DASARATHA

(As the red-gold chariot driven by the ever-loyal Sumantra made its way to the forest, all of Ayodhya, except the emperor's wives, followed the prince and his companions in exile. The sun set as if loath to see them leave, and the sky grew dark as the mind of Kaikeyi poisoned by Mantara.

After a while, they reached a fragrant grove full of birds, two

leagues away. The devastated men and women who had followed
the chariot, a crowd so thick that a sesame seed falling on them
wouldn't have reached the ground, spread themselves on the grass
in exhaustion. But try as they might, they couldn't sleep.)

All of them, men and women, lay anywhere and anyhow,
their hearts heavy with sorrow and finally found fitful sleep.
Some lay sprawled on the rocky ground and others flopped
down, heads resting on their hands.

Some young women, their breasts coated with dust like
saffron hills covered in mist, lay around haphazardly. Mothers
with lotus-faces, their children's hands on their breast, lay
heartbroken on the ground, like heaps of leaves.

Rama himself, sleepless and sorely distressed, called
Sumantra and said, 'Noble one, I am in a fix and need your
help. These loving people, I can't send them back by force.
And to leave stealthily would be wicked.

'If you, my father, will drive quietly back, they will scan
the trail and think I've gone back and themselves return to
Ayodhya. Kind sir, please do me this favour.'

'Noble prince,' said Sumantra, 'if I return in this fashion,
what will I tell those whom I see? What should I tell the dying
king? That I am the bearer of glad tidings from you, or a grim
messenger from the god of death?

'Shall I tell him that the lion cub he secured with such
effort and sacrifice, is now forever gone? That will make me
worse than Kaikeyi.'

Deeply troubled, Rama embraced Sumantra and dried
his tears saying, 'Is Dharma to be pursued only if pleasant,
and given up when it causes pain?

'My noble father sent his beloved son to the forest to maintain
Dharma and it is my duty to obey him. Please, please go back
and first see sage Vasishta and tell him all I have told you.

'Ask him to apprise my father of my innermost thoughts
on this matter. Ask him to tell my brother that an ideal ruler
he should be.

'Since I don't in the least bit think that Kaikeyi has done
me wrong, ask the sage to tell my father he should bear her

no grudge whatsoever. And, above all, console my father and
be with him.'

'Lord, what can a servant do but obey, though it might
break his heart?' said Sumantra. He then turned to guileless
Sita and she said, 'First pay my respects to the king and my
mothers-in-law. And ask my beloved sisters to take good care
of my golden mynah and green-hued parrot.'

Overwhelmed at such innocence, Sumantra wept.
Turning to Lakshmana, he asked whether he had any message
to give.

Said Lakshmana bitterly, 'What is there to say to that
truthful king who promised the kingdom to my noble lord
and broke his word to please a woman?

'While his good son feeds on grass in the forest, let that
truthful king feed on choice delicacies and cling to life without
sparing a thought for the life hereafter.

'Tell Bharata, that valorous king, that I have no brothers,
not Rama, not he who usurped his kingdom, nor that other,
my fake younger brother. I am alone, in myself secure.'

Thereupon, laden with a heavy heart, Sumantra yoked
the horses to the chariot and drove off noiselessly, leaving no
sign of his departure save a visible track. The three of them
too left unnoticed in the middle of the night.

Within two hours, Sumantra sighted the ramparts of
Ayodhya. Going straight to Guru Vasishta, he related all that
had happened. Heart distressed and knowing what was to
come, Vasishta sighed, 'This is the end of the king.'

When the grieving monarch heard the excited
exclamations, 'The chariot is here, the chariot is here!' he
thought Rama had returned. Opening his eyes and seeing
Vasishta by his side, he asked in a hope-filled voice: 'Has he
come?'

When the anguished sage said nothing, he read his face
and fainted away. Reviving a while later, he asked Sumantra,
'Is he near or far away?' On hearing him say, 'Rama and his
brother have gone with golden Sita into the forest deep,' the
king died.

Detecting neither breath nor movement, Kausalya fell

upon his body. Realizing that his precious life had seeped away, her mind whirled and she writhed like a worm in the sun and wailed uncontrollably.

'Should the great king owe his death not to disease or sword or spear, but like a crab or an oyster, a banana or a bamboo, to one begotten by him? O heartless Kaikeyi! Your wild ploy to obtain a kingdom by a boon unbreakable has borne fruit.'

While she wailed thus, Sumitra drooped, half dead. Dasaratha's lesser wives cried aloud in tumultuous grief, clutching the body of that king who had parted with his son and his life to redeem the bitter promise forced out of him.

They clung to him as if the boat that would take them across the great sea of life was infested with the sharks of delusion.

(Sumantra went to the royal preceptor, Vasishta, with news of the king's death. Deeply distressed, he sobbed his heart out at the strange ways of Fate. But he was assailed by thoughts of attending to the immediate practical problems arising from the situation.)

'There is no son around to do what is to be done. Word must be sent to Bharata in the Kekaya capital to come back with all dispatch. Meanwhile, the king's body that lies surrounded by a sea of women, should be plunged in a sea of oil.'

(To return now to those hapless people who had followed Rama to the edge of the forest:)

On waking and not finding Rama there, they were bewildered. Wailing bitterly, 'Our eyes that should never have closed have betrayed us,' they ran helter-skelter in all directions. Then, spotting the tracks made by the chariot, they decided to follow it.

Suddenly, it struck them that the tracks led citywards and they were filled with joy at the thought that Rama had gone back to Ayodhya. Their joyous uproar sounded like the sea and the sky had joined hands and clapped in unison.

Their happiness knew no bounds. It was as if the sea,

having inundated the universe at the end of the yugas, had retreated to its old place, leaving the earth as it once was. Back to Ayodhya its citizens went.

Alas, soon enough they learnt that the king had departed to heaven and that their Rama had not returned as they had surmised. Their hearts broke at not having been there for the grieving king in his hour of need or much help to the prince who had gone to the forest. Thus were they trapped in a prison of endless sorrow.

THE GANGA

(The next morning, alone at last, the three of them walked at a leisurely pace. Those who saw them were struck dumb and gasped, 'What a sight! Black magic? A jade mountain? A rain cloud? The rolling sea?' Rama and Sita were happy beyond words, struck with wonder at each other's beauty, set off by unfamiliar surroundings. As if for the first time, Sita saw how Rama's feet outshone the bee-haunted lotuses, and laughed. Rama was thrilled at her dainty beauty, her swelling breasts decked with jasmine, her hair a dark cloud, and her eyes the blue lilies that farmers were weeding from the streams.)

Thus they walked, hand in hand, admiring the beautiful countryside: tanks overspread with lotus creepers, groves with swans, sandbanks with shells, thickets shedding flowers, and streams flinging gold.

On seeing them, buffaloes, mouths drooling the corn they were munching, dashed about in happiness.

Startled bees scattered from lotuses; the fish in the water leapt about in joy; and maidens, looking like red-webbed swans as they bathed in the streams, looked up admiringly.

Walking past fertile fields and magnificent groves, they reached the wide expanse of the Ganga, on whose banks lived sages of ancient lore. The tapaswis were exultant that the God they sought through harsh penances had come of his own will to their doorstep.

They took them to their ashramas with the joy a parent feels when, having searched for his long lost, but never forgotten, child he sees him face to face at last.

Bidding them bathe in the holy Ganga, they scoured the woods for the best of vegetables, fruits and roots, to serve their austere fare, but sweetened with the nectar of their love.

As Rama and Sita entered the waters hand in hand, the eternal Ganga appeared, palms folded in greeting, and said, 'Men and women from all quarters bathe in my waters and lose their sins. But when you, my father, bathe in the same, I lose *my* sins and gain my soul.'

With his arms extended, Ganga water dripping from his matted locks and Sita by his side, Rama resembled at that moment, the crescent-crested one dancing in front of Parvati.

As he stood in the middle of white-foamed Ganga with his slender wife beside him, he was Vishnu himself on the milky sea, rising, as of old, from his bed.

The *vanchi* creeper was shamed by Sita's waist, the swan by her gait, the lotus by her foot and the carp by her eyes. They all hid themselves when she dipped her soft soles into the water.

The maiden's stack of rain-cloud hair floating on the waters of the river made it look as if the dark stream of Yamuna had suddenly flowed into the Ganga.

She plunged and rose again and again from the swirling river, looking like Lakshmi herself rising from the milky ocean.

Bath over, he went to the dwellings of the vedic sages and prayed to the gods worshipped by them, performed the ordained rites, and partook of the feast they had prepared out of their love for him.

He, who would not even taste the nectar he had procured with such difficulty and gave it all away to the gods instead, was happy with the simple fare the sages provided. Is there anything that cannot be achieved if the heart is true?

GUHAN

(To Rama, who had been staying with the rishis, came Guhan, a tribal chief and lord of a thousand boats that plied on the Ganga.

*A giant of a man who wore a red skin round his waist and a tiger's
tail for a belt, his humility was all the more striking for his being tall
enough to plumb the Ganga. Standing outside Rama's hut with his
offering of fish and honey, he called out, 'Lord, I, a mere dog, have
come in good time to wait on your pleasure.' To Lakshmana, who
came out on hearing his stentorian voice, he said, 'I, a boatman and
a hunter, am your servant, a dog come to pay my respects to Rama,
the incomparable.' A duly impressed Lakshmana reported his arrival
to his brother, who bade him bring the huntsman in. Refusing to sit,
he begged, 'Lord, I have brought you honey and fish. Would you take
a taste of it?' Rama graciously accepted his gift and told him of his
plan to cross the river the next morning, seeking the huntsman's aid.
Guhan eagerly agreed to help and with Rama's leave spent the night
there, standing guard along with his men, bow in hand and arrows
on the ready. Lakshmana, too, did the same, eyes unwinking. When
Sleep approached, he told her sternly, 'Come to me in Ayodhya.'
Loath to defy him, she bowed in deference to his wishes and left.
Then came the dawn.)*

As if to spur feckless earthlings to imagine a state
beyond heaven itself, the sun, itself never born and therefore,
deathless, had earlier shown what death was by setting. It
now rose to show what birth meant.

Morning prayers and oblations done, Rama asked Guhan
to bring the promised boat. Loath to part with his hero so
soon, Guhan said, 'We are plain folks, lord, and the forest
is our home, but we lack nothing. Prince, we are strong and
shall willingly do your bidding. Consider us your kinsmen
and stay with us.

'We have honey and meat to satisfy the gods themselves,
and men to guard you like faithful dogs. We have the forests
for sport and the very Ganga to bathe in. Come with us and
stay as long as I live.

'We have animal skins for clothes and straw mattresses
for beds and huts to stay in. We have many pairs of swift
feet and hands to fetch whatever you need from the sky
itself.

'Five hundred thousand hunters, armed with bows and

stronger than gods, are at my command. If you should but stay a single day with us, blest we shall be beyond anything else.'

The prince heard him out, heart brimming with love. Flashing a smile, he said, 'Heroic soul! We will certainly come to you in a few days, once we are done with visiting all the sacred rivers and holy sages.'

Guhan swiftly went and brought a long boat. Rama took leave of the sages, and with his dear brother and moon-browed Sita, got into the boat.

The boat sped along, like a huge crab on long legs, spurred on by its mighty oarsmen. Sweet Sita and sun-like Rama sported, splashing water at each other.

No longer a river, but a woman, Ganga, with sand dunes for ample breasts, decked with sandal, gems and flowers, lifted the boat with her hands, and carried the three of them across without effort.

Reaching the shore, Rama asked Guhan, 'Which way to Chitrakuta?' And he, who would have given Rama his life if need arose, said, 'Lord, I, your dog, have something to say.

'Expert in the intricate paths of the forest, I can search and get for you the best of fruits, vegetables and honey and put up a hut for you to stay in. I will never desert you even for a minute, if only, dog that I am, am allowed to go with you.

'I can find my way in the dark and drive away ferocious beasts. Can dig rocks for roots, go any distance to bring you life-giving water, provide an army of bowmen to guard you. I fear nothing, doughty prince, and I shall never leave your flower-like feet.'

Rama replied, overwhelmed with love for this hunter, 'You are my life and my brother is your brother. This bright-rowed lady is your friend and this sea-girt earth is all ours. I will serve you forever.

'We were four brothers once. But since love is a boundless thing, from now on we are not four but five. However, we each have our different duties to perform. Into the forest I must go, and you must stay behind, to look after your people who are now mine. I order you to do so!'

Unable to disobey him or suppress his sorrow, Guhan took his leave, looking like an ailing man. And Rama, with his lovely wife and loyal brother, set out on a long trail into the dense forest.

CHITRAKUTA

(Early summer, fickle as a prostitute's love, for once was kindly disposed. It welcomed them with a cool fragrant southern breeze. The dark clouds that hovered above made the sun's rays mild, like those of the moon. Trees gave shade, clouds raindrops, and dancing peacocks made their journey pleasant.

Enchanted with the beauty of it all, Rama pointed out the delights to Sita, never failing to add that none of them, the peacock or the parrot, or the trees whose golden flowers prodigally scattered pollen on the rocky ground, was within hailing distance of her own beauty and grace.)

'Look at the "eyes" of the peacock taking in your beauty. Their plumes, usually furled in shyness, are now outspread in dance, with bees as musicians and the drumming of rain as the *taala*.

'Look at the way the deer flock to you as if you were one among them. The birds are deluded by your bearing, the animals by your lovely eyes that are spears kept in trim with collyrium, too large for any hand to grasp.

'Look at the way lion cubs and elephant calves gambol as one, not in the least hostile but rather, unwilling to part from each other.

'O fragrant-haired princess! Look at the plants dip their jewel-like flowers into the river, as if they were young women dipping their tender breasts in the streams to cover them with the white silk of the river's foam.

'Look at the numerous male bees, blind-drunk with honey, using the humming of the females as their eyes to find their way! My love, sweeter than a heavenly nymph! See the fragrant pollen scattered on the rocky ground, like so many beauty spots on your lovely breasts.

'Look at these trees that have shed their flowers, lest your feet, unused to rocks, should be hurt. And koel sweet! Look at the creepers shamed by your waist, weighed down by their load of flowers.

'Sword-eyes! Look at the bees that haunt your lotus-eyes and your sprig-like legs. Look at those clouds dark as your tresses, and those bamboos, slender as your shoulders.'

(And so they walked on till finally they spotted that holy hill, the abode of rishis. Even as they approached, Sage Bharadwaja emerged from his hut. Hair matted, chest hirsute, clad in deerskin, he walked with deliberate steps, kamandala and umbrella in hand and the four vedas on his lips.

Surprised and delighted, he welcomed Rama: 'Great warrior, what brings you here in this garb?' Rama told him everything that had happened. The great sage said despondently, 'Can such things happen in our time? How fruitless is Earth's penance!' He then added philosophically, 'But isn't life a cycle of sorrow and joy, of good deeds and bad? What use distressing oneself?'

He then took them to his abode, showed them a place to stay and gave them fruits and roots to eat. They were filled with happiness and contentment.)

After a while, the rishi said, 'Handsome prince! We lack nothing here; there's water in plenty, flowers, fruits, roots and vegetables in abundance, no evil and no dearth of good. Ganga, Yamuna and Saraswati come together as one here. Stay with us. No sweeter place can be found.'

Rama replied, 'Noble sage, though some distance from Kosala, this is not far enough for my people to cease to come here to see me. This will create problems for all.'

The great sage saw the point and said, 'Ten leagues from here is Chitrakuta, sweeter than even heaven. Make it your home.'

(The three touched his feet with reverence and departed.)

Crossing the *mullai* land, the sylvan terrain where cowherds play on their bamboo flute, and then *kurinji*, the hills where lovers meet in secret, they reached the banks of the Kalindi river where fawns were wont to quench their thirst.

The noonday sun was at its zenith then and they greeted the river with joy, plunged deep their dust-laden bodies into its waters. Having helped themselves to some roots and fruits, they drank deeply of the plentiful water and then wondered, 'Now, how do we cross the river?'

The ever-ingenious Lakshmana cut some bamboos and tied them up with the *manai* creeper and readied a makeshift craft. Seating his brother and his wife in it he ferried them across that broad river, using his hands as oars.

They then reached *palai*, the desert land, which burnt branch, root and the earth and even the very mind that thought of it. Even as anxious Rama worried that Sita couldn't possibly cross this parched land, the sun miraculously shed its heat and made its rays cool as moonbeams.

Withered trees burgeoned afresh and the hot earth became a lotus field; sharp stones became soft and cool like flowers freshly plucked.

Creepers sprouted new shoots, white clouds rumbled and dropped cool rain; fawns suckled tigers that seemed to have lost their hunger, hostility and rage.

The grass grew wide and high, a green carpet for peacocks to dance to the music of the humming bees. Fruits ripened out of turn, plants emerged unplanted, flowering like maidens coming of age.

Like the heart of a maid awaiting her beloved on the day promised by her husband gone away on war or business, the wilderness cooled down miraculously, as did the maidens when the hero did indeed keep the date.

Crossing the stretch, they saw in the distance the Chitrakuta hill, the top of which almost touched the sky. From afar the hill looked like a male elephant extending its trunk to seize its lover, a cow elephant in the guise of the moon, obscured by a dark and thundering cloud.

On reaching Chitrakuta, that hill of incomparable beauty, Rama delighted himself in showing to Sita the myriad wondrous sights of their new abode.

'Come and see the blood-stained pearls scattered in a fight between an elephant in musth and a fell lion. They look like jewels strewn in a mire of saffron in a love-tangle between a man and his love.

'O lovely sprig no thicker than a thread, carrying those bejewelled breasts! Look at the moon, making his way through the groves of sandalwood, bent upon obstructing him.

'Look at that crescent-tusked elephant, feeding a pregnant cow with the honey he has brought from a cave swarming with bees.

'Look at the horse-faced kinnaras reflected in the crystal of the rocks. Are they not like God who only reveals Himself, once in a while, to self-denying yogis whose hearts yearn for Him?

'O incomparable koel, prettier than a dancing peacock, look at the mountain lasses who have been provoked by the kinnaras to give up their sulks and seek their lovers!

'Look for the dainty footprints left on the jade rocks by swift-footed Vidyadhara girls, who have scampered away after love play with their husbands. But you'd hardly see them, for the red-colour would merge with the hue of the ruby rocks!

'My very life, O complete woman! Look at the male monkey drenched by his mate with water from the waterfall. He, in turn, is almost drowning her with water he has shaken from a cloud.

'Tender sprig, look at the spear-eyed kurinji girls guarding their millet fields by pelting the birds with small red gems, each one a glittering star.'

(All this and more did Rama show Sita, who listened rapt in wide-eyed wonder. He also pointed out how the animals and birds lived in perfect harmony with the sages and assisted them in their holy rituals. Monkeys tenderly led by the hand aged rishis with fading sight and brought them sweet mangoes, jackfruit and bananas. Snakes made staircases of themselves for the hermits to tread on. Boars brought them roots they had dug up. Parrots, with beaks red as Sita's hands, supplied the sages with mountain-rice, millet, grams and pulses.)

Soon the sun descended in the west like the asura Kalanemi who sank without a trace when Vishnu's discus decapitated him and left the sky red with blood. Then the moon appeared, like a fang knocked out of the same asura's mouth.

Lotuses, having bequeathed their beauty to lovely women, folded up. Other fragrant blooms too shut their petals, but the flowers of the night blossomed. Monkeys, male and female, went looking for their homes in the trees; elephants returned to the mountain slopes, and birds, the day done, sought their nests.

(While Rama was looking at the sky in wonderment, Lakshmana, ever the practical one, was busy building a hut for his brother and his wife. Erecting a vertical frame with pieces cut from a bamboo, he provided a long beam and a roof by binding a series of transverse laths and spreading mats of palm leaf over them.

For the roof he used teak leaves and reed grass. All around the vertical frame of the walls, he plastered wet mud to hold the structure together. He made, as set down in the books, two rooms—one for Sita and another for Rama, and beautified the inner walls with red mud and gems and pearls fetched from the river.

Deeply moved, tears in his eyes, Rama exclaimed in wonderment. 'Lakshmana! When did you learn all this?' And then, somewhat downcast, 'What use is my fame and glory, my insistence on maintaining Dharma by obeying the wishes of my father at all cost if all it means endless trouble to you?' But Lakshmana made light of it all, and their new life began.)

THE FUNERAL

(The messenger sent by Vasishta to summon Bharata and Satrughna back to Ayodhya from their grandfather's palace reached the Kekaya capital with all dispatch and was promptly shown to the presence of the prince. He handed the scroll to Bharata who received it reverently. Beaming with pleasure, Bharata read the contents. He then took leave of everyone, said the farewells that needed to be said, and ordered the chariot to set out for Ayodhya,

unconcerned about day or time. After full seven days of travel,
during which they crossed many rivers, forests and mountains,
Bharata and his rumbustious entourage reached the Kosala border.
Suddenly, he realized something was amiss.)

The fields were unploughed; no garlands adorned young
men's shoulders; paddy-fields were untended. Lakshmi, Goddess
of Fortune, seemed to have deserted both her lotus and the land.

Overripe fruits had fallen unplucked into streams; flowers
that hadn't been gathered, had withered and fallen off the
creepers. Weeders neglected their work, like sulking women
refusing to yield to their husbands.

Parrots were silent. Go-betweens carried no messages from
one lover to another. Silenced were the drumbeats, and the
golden streets remained untrodden by festive processions.

Dance halls and bathing pools were deserted. Faces knew
no laughter and heads had lost their chaplets. Lamps were
either dim or unaccompanied by flame.

Not aware of what had happened and distressed at what
he saw, Bharata's mind filled with fear, even as he proceeded
step by weary step towards the palace. At the city gates he
noticed that the customary forest of flags was missing; missing
too were the sounds of drumbeats that used to proclaim,
'Come, help yourself to whatever you want.'

Bereft of chariots, horses and elephants, palanquins and
wagons had none to ride them. The streets of Ayodhya had
lost their beauty, like a riverbed all dried up. His mind filled
with undefined fears, Bharata reached the emperor's palace.
Not finding him there, he was beginning to get even more
alarmed, when he was hailed by a royal maid.

Bowing low, she said, 'Noble lord, your mother wishes to
see you.' He went at once to her palace and touched her feet
with deep respect. 'I am eager to touch the lotus feet of the
king among men whose love for me is irrepressible. Tell me
where he is,' he begged.

Plied thus with eager questions from her son, she,
unperturbed, said, 'The mighty king who had laid low the
might of rakshasas has gone to heaven to the welcome of
adoring gods.'

When he heard these burning words, down he fell and measured the earth like a lofty tree struck by lightning. His bright face dimmed, his lotus eyes streaming tears like a waterfall, he said, 'You have fed my ears with fire.'

Addressing his dead father, he wailed, 'O king! You have cut the very root of virtue, murdered grace, and dimmed the brightness of your excellence by dying thus. What greater blot on your spotless reputation than this?

'O king of kings! You who renewed over and over again the valorous deeds of your ancient race, did you go to heaven searching an equal, since here on earth, every king had become your vassal?'

All this and more he said, disconsolate, eyes streaming and bones melting. Gradually bringing his emotions under control, he said, 'With father gone, to Rama's side I must hurry. He, virtue infinite, is my all, my father and mother, my lord and brother. Until I bow to his feet, I will feel this sense of disquiet.'

Adept at delivering shock and thunder, she said at once, 'Dear son, with his wife and brother, Rama has gone away to the forest.'

The forest! When he heard this, he stood stunned, as if he had swallowed fire. 'What more has Fate in store for me?' he asked, 'What fresh disaster remains for me to hear?'

Shocked and distressed, the great prince persisted with his queries: 'Did he go to the forest because of some crime he committed? Or did he provoke some god's wrath? Or was he sent there by Fate insuperable? For what reason did he undertake such a journey?

'And if Rama himself did commit a wrong, would it not have been for the greater good of mankind, like a mother forcing her child to obey? Did he go after my father died? Or was it before? Be pleased to tell.'

'He despised no elders,' she replied calmly, 'nor was he guilty of the insolence you speak of. Nor was he sent there on account of a god's wrath. He went to the forest even when the sun-like king was alive.'

'If there was no crime and no enemies hot-blooded, nor

any god displeased, how, explain to me, could a father stay back, while his son departed to the forest?'

'Through boons I'd obtained long ago, I sent the son to the forest. And by doing so, I got the kingdom for you. Unable to bear this shock, the king gave up his life.'

These words had hardly reached his ears, when his lotus-hands shot out to shut them off. His beetle eyebrows danced up and down and fire mingled with his sighs. His eyes shed blood.

His cheeks trembled and fire and smoke issued from the pores of his skin. His long hands beat each other, making a noise that split the earth and frightened thunder.

The gods were frightened and many asuras died. The elephants guarding the quarters went mad. The sun went down, and Death himself, ever angry, closed his eyes in fear.

A lion enraged, he spared the cruel queen not because she was his mother. It was for fear of invoking Rama's disapproval that he decided merely to chastise her.

In a voice resembling thunder, he said, 'Your fell plot made my father die and my brother turn into a sage! I have heard this from you and yet not torn your mouth! Am I not guilty therefore, of the greed to be king?

'You still stand here! And I too! In the twinkling of an eye I should have felled you. What has spared you is not the title of mother that you bear, but my fear of displeasing Rama, the true mother of all living things.

'A king is to die for a thoughtless word, a hero is to give up this world and Bharata is to rule a world thus got! Can there be a more perverted Dharma than this?

'Through the cruel plotting of a crafty mother, an ancient tradition is being broken. Bharata becomes king! What greater scandal?

'You were a snake the valorous king lodged in his house and you struck at his root under cover of a boon. What else will you be wanting now? You are not a disease that killed your husband and departed with him. You are a demon that survives his death. You deserve to die.

'You are indeed my mother who fed me milk and

deathless shame. What else do you have in store? You ate up alive the ever-true king and won through a boon, not just a kingdom, but eternal shame.

'Parted by force, like a cow from its calf, Rama left and yet your selfishness left you unmoved. My father died to keep his word. And my brother, convinced that this was Dharma, gave up a kingdom. Would I, born with him, be able to bear the shame of ruling a kingdom obtained for me through a mother's fraud?

'Did he, who should have been the ruler, not anticipate that the king would surely die if he left for the forest? Would he not have thought that you were willing to take the blame, but must surely have been set on this course by me?

'It matters not what the king of ancient lineage thought. But that Rama should think that I, his devoted brother, would be so sinful! O what a treasure my mother has got for me!

'When that good man heard that the great bowman had left for the forest, he died at once. But here I am, neither having killed that venomous woman, nor having died myself. Have I not earned the world's censure for being a smug hypocrite, who merely lamented aloud the exile of Rama?

'The Goddess of Fortune will quit this land. Whom did you consult? Who advised you? What have you got by destroying Dharma, that noble tree, root and branch?

'Through your murderous mouth I have killed my father. More than that, I've sent my brother into exile. If I still stay here and rule this land, it will be not your sin but forever mine. To expiate that great sin of having lain in your hellish womb, I shall undertake a great penance. Let the god of virtue be my witness.

'Let me give you a piece of advice. Give up the life I have spared. They may yet say that you did not mean what you did. Having been thus absolved of the crime you committed, your life wouldn't have been in vain. There is no other way but this to salvage your name.

'I will not stay with a sinner whose wickedness in words I can't describe. To rid my sorrow, I shall go and fall at pure Kausalya's golden feet.'

On reaching Kausalya's palace, he fell at her feet, throwing himself headlong on the ground. Holding her small feet in his large hands, he wailed and lamented.

'The wicked who should have died are still alive. How can I utter these words and continue to breathe? I, a thief born to that cruel woman! Let me end my life and my grief.

'O that a blot called Bharata,' he mourned, 'should have been born in that lustrous race, whose progenitor is the very Sun, who daily dispels the darkness of the world.'

When she heard Bharata lamenting thus, the high-born Kausalya, patient and chaste, was convinced that his heart was pure and he had no desire to be king. Wrath gone and heart melting, she said, 'It is plain you knew nothing of your dear mother's dark designs on your behalf.'

When the prince heard those words, he roared like a lion caught in a death trap and let fly a series of terrible oaths, enough to frighten even eternal Dharma.

'O that I be quickly dispatched to the fiery hell reserved for one who subverts another's virtue, a heartless wretch or an adulterer, a man of wrath or a butcher, a tormentor of ascetics or a slayer of his teacher's wife!

'To that fiery hell meant for the one who betrayed his prince, or a coward who ran away from foes, or a robber of a beggar's all, a denier of Vishnu's godhead or an offender of virtuous brahmins, or a fool who says that the vedas were the products of mere men!

'To the fiery hell where goes the sinner who fills his wretched stomach while his mother starves and wilts, or the man who forsakes his chief!

'May I be dispatched to the fiery hell where goes the coward who, to save himself, will hand over a refugee to his enemies, or the one who never thinks of Dharma. The hell into which these fall, never to return, may I too be thrown into the same inferno!

'The man who bears false witness, the man who is afraid to fight, the man who robs one in danger, to the hell meant for these, may I go. The man who sets fire to another's house, the killer of children, the partial judge, the abuser of gods, O!

that I would fall into the hell reserved for such as these!

'The man who deprives the calf of its milk, the sly pickpocket, the ingrate with an evil tongue, let mine be the same hell as theirs!

'The man who, to save his life, will forsake a woman set upon on the street, the man who eats while others starve, let mine be the hell that is their fate!

'The man who yields to the enemy in war in order to somehow save himself, the king who helps himself to more than is set down in the shastras, let mine be the hell into which they will fall!

'Let me fall into the hell meant for that blameworthy sinner who, having become king, forgets the prescribed ways and acts in a manner unworthy of his position, simply because he can now do what he likes!

'Let me suffer the fate of those who would force a virgin or a teacher's wife, drink in excess or be an accomplice in an act of burglary!

'Let me suffer the fate of one who, like a dog, eats what he should not eat, is neither male nor female, ignores the advice of those who warn against hell and is given to speaking ill of others!

'Let me suffer the fate of one who would blacken the names of families old and spotless, scatter a poor man's food in a famine and eat in front of the hungry, making their mouths water, without sharing so much as a particle with them!

'May I set aside my bow and sword, and embracing for a few more days this unreal life, be forced to stretch my hand for any morsel my sneering foes may deign to give!

'May I go to that corner of hell reserved for that dithering fool, who will neither give nor refuse those who beg, but will only make them waste endless days seeking such favours!

'May the contemptuous laughter of girls echo around me, as I, armed with the sword that could have cut my enemy down, bow my head low, clinging to a diseased and stinking body!

'While my foe enjoys my fields and forests of sugarcane

and red rice, may I, just to preserve my life, be dragged before him on fettered feet!

'With God as witness, if I had prior knowledge of the wicked deed of that cruel woman, may I, a cur, fall into the hell meant for those who injure the good!'

Hearing all these terrible oaths that proved his innocence, Kausalya wept and embraced the son who stood in front of her, seeing in him the one who had renounced the kingdom and gone away to the cruel forest.

Realizing that his heart was true and his mother's evil self-taught, she wept. Her face swollen with tears, she hailed him 'king of kings', and blessed him. 'Who could ever have been your equal among all your ancestors of this high-born race,' she commended.

When Vasishta, the royal guru, entered, the prince fell at his feet. 'Tell me, O holy sage! Where is my father?' Distressed and confused, Vasishta stood speechless.

'Spotless son, it is seven days since your generous father died,' he said at length. 'Finish the rites a son should perform.'

(With the sage beside him, he went and looked at the body of Dharma incarnate.)

Made golden by the bath in oil, the body was now bathed afresh by Bharata's tears. Men well-versed in the four vedas lifted the king's body, and to the beat of the royal drum, placed it on a hearse of gold.

With Sumantra, the charioteer, in the lead, the funeral procession set off accompanied by great ministers, the army chiefs, and innumerable others. Silent tears fell from the eyes of the city's maidens, watching the heart-rending sight from cloud-capped towers. The 'eyes' of the drums let out piteous cries, and conches and clarions wailed.

On horses, elephants and chariots, went the many kings, the brahmins leading Dasaratha's many wives.

On reaching pellucid Sarayu with its leaping waves, they performed all the rites described in the vedas and laid the precious body on the royal pyre.

As Bharata rose to perform the obsequies, holy Vashista

said in accents of deepest sorrow. 'In his great anguish caused by your mother's wickedness, the king disowned you before he died.'

When he heard this, Bharata felt as if his very birth had destroyed Dharma. He perceived himself dead, as if what remained of him was another being.

Like a dreadful snake that feared thunder, he fell upon the earth; unable to suppress the sorrow that surged within his breast, he sobbed:

'Unworthy to perform rites for the dead, I am deemed fit to rule the living! Who, among all my ancestors in the solar race, was as great as I!

'I am the husk, the outer petals of the fragrant screwpine. Such is the honour my mother has given me, she who brought me forth and nursed me to life.'

He stood apart, steeped in sorrow overwhelming, as the sage, well-versed in the vedas, had Satrughna perform all due rites.

The rites ended, those 60,000 other wives, their faces like the lotus and the moon, came together and unhesitatingly fell into the fire. Through a fire cooler than water, they reached the heaven reserved for those who refused to survive their husbands.

All rites completed, Bharata went back to the palace with a heavy heart. The next ten days dragged like aeons and he was plunged in a sea of sorrow. Then it was time for the next step to be taken.

Accompanied by all the wise men of that land, Vasishta went to meet Bharata, still in deep depression, to decide what next to be done. A land without a king would only breed anarchy, a prospect unthinkable.

ROAD TO RAMA

Blessing Bharata, the sage began, 'O virtuous one without a stain to his name! The reason we are all here is to ensure that justice and virtue do not go unprotected.

'A land without a sworded king is like the day without a sun, the night without a moon and stars, the body without a soul. Neither on earth nor in heaven, neither in the realm of the gods nor of demons, have we ever seen a kingdom without a king.

'Virtuous soul, your famous forebears from Brahma down have ruled this land without interruption. If it should now lack a ruler, it will be like a shattered boat in a turbulent sea.

'Your father is dead and your brother has gone away to the forest. Through your mother, you have obtained an ancient kingdom that you must now guard. This,' he said, 'is our considered view.'

Bharata was stunned, more shocked than one obliged to swallow venom, his eyes a stream of tears.

His body atremble, tongue wordless, eyes shrinking, he lost consciousness. Recovering, he spoke up, clear-sighted, his mind made up.

'If what you've now expounded is Dharma, that I should be crowned while my elder, the one who is fit to rule all three worlds, is still alive, then, surely, my mother has done no evil by doing what she did?

'If her wicked deed meets with the approval of good men like you, I have to infer that, having skipped the two yugas in between, the dark age of Kali is already here.

'If from the days of Brahma, there has ever been a precedent, where the younger has ruled while the elder was still alive, then you, who were the king's counsellors, find out when that aberration occurred and prove it to me.

'Even if it is right, I cannot bear the burden of this world and continue to live. I will bring Rama back and have him crowned, as is only fit and proper. If I cannot do as I have promised, I too shall gladly stay with him in the forest and do penance. One word more from you on this subject, I'll kill myself,' said he, resolution personified.

Struck speechless by what they heard, the stunned assembly recovered enough to say, 'When the great king was still alive, Rama accepted the gem-set crown. But you refuse the crown you have inherited at his death. Who among princes can match you in righteousness?'

Bharata called Satrughna and told him, 'Proclaim by

beat of thunderous drums that we are bringing back the rightful king and order the army to get ready quick.'

When the citizens of Ayodhya, steeped in woe, heard Bharata's words broadcast thus, they acclaimed his decision, as if nectar had restored life to the dead.

Sounding like the seven seas at dissolution, the huge army rose, Kaikeyi's hopes came to naught and sorrow fled.

The grand march to the forest began. Dust rose to the sky obscuring it completely, as the men and women of Ayodhya followed the army. The din that arose resounded in all four directions.

As that huge concourse disappeared into the jungle, the city faded from sight, shrinking like the sea when Agastya, the dwarf, had drunk up its waters.

Seeing that this earth could bear the weight of that humongous army that narrowed the quarters, could those poets who describe her as a woman, be deemed to be in their right minds?

Bharata, clad in bark, walked in front followed by his mothers, the sages and his father's counsellors. Satrughna, the younger prince, spotted Mantara, death in person, pushing herself forward in the crowd.

He caught hold of her, ready to dispatch her to her maker, but Bharata stopped him and said, 'I did not hack into bits that sinner who destroyed the ancient tradition, not because she was my mother but because Rama would not have approved.

'Let's leave the crookback alone, however angry we may be for the endless woe she has caused.'

He stayed the night in the same grove where Rama had rested some days earlier, laying his head on the same grassy mound on which Rama himself had slept.

GANGA SIGHTED

(The next day, Bharata reached the banks of the Ganga with his huge army comprising some 60,000 Akshauhinis, and about 200,000 elephants, horses and men. Sighting them from afar, Guhan, the great boatman, jumped to all the wrong conclusions. This huge

host could not have come except to wage war against his beloved Rama. Strong as Death the army, he guessed, from the dust raised by the marching multitudes.)

Laughing with derision, eyes darting fire and smoke issuing from his nostrils, a dagger in his belt, a horn and a tabor in his hands, shoulders heaving, he scented war and sneered aloud, 'An army of rats.'

He told his assembled huntsmen, 'This host bent on mischief shall be sent to heaven and the great kingdom shall be restored to my bosom friend. Be on the ready.

'Beat the drums, destroy the paths and fords on all sides; ply no boats. Keep guard. Seize whoever comes this way,' he ordered.

'The treacherous usurper who has done my dark-hued prince out of his kingdom has come. It's time for red arrows to fly, belching fire. Should he escape, wouldn't I be called a cur?

'Am I a bowman to be frightened by elephants? If I let him cross the river, wouldn't the world sneer, "That wretch of a hunter was better dead"? Is not that rare word "friend" worthy of treasure?

'Shouldn't you attain the renown of hunters by defeating an army marching with banners, and restore the land to its rightful owner? Can you not see how this man, whom my lord endowed with his land, is loath to let him enjoy even the forest, which is ours?

'Is a king's neck immune to a hunter's arrow? Come what may, before they can reach my dear friend, he and his army will first have to escape my hands.

'Will not my arrows destroy the army of one whose mother gave my friend bark to wear and sent him into exile? Come, let us annihilate all of them.'

Sumantra, the veteran charioteer, saw from afar the great bowman. He approached Bharata and told him, 'That is Guhan, who owns the banks of the Ganga. A bosom friend of your brother, he has a sea of an army and countless boats to do his bidding.

'His strength is a rock, his love a sea. There he stands,

beautiful as the dark night, eager perhaps to meet you.' Bharata, pure of heart, replied, 'If he is dear to Rama, I'll go to him before he himself comes to me.'

Saying this, he rose. Across the river, the king of hunters saw astounded, a bark-clad figure covered with dust, face unsmiling, like the moon shorn of rays.

'He resembles my chief,' he thought, 'and his garb is an ascetic's. His grief seems endless. Can such a brother ever harbour sin in his heart? I will soon find out.'

'Guard the paths,' he ordered his men, and left alone by boat to meet Bharata halfway. As the two came face to face, Guhan fell at Bharata's feet. And the one, whom Brahma himself would not hesitate to worship, touched Guhan's feet.

Guhan, happier than a father on seeing his son, raised and embraced him. He then asked, 'O doughty prince, what brings you here?' Bharata said, 'I've come to set right a wrong done by my father and take Rama back.'

On hearing those words, the hunter-king, so pure of heart, heaved a deep sigh. Joyously, he fell on the ground a second time, locked with his hands the prince's lotus feet and said,

'The kingdom your mother got for you, you have spurned as sin. O prince beyond all praise, can even a thousand Ramas equal you?

'O prince as virtuous as you are mighty, what praise can a poor hunter shower on you? Like the sun whose rays make all other light look dim, you have by your action put in the shade the fame of your ancestors, gathering it all up and making it your own.'

An ocean of grace and virtue incarnate, Bharata bowed in the direction of the south and asked him, 'Where did our brother stay?' And the hunter-king said, 'Come, prince, I will myself show you the way.'

Fleeting like a cloud, Bharata rushed forward and saw the bed of grass amidst the rocks, where the bowman must have rested. Plunged in a sea of sorrow, he fell down and bathed that place clean with his tears.

'You know you had to suffer all this because of me. You

supped on roots as if they were ambrosia; slept on grass; and I, knowing this, am yet alive. All I have to do is to wear that priceless, glittering crown!'

The mighty prince had more questions, 'If this is where the great one slept, where did he, the one who walked away with him out of his boundless love for him, rest?'

The hunter replied, 'O mighty one! While the handsome prince and his wife slept, Lakshmana, bow in hand and wide awake, kept vigil through the night.'

Deeply pained, Bharata said, 'We are both by birth Rama's brothers. But while I caused him endless woes, the other wiped away his suffering. How boundless his love! And me? What price my service?'

He lay down that night on the same dusty ground and requested Guhan, 'O great hunter! If you'll carry me across the Ganga, you'd be taking me across a sea of troubles to Rama.'

'Very well,' said Guhan and went to his kinsmen. 'Bring the boats!' he ordered, and they came in a heap as if Siva's silver mountain, golden Meru, and Kubera's flying chariot, shy of their single status, had split themselves into numerous forms.

The boats, whose gait put women and swans to shame, covered the Ganga completely from one bank to the other. As they bobbed about on the waves, they resembled the traffic between heaven and earth, virtue and sin alternately ascending and descending.

'Countless boats have arrived, prince,' Bharata was informed. 'What is your pleasure?' And the prince looked at Sumantra and said, 'My father, let the army embark quick.'

Commanded thus, Sumantra saw to it that the loading went off without disorder.

Looking like the thunderous clouds at Dissolution that drank up all the waters of the seas, the elephants, trunks raised, swam across the river. Musth streaming from their bodies, only the tops of their heads showed. Slashed by the undulating waves, they looked like the breasts of Ganga.

(Soon that vast army and the multitudes of Ayodhya had left the river behind. Only when he saw that they had reached the other shore, did Bharata get into another boat with Guhan, his three mothers and Sumantra. As the boat began to move, Guhan looked at Kausalya and asked who she was.)

Bharata said, 'She is the first wife of the one at whose courtyard kings would wait. That fortune that was her due, for having given birth to the one elder to Brahma, she has lost through my birth.' At this Guhan wept and fell at her feet.

Distressed as a heifer that had lost its newborn calf, Kausalya asked Bharata who the mighty oarsman was. 'A dear friend of Rama, and elder brother to Lakshmana, Satrughna and me. A prince by the name of Guhan,' said Bharata.

'Sons,' she blessed them, 'no longer should you feel desolate. Even the exile of the two heroes has borne fruit; with this powerful tusker, you are not four but five, and together you should rule the whole world as one for a long time to come.'

Guhan then turned to the one who stood by herself, Dharma incarnate, and asked, 'Tell me, prince, about the one who looks so sad.' And Bharata replied, 'She is the younger wife of that king and the mother of the one who refused to be parted from Rama, proving to the world that Rama has a brother.'

When Guhan asked, 'Who is this?' of the one who sent her husband to the pyre, dispatched to the forest that ocean of grace and thereby plunged her son in a sea of woe, Bharata replied,

'The mother of woes, the foster mother of all blame, the one who carried me in her sinful womb a long, long while, so that I may pine and waste away for ever. If you must know the only one whose face is untroubled, let me introduce her to you—she is my mother.' The hunter greeted her, the ruthless one, as reverentially as he had the other two.

(Soon, moving gracefully like swans, the boats came ashore. The women got into the waiting palanquins. Then, with Guhan beside him, eyes brimming with tears, Bharata walked the long distance to the hermitage of Bharadwaja, who met him halfway and welcomed him warmly.)

SANDALS CROWNED

Bharata bowed to the sage who showered endless blessings on him and said, 'How is it, that you, who should be wearing the crown got for you by your mother, are now in ascetic's bark, matted hair and all?'

Bharata replied indignantly, 'How is it that, you, the all-knowing sage, ask me a question that does not become your own learning and status? Will I, against the rule, rule the land? And if the true king does not agree to do his duty, I too will forever stay with him in the forest.'

(The great sage was deeply moved by such selflessness and saw to the comfort of his royal guests. He arranged for a feast and entertainment, conjuring up with his magical powers celestial apsaras to delight them with dance and music. While everyone enjoyed these sights, Bharata himself fed on roots and vegetables, laying his golden body on the dusty ground. When the dark night ended, all luxury faded away as if it had been a mere mirage.

Taking leave of Sage Bharadwaja, Bharata and his entourage moved on towards Rama's abode at Chitrakuta. Lakshmana saw from afar the arrival of the army amidst the dust and din caused by their movement.)

As was his wont in matters concerning Rama, he hastily concluded that Bharata's intentions were hostile. Rage roaring through him, he thought,

'This is Bharata, plotting evil with a malicious heart, now come with an army. Not content with the kingdom gotten through foul means, he is now determined to war with one bent on penance.'

He leapt up, reducing to powder the rock he had been sitting on, rushed to Rama and reported indignantly, 'Defiant

Bharata has come in haste with a huge army to war against you.'

He fastened his anklet and picked up his dagger, placed the quiver of arrows on his shoulders and buckled a mail to his chest. He then took up a well-thronged bow. Touching Rama's feet, he said, 'You shall now see your two brothers in deadly combat.

'Bharata, who has lost both earth and heaven, but has the might of an army behind him, not to mention his own strong shoulders, pitted against me, the one who has come away with you to the forest, with naught but my own unique strength. Your heart will rejoice.

'You shall see the rivers of blood let loose by me carrying away men, along with their mounts and chariots. My fiery arrows will pierce the weapons, hands and mailed breasts of a thousand warriors and slay them all.

'You shall see, my lord, the small eyed demons and devils dancing in joy with headless corpses, keeping time with the shields seized from hands cut down by me.

'You shall see my sharp shafts slash men, powder their chariots, slice off the legs and heads of elephants and horses, and the limbs and shoulders of those astride them.

'You shall see my golden arrows, well feathered, pierce the hearts of those two princes, and invite the birds to feed on their flesh.

'For love of a woman, and to the distress of the world, the king ordered Bharata to rule the earth. Now, you shall see how, ordered by me, he will leave the earth to rule in hell.

'You shall see Kaikeyi, that acme of scandal, eating dust and wailing aloud—she who rejoiced at your mother's distress, when Fate made you exchange a kingdom for a forest.

'O faultless spearman, I shall in a second dispose of this army with a single arrow like Siva, the Destroyer, and get back to you in no time.'

To Lakshmana thus ranting vengeance, gentle and generous Rama said, 'O my guardian angel! Listen to me for a moment. If you set your mind to confound all fourteen worlds, none can stop you. But let me tell you something you might want to chew on.

'Mighty bowman with pillar-like shoulders, of our ancestors, too numerous to be counted, can you recall any that has ever sinned?

'Everything the vedas prescribe, Bharata's conduct exemplifies. His deeds are not the horrid things you have described in your great love for me. Is it wise of you to think that the great one has come here to wage a war against me?

'It is more than likely he has come to give me the kingdom out of his boundless love for me. How can anyone think of him as anything other than a towering image of Dharma and the very linchpin of virtue?

'He has come, I am certain, only to see me. You yourself will soon see that this is the truth.'

(*Meantime, Bharata had ordered his army to stay behind and walked forward with Satrughna to meet Rama. As he advanced, palms folded, body withered, eyes brimming with tears, he was the very picture of woe—this was what Rama saw from a distance.*)

He turned to Lakshmana and said with affectionate exasperation, 'You, sir, with your resounding bow, have now a good look at him, come here with an army, dressed for war.'

His anger-ravaged face dimming, Lakshmana stood astounded. Seeing Bharata, body emaciated and face savaged by grief, Lakshmana's bow, along with his tears, fell to the earth.

When he saw Rama, Bharata's eyes brimming with tears, quite forgot the reproachful words he had rehearsed a hundred times—'You didn't think of Dharma, withheld your grace, and abandoned tradition.'

Speechless, he could only fall headlong, as though he was sighting his dead father. The tears from Rama's lotus eyes that saw Bharata's form so shrunk, flowed down and bathed his matted hair.

Embracing him, he scanned many times the garb he

wore, several thoughts spinning through his head. 'You are sunk in sorrow. Is the valiant king well and strong?' he asked.

Bharata replied brokenly, 'Unable to withstand the disease of separation from you and with Death having established his rights, through the agency of my dark mother's boon, he has departed to heaven.'

Before the cruel words could enter his ears like a spear in a sore, his eyes and heart whirling madly, the lord of heaven fell down on the ground.

Like a snake struck by thunder, he briefly lost his senses, ceased momentarily to breathe. Upon recovering, he broke into a lament:

'O chief! A lamp forever aflame! Father of the land! Mother of virtue! Fountain of mercy, lion to your enemies! My father dead? Who will be Truth's kinsman now?

'O victorious and deadly spearman! You obtained the grace of that renowned sage and performed those faultless *yagas*, only to get me, the cause of your death?'

'You whose garlands scattered gold, is this the way you take your rest, leaving the burden of kingship to me? Am I, your murderer, fit to be king?

'I, a wretch who gave the world only trouble, accepted the kingdom, which even those who want everything did not want. Now for whose sake, should I cling to this unreal body and rule?

'You could not bear that I should leave Ayodhya's honeyed groves for the forest and therefore died. But I? Greedy for life, I linger on.'

His strong brothers and the kings who'd come with Bharata attempted to comfort that high-shouldered lion. And the great Vasishta consoled him thus:

'Man's only hope of salvation lies in following the path of Dharma and renunciation. You who have crossed the sea of the vedas, have you forgotten that birth and death are inevitable?

'When one realizes that life is an illusion and that it takes many thousands of forms, both happy and sad, is it right to expect from Death any kind of compassion?

'Have you not seen some creatures die even before they are properly born? When a man who has ruled the world single-handedly for 60,000 years departs, is it right to mourn?

'Can even those three, the primeval gods, one righteous and creative, the other bearing the trident, and the third the discus and the gift of speech, escape the ensnaring coils of Time?

'When the five elements on which depend our five senses themselves cannot escape death, should you lament the passing of a single life?

'Life is a flame made possible by the wick of Time and the deeds of our past is the oil that feeds it. When they end, life too must end. How can it be otherwise?

'Is it possible to count the number of wombs responsible for those who live in sorrow, die, suffer sorrow in hell and are reborn to more sorrow?

'It is foolish to cry over life, which is but a drop of rain. Water from your eyes won't bring him back.'

Then Rama, the soul of all living things, went with the sage to the river and plunged into its waters. Later, guided by that same holy man, he offered water to the spirits of the dead.

The rites duly performed, they all went to the hut where Rama gently broke the news to Sita. Heart throbbing, eyes stirring like two seas, she rested her hands on her foster mother, the Earth, and broke into a keening lament. The wives of the sages comforted her and led her to bathe in the sacred river. Her sorrow abated, she joined her husband.

Sumantra then took them to the three waiting mothers. They embraced the grieving Rama, themselves breaking into sobs of unsuppressed grief. Then they clasped Janaka's daughter to their bosom, whereupon they wept with renewed despair.

(*The next day, surrounded by his brothers, sages and kings, Rama held consultations with Bharata.*)

'The emperor is dead and by his order the kingdom is yours. How come then, that instead of a crown, you have assumed this garb of an ascetic?'

Bharata bowed low to his elder brother. Looking hard at him, he countered, 'You who are Dharma personified, have yourself retreated from it. Why?

'Through an improper boon you were put in an improper place, and I, the proper son of that woman who so improperly killed her king, may I not do a penance improper?

'Born of a sinner and a sinner myself, I may neither commit suicide nor be allowed to do penance. How then am I to save myself?

'Can the sin of a woman unchaste, the sin of penance devoid of patience, the sin of virtue without grace, rival the sin of giving a kingdom away, against the norms set by our ancestors?

'When you can give up a place which is yours and by tradition inalienable, and decide to do penance, can I, even unconsciously, take the reins of a kingdom that will henceforth be deemed a destroyer of Dharma?

'When the king has died for love of you, and you have withdrawn into a burning forest, am I to be a fell opportunist and seize the kingdom treacherously?

'My father, erase the sin your father committed and the horrible pain my mother's crime has brought to this world. Resume charge of the kingdom,' he said, pouring out his pain.

Hearing the firm words that revealed his determined heart, Rama, moved, said, 'Bravo, hero, but listen to what I have to say.

'Conduct, truth, justice, praiseworthy loftiness, and all the good ways of Dharma have been laid down according to the shastras.

'Great bowman! Understand that learning, good sense, right conduct and high deeds are only what our worshipful gurus describe.

'My son, if you investigate who those great gurus are, you will realize that they are none other than one's father and mother.

'O prince, learned in the vedas, I followed the Dharma of our race in obeying my father's command that resulted from a boon my mother had obtained. Would it be right if I renege upon it now, because of your appeal to me?

'Are sons born to endow their parents with glory through their good deeds or to bring on them unforgivable infamy by the sins they commit? Should I make my father turn in hell, for having uttered a falsehood here on earth?

'Should I allow greed to take an upper hand and accept your offer and rule the world tempted by the pleasures of its fleshpots?

'Since the kingdom belongs to you by virtue of the boon your father was committed to, and you by birth are equal to the task, it is all yours to rule.'

'You were born before me,' Bharata persisted, 'and there is none in the three worlds to equal you. If this earth is mine, then I give it to you. Come and be crowned.

'While the entire world stands perturbed and sorrowful, will you, valiant brother, do as you please? Put an end to their misery and despair,' he begged, and clasped Rama's lovely feet.

'If out of your love for me, you give me this kingdom,' Rama said, 'is it right? Can all the years in the forest I promised my father be over in a day?

'Can the world regard anything but Truth as the highest form of purity? Is there a greater evil than that which departs from it?

'While I stay in the forest for fourteen years, you rule the kingdom given to you, and thus preserve Truth. This is my command to you.

'When the king asked me to take the crown, I agreed only because I wouldn't disobey him. Can you disobey me now? Do what I tell you. Don't wilt in sorrow.'

At this point, Vasishta intervened and told Rama where his duty lay. 'I have lovingly taught you, Rama, the arts and sciences that will guide you in this life and the one that lies beyond. Do not refuse my command. Come and rule your land.'

Rama joined his hands in reverence before his guru and made his submission: 'O Son of Brahma, tell me this: can one, teacher, son, or whoever, tender a solemn promise and renege on it?

'If one does not obey with reverence a mother's commands or a father's orders, is he not guilty of behaving like an outcaste? Isn't he no better than a wild dog that runs amuck?

'I have on my head an earlier order that I had promised to fulfil. Now, you, sage, command me to do the opposite. What should I do now? Learned one, resolve this dilemma for me.'

The sage had no answer to this and held his peace. Then the younger prince said, 'If that is you decision, let who will, rule the land. I'll stay with Rama in this fearsome forest.'

The gods who were witness to this argument thought in panic: 'If Rama is thus taken away, our work will come unstuck.' They then intervened, saying, 'Worthy Rama has the right to obey his father and go into the forest; and it is your duty to rule the land for fourteen years. Both must be done.'

Rama said, 'This is an injunction that cannot be defied. I asked you earlier, now I must order you: rule the land for the time prescribed.' And he caught both Bharata's lotus hands in his.

'If I agree,' said Bharata, 'you must come back after fourteen years to that great city and rule. Otherwise, I swear by you, I shall enter the fire and die.' And Rama, seeing his brother's firmness of mind, melted, and agreed that it should be so.

With no other option left, Bharata sobbed his heart out and pleaded with infinite sadness, 'At least give me your two blessed sandals.' Rama, the giver of all things good, readily agreed.

His resplendent body covered with dust and eyes brimming with tears, Bharata placed the sandals reverently on his head, saying, 'These two will now be my crown,' and left.

The mothers and other relatives, the good men and the sages, the massive army and, finally, Vasishta, all left with him.

Sage Bharadwaja, skilled in ancient lore, too, left for his ashrama as did the denizens of wave-tossed Ayodhya. The gods left for their heavenly abodes, and, at Rama's command, Guhan, too, left.

With Rama's sandals on his head, Bharata crossed the pellucid waters of the Ganga. He did not enter beauteous Ayodhya but instead spent a sleepless night on the river bank.

Passion renounced and eyes never lacking tears, he began his rule from Nandigram, as proxy to his master's sandals.

Fearing that his very dear subjects would forever pine for him if Chitrakuta, close to Ayodhya, became his abode, Rama too embarked on a southward journey with his guardian brother and dear wife.

ARANYA KANDAM

(*Journeying southward, the trio met many single-minded rishis engaged in severe austerities. The first such sage was Atri, who welcomed them with great joy. They stayed with him and his incomparable wife, Anasuya, for a day or two and then moved towards the thick forest of Dandakaranya. Here they encountered the first of many rakshasas, forever harassing the sages, Virada by name. Of fearsome proportions, his jet-black chest adorned with huge pythons for necklaces, he was devouring elephant after elephant with a hunger unappeased when they came upon him.*)

In the twinkling of an eye, he seized swan-like Sita and rose to the air. Then ensued a fierce battle, the two incomparable bowmen sending shaft after shaft to shatter the many weapons he sent down, including his fabulous trident, and hills and trees uprooted and hurled with ease.

After an earth-shaking and sky-splitting battle that lasted a while, Virada fell down, badly mauled. But even as Lakshmana, on Rama's orders, was preparing a grave for him to be buried alive, Virada transformed himself from a frightening rakshasa to a new being, like Brahma emerging from the primal egg.

Singing hymns in praise of Rama, he told the story of his curse. Known as Tumburu, a celestial being in his former life, he had once in a fit of lust embraced Rambha, the heavenly nymph, even as she was dancing.

For this transgression he was cursed to be born the son of a rakshasa called Kilinja. When he prayed for forgiveness, he was told that the curse would lift when Rama's feet touched him. After this happy conclusion to a fierce encounter, Rama blessed Tumburu and continued the journey to yet another cluster of ashramas.

(*Moving on, they met Sage Sarabhanga, who welcomed Rama eagerly and told him an unusual story. Brahma, the four-faced god,*) was so pleased with the rishi's penance that he sent Indra to fetch him for he wished to share his abode with the sage. Sarabhanga politely refused the offer, saying that Brahmaloka was but a trifle: his penance was not for 'worlds fleeting as painted pictures. His aim was to go where there was neither time nor change, no expansion or contraction, no transformation and no ruin, even at the time of Pralaya, the great Dissolution.' He said that he had been waiting all these days only to immolate himself in the presence of Rama, the only God.

When Rama heard this, he demurred. But the sage insisted, 'Now that I have seen you, my earthly bonds have snapped and I have no more desires left. I refused Brahma's offer, because I wanted a higher, everlasting world. Please grant me permission to die in your presence.' He then entered the fire along with his wife and reached that supreme abode he had desired.

Depressed though they were by this fiery departure of the great sage, the three moved on past many pleasant hills and groves, shining rocks and purling streams, meeting men and women of many tribes as well as the sages of Dandakaranya. Once again Rama was told of harassment by the rakshasas. He reassured them that his great bow and quiver of arrows were forever at their service. 'Even if these evil doers were to be protected by Subramanya, Vishnu or the great Siva himself, if they dare stand in the path of virtue, I shall cut them to pieces. Never fear.'

Rama then met Agastya, the father of Tamil eternal, who embraced him, eyes brimming with tears. 'Stay here,' he pleaded, 'and perform all the penances you wish. And if the rakshasas appear to ruin our penances, you can kill them and end our misery.' Rama replied tactfully, 'Isn't it better I move on to meet these asuras head-on than wait for them to come here? What is your pleasure?' Agastya consented to let them go and told Rama of a cool grove further on by name Panchavati, surrounded by towering hills and a river, divine as the Caveri. There was an abundance of honey and fruits of every kind and storks and swans to entertain Sita. Seeking the sage's blessings, they moved on to this place suggested by him. They walked many leagues, crossed many rivers and negotiated many hills. They then sighted Jatayu, the king of eagles.

With feathers as of molten gold, he was perched atop a mountain, the darkness of the sky illumined by his wings while his red talons, that looked like a coral creeper, lit up all that was below. Pure-minded, learned, ever curious, sharp and truthful, he was a wise counsellor, able to see far, small though his eyes were.

The threesome at first looked at him with suspicion, wondering whether this enormous bird was a rakshasa in disguise. They couldn't be certain. Maybe, they then thought, it was Garuda, Mahavishnu's mount himself, who had stopped there to rest for a while.

Jatayu too, wondered at the identity of the young trio. 'They wear their hair matted but look like gods. But gods they cannot be, for I know all of them.

'Their looks are such that they could make the three worlds their domain if they so wished. The eldest resembles my old friend Dasaratha, the emperor. Could he be . . . ?'

On approaching him, Rama said, 'We are Dasaratha's sons and this is Sita, my beloved wife.' Immediately, Jatayu flew down from his perch, love swelling within him like a sea.

He asked after Dasaratha and was told he had departed to heaven. The great bird fell down, as if struck by lightning. Recovering, he wailed, inconsolably, recalling his many happy associations with his old friend.

He then introduced himself. 'I am Jatayu, king of the eagles, son of Aruna, and the younger brother of Sampati. Dasaratha was a very close friend. I have been around since the days of gods and castes.'

When they heard this, their hearts filled at once with sorrow and joy. Sorrow because they remembered their father's death and joy because they found a surrogate father.

Jatayu said, 'Children, you must now perform my last rites. We, your father and I, were two bodies but one soul and now that he has left, I too cannot bear to live.'

Rama said, his eyes filling, 'Deprived of our father, separated from our mothers and exiled from our city, we entered the forest and chanced upon you. Will you too now leave us in the lurch and depart?'

His heart melting, Jatayu said, 'My children, stay here and do your tapas. I will guard you against all danger.' Rama then told him of the place that Agastya had recommended. Jatayu took them there, guarding them like a mother bird its young ones.

SURPANAKHA

(They then saw the river Godavari, spread like an ornament of the earth, flowing majestically over the five tracts described in classical poetry. Its waters blessed the people with rare goods fit for the gods.

That goodly river looked as if it had come there to adore these god-like children, its face shining with lotuses, its eyes tulips, its hands the waves that scattered fragrant flowers at their feet.

They then reached Panchavati, cool and divine, on the river. There, in a quiet and lovely grove, Lakshmana put up a hut. Soon enough, they had their next adventure in the form of Surpanakha, Ravana's sister.)

A fell disease from her birth, born to destroy root and branch the rakshasa clan, she was, for some unknown reason, staying alone and roaming freely in that forest. Impelled by fate, she arrived one day at Rama's hermitage. On seeing him, she mused,

'The mind-born Manmatha is said to have no body at all. Can it then be, that the god of love, burnt to ashes by Siva's wrath, has obtained through long penance this form, more lovely than the one before?

'No tree or mountain can ever match his hands,' she thought. 'The abode of beauty, hands stretching to the knees, as prescribed in the books, and very much like the trunks of the *diggajas*.

'How lucky is the sea-earth with her elephant's gait to be a woman! When this rare being walks on her, she should be trembling with joy.

'No hill of rock can ever compare with this bowman-hero's shoulders; even Meru, famed and golden, cannot rival this sapphire mountain. Why does he, of such rare looks, submit his body to penance? What penance has penance done, to be wooed by such beauty which does not sate, no matter how long one feasts on it?'

The flood of love in her heart, greater than any tide in river or sea, submerged her sense. And her modesty, like a miser's fame, grew less and less. Her heart scorched and dry, she fixed her gaze on the hero's shoulders and was unable to pull it back.

'A rakshasi fanged he will reject at once as one who gobbles up all life; it is better therefore that I appear before him as a lisping koel and a pretty peacock.'

Invoking goddess Lakshmi with a mantra she knew, the frightening rakshasi gained a face brighter than the moon that glows in the sky.

Tripping on lotus feet she came, a shimmering peacock, a gliding swan, a lightning liana, a witching siren. The tinkling sound of her anklets and waistlets, the humming of the bees in the flowers she wore in her hair, announced her approach.

Rama, who turned that way, was surprised to see before him a bowing figure with burgeoning breasts and a face that looked as if sweet nectar had dropped from heaven. Seeing that form, unequalled in heaven, earth or the netherworld, Rama wondered, 'Who is this? Is there a limit to her beauty or her equal in adornment?'

She, her heart filled with love, looked at his face and touched his feet. Standing aside like a shy fawn, she darted her spear-eyes in a sidelong glance.

'Fair one, may good attend your arrival, indeed a blessing to us! Where do you come from? What is your name? And who are your kinsmen?' asked the first of the vedic gods.

And she, poor fool, said, 'I am Brahma's great-granddaughter, sister of Kubera, Siva's friend. Also of the one who quelled the *diggajas*, hefted Kailasa and now rules the three worlds—a maiden named Kamavalli.'

Rama heard that and grew suspicious. 'This doesn't seem right and must be explored further,' he thought, and said, 'If it is true that you are the sister of that fiery-eyed and fearful demon, tell me truly how you have acquired this form.'

Hardly had he spoken when she said without hesitation, 'Though I am one of them, I hate their ways. I detest their deceit and violence. Having chosen good and rejected evil, I have done endless penance to expiate my past sins. Thus it is that I obtained my present form.'

'Sister of one who has Indra for his servant and rules the three worlds, how is it that you have come thus alone, without pomp and circumstance?'

Sly as ever, she replied, 'Spotless one, I no longer belong to that lawless crew. I am now on the side of the gods and the noble sages. I have sought you for something I want.'

Rama thought, 'A woman's mind is too deep to plumb! I shall know the truth as I get along.' To her, he said, 'What do you want of me? I shall help you if I can.'

'It is not proper for well-born women to declare the love they feel; but, enamoured, I pine; what can I do with none to help me? Save me from Kama!'

As she spoke, her eyes stretched and contracted, scattering rays, now bright, now dim. Her breasts rolled and heaved. 'A shameless woman,' Rama thought, 'low-born with no good in her.'

But he said nothing. Not knowing what he thought, that dissembler wondered, 'Have my words moved him or will he reject me?' Unable to bear the quivering suspense, she decided to speak again:

'O beauty past painting, I did not know you were here. Else I would not have wasted my youth and womanhood in following the routine prescribed by the sages.'

'This sinful rakshasi knows no law and has come with evil intent,' thought Rama and demurred, 'Fair lady, what you ask is against the traditions of caste. You are a brahmin and I, a kshatriya.'

'My father,' she replied, 'was a vedic brahmin; my mother, chaste as Arundhati, was the daughter of King Chalakantaka, a spearman. Your objection is invalid and I am saved!'

A mischievous smile wreathed the face of the blue cloud at these yearning words. 'The learned, dear lady,' he said, 'won't approve men mating rakshasis.'

'I am now a rare Vidyadhari and made a mistake when I said that I was Ravana's sister. Haven't I already told you how I pleased the gods and sloughed off my sinful birth?'

'One of your brothers is monarch of the three worlds. The other is Kubera, lord of wealth. I will accept you if they offer you to me. Else, seeing how lonely you are, you should seek elsewhere your desire's fulfilment,' he said, fending off her advances.

Whereupon she replied, 'O one with shoulders like hills! The vedas themselves have sanctioned the gandharva marriage for a man and maid deeply in love. My brothers will come around after our union.'

'The grace of the rakshasas, no less! The joy of life inseparable with you—how many boons my penance has obtained since leaving Ayodhya!' he said, laughing.

At that moment appeared Sita, as if she were a gift from the gods, a queen of heaven sprung from the earth, that rare jewel-like sprig, whose beauty dazzled the denizens of heaven, earth and the netherworld.

That foolish, insensitive carnivore saw before her a flood of light issuing from the flower of chastity, which would one day burn down the forest of warring rakshasas.

Surpanakha gazed long at the newcomer, trying to fix that vision in her mind. 'There is no end to beauty,' she thought, 'only limits to an artist's skill. I cannot take my eye or mind off this vision divine. And if I, a woman, think this way, what would men feel in her presence?'

She stood transfixed, gazing alternately at him and that miracle of vision. 'There is nothing more to think,' she mused. 'Brahma himself, after much thought, has created an acme of beauty in these two. There is none to rival them in all three worlds.'

'This rare jewel couldn't be his lawful wife. She too, peerless and tender of feet, must have happened along like me and been given protection.' Thereupon she said to Rama,

'This woman is a fraud, a rakshasi. Her form is false; she lives on flesh. Put her away!'

'Your shrewdness is amazing indeed,' said he, smiling. 'Who can cheat you? Your transparent goodness reveals your thoughts. Is she indeed a deceitful rakshasi? Look at her carefully.'

When she, ambrosial, chaste as Arundhati approached the hero, Surpanakha, her black heart afire, screamed, 'How dare you, a rakshasi, interfere?' Terrified, her slender waist shaking, her soft soles aching, she hugged Rama's shoulders, a coral creeper against a raincloud.

Rama, who knew that even jesting with rakshasas might prove dangerous, told her, 'Forbear, woman, from your pranks. My brother will be furious if he knows about this. Get away, quick.'

That winsome rakshasi replied, 'Brahma, Vishnu, Siva, Kama and all other immortals are engaged in penance in order to obtain me. How is it that you despise me, all for the love of this forward cheat?'

'This lustful creature will not go away even if I rebuff her,' he thought, and retreated into his hut with Mithila's daughter.

Left alone thus, Surpanakha thought, 'If I cannot embrace him today, I'll die.' And even as the sun turned west, she entered her room of crystal in a golden grove. As she languished, her heart broken, the love within her spread through her like poison from the fangs of an angry cobra.

Morning came and the fiend, still tormented with unappeased lust, said to herself, 'So long as that other one is around, he won't look at me. I will spirit her away and hide her somewhere and then live happily with him as his love.'

She repaired to the great one's hermitage and found he was away at the river for his morning rites. In the dim-lit hut, she failed to see his brother Lakshmana, guarding Sita as a miser minds his hoard.

'She is alone, my plan will succeed; I need not waste any time,' she decided. Full of malice, she began to trail Sita when Lakshmana, ever the vigilant guardian, saw her.

'Stop!' he shouted. Finding the intruder a woman, he refrained from using his bow. Instead, he caught by the handfuls her flaming red hair and twisted it. He then gave her a kick and pulled out his dagger.

'I will lift him to the sky,' she thought ferociously. But he threw her down with ease. Telling her to 'desist from evil,' he cut off her nose, ears and nipples. This done and his anger spent, he let go of her hair.

The scream that issued from her mouth filled the earth and entered heaven. The blood from her nose overflowed and dissolved the world!

It was that bright sword which cut off her nose and nipples, but spared her life, that sowed the seed for the war that was to end with the hacking of the ten crowned heads of Ravana.

She wiped her nose, sighed like a furnace and beat the earth with her hands; felt her breasts and looked at them, dismay writ large on her face. Whirling around, perspiring but still besotted, she collapsed.

Blood flowing as from a fountain and making a mire all around, she screamed so loud in her agony that even the gods in their lofty abodes could hear her. Invoking her kin whom even Death feared, she broke into a long lament:

'O mountain unique, who lifted the peak on which rests Siva, is it not a shame that while you reign, ascetics roam around, bow in hand? Are you concerned only with preventing gods from raising their heads? Won't you bother yourself with what is happening here on earth?

'You made slaves of every god in sight—of wind and water, fire and death. Can you not then control mere mortals, such as these two? What has happened to you, mighty warrior, who was bequeathed a sword by Siva himself?

'You have broken off the tusks of elephants and reduced mountains to mere powder. These men are not even worth the dust under your sandals. Perhaps you deem them beneath contempt?

'Has the famed strength of Ravana and his brother, the might that subdued even the gods, taken flight? Is it now the property of mere men, the meat we rakshasas feed upon?

'Indra, Siva, Brahma and all other gods obey you; apsaras invoke your blessings. All the seven worlds are yours to rule. How can I enter your court now and show my face without shame?

'Brother, O brother, who hefted Siva's hill, here, in this forest that is Khara's domain, a mere man has kicked me around and cut off my nose, exulting in his strength. And all I can do is wail and beat my breast.

'O Ravana, O Ravana, you achieved renown by breaking off the tusks of guardian elephants! Won't my nose thus cut off, smirch your fearsome reputation? What a scandal!

'O nephew, dear nephew, you destroyed demons, imprisoned Indra and enslaved the gods. Mere mortals have disfigured me! Am I destined to die here in shame?

'Once, O nephew, with a single bow, you set the seven worlds ablaze, destroyed all the quarters in anger, and fettered and imprisoned Indra. Won't you come and see what these men have done to me?

'O Khara! O Dushana! You who are of the race whose bright jewels can pierce the night and who have weapons that can split the rocks! Have you too, like Kumbhakarna, fallen into unbreakable sleep and can't hear my cries?'

Even as she lamented, rolling on the steps of that hut, Rama arrived, bow on shoulder, having completed his daily rites by the river.

She looked up at him. Beating her breast, her tears and blood making mire, she fell before him. Lamenting loud, she said, 'Alas! See what I've got for loving you!'

His guessed accurately that his brother must have disfigured her for committing a grave crime. 'Who are you, lady?' he asked.

'Don't you know me? I am the sister of one whom none dares oppose, of one who owns all the worlds from heaven downwards.'

'What brought you from a rakshasa's palace to this forest, where we have come to do penance?' he asked quietly. 'O balm for the lovesick, didn't I come here yesterday?' she asked, taken aback.

Feigning surprise, he wondered, 'Could you be the same person who came yesterday?' Reproachfully, she answered, 'My lord, if one has her breasts, ears and nose cut off, will she still look beautiful?'

Rama smiled. Looking at Lakshmana, he asked, 'What was her fault that you decided to cut off her ears and nose?' To which that hero replied, 'Whether she was in search of something to eat or was set up by a band of sinners for some fell purpose, I do not know. But I saw this sinner attempting to seize Sita.'

Before the bowman could finish, the rakshasi said, 'Haven't you ever come across a jealous frog provoked to rage at seeing another near her mate? Where is the heart not inflamed by the sight of a co-wife?'

'We have come here', said Rama, ineffable, 'to destroy the entire rakshasa race, notorious for waging treacherous wars. Don't lose your life through such wicked talk. Run away from this holy forest.'

To this Surpanakha replied, 'Innumerable gods from Brahma downwards, their hair never greying, their skin never shrinking, are Ravana's subjects. Your hasty deeds are foolish. If you have any sense, listen to what I say for your own good.

'If someone were to tell Ravana, "Your sister has lost her precious nose", he would lose his tongue for daring to lie. In your savagery, you have sliced off not only my nose but also your race. You cannot escape now.

'If you protect my life, I will save yours. Else, while Ravana lives, none in heaven, earth or the netherworld can save you.

'Women of character never boast. But it is my passion for you that makes me talk thus. Won't you tell your younger brother that I, sister of one stronger than the gods, on my own am stronger than either of you?

'I can protect you in a fight by carrying you to the sky when attacked by terrestrial enemies. Why hate those that can guard you? I can give you whatever you want.

'Tell me, what use is this fragile flower? Name if you

can, another woman, either here on earth or in heaven, high-born like me, unmatched in beauty and goodness.

'True, you have cut off my nose—so what? Isn't a long nose a blemish in a woman? If you will accept me, I can conjure myself another nose and become a beauty once again. If you will look upon me with grace, I'll give you everything a woman can give.

'Like and dislike are all in the mind. If you accept my love, my very life is yours. Isn't the beauty that pleases all a poison in itself? Is it not enough if I please you alone?

'O hero, why did you disfigure me, if not with the thought that, beauty marred, I have no choice but to stay with you? You have done no wrong and I know it. My love for you is now doubled, for I am no fool!

'If the fierce rakshasas happen to set eyes on my face, they will destroy the entire world out of their hatred for you. High-born men like you dedicated to Dharma can't cause such calamity. So, stay with me,' she finished audaciously.

'I have still with me,' said Rama, 'the shaft that took the life of Tataka, your mother's mother. And I have vowed to destroy the entire rakshasa race. So, foolish woman, stop at once all this idle talk and go away.'

Replied the rakshasi, 'King of a land well-watered and fertile, you claim to want to destroy the rakshasas. Very well then, if you can ignore my gaping mouth and fangs and accept me, I will teach you to master their tricks and sorcery and help you win the war against them.

'If you wish to defeat those strong and treacherous demons by using their own magic and witchcraft against them, I can help you. I am familiar with all of them and know well how to prevent the effect they will have on you. It is said that only a snake knows the ways of a snake, and surely you are aware that one must set a thief to catch a thief?

'Even if you won't give up this slender-shouldered woman, why think of me as superfluous? If you hesitate to accept me because your lover is with you, very well then. After the three of us destroy the demons, you might consider marrying me off to your younger brother here!

'When you return to your city, I shall assume any form you wish and be a good wife to your brother. If your brother, his anger now quenched, objects to a wife without a nose, you can tell him, "Have I not spent all my life with a woman who has no waist?" '

Lakshmana eyed his spear and told his brother, 'Unless we kill her, our troubles won't end. What is your pleasure, lord?' Rama gave permission, 'Yes, if she won't go.' Frightened at last, she thought, 'If I stay any longer, I will lose my life.'

'Did you think I would stay with you after losing my nose, my two ears and breasts? I only said what I said to find out your true nature. I'll confront you with Khara, swifter than the wind, more fierce than fire, who will prove the death of you.'

And with that she left, her malice deep and implacable.

KHARA KILLED

Blood guttering through her nose, locks outspread, mouth agape, Surpanakha fell at Khara's feet like a dark cloud rendered ruddy. Her cry sounded like a drumbeat tolling the death of the rakshasas.

She rolled on the ground like a snake wilting under fiery lightning. 'Who dared do this to you?' he thundered. And she, almost blinded by the blood spurting out of her nose, said bitterly,

'Two men, ascetics, with bow and sword. They are apparently bent upon killing the rakshasa race, root and branch and establishing righteousness on earth.

'And a girl with them, the like of whom cannot be found on earth, heaven or elsewhere—a rare sight to see or describe.

'I thought, this beauty I should take to Lanka's king. When to do it I seized on her, they got enraged and cut off my nose.'

'Bring my chariot,' he ordered, furious. At once fourteen men, each a hill with two hands, and who, with just one, could have lifted the world, begged him to leave this task to them.

Armed with spears, swords, axes, pestles, wheels, nooses and heavy clubs, their roar alone was enough to frighten the world. 'Well spoken, indeed,' said Khara, delighted. 'If I myself went to fight these weaklings, the gods would laugh. Go you forth and kill them; drink their blood and return victorious with that girl!'

Happy with the task assigned, they bowed to him and, guided by that shameless woman, Death's own messenger, went to that lovely grove. She pointed with her finger at the lotus-eyed discus-bearer, the one with a thousand names, who happened to be engrossed in deep meditation.

'We'll seize and throw them up to the sky,' they said. 'We'll catch them with our noose,' they boasted. 'We'll finish them off as we were told.'

They stood around like so many mountains, in battle readiness. Rama, the refuge of all things living, saw them. Instructing his brother to 'look after the lady,' be picked up and slung on his shoulders his bow, as if it were the *karpaka* tree in flower.

Sword in hand, he sallied forth to confront the fiery rakshasas come to fight him. With his sure shafts he brought down the twenty-eight hands carrying swords, battleaxes and gleaming tridents.

Like trees mown down, their arms and weapons fell to the ground. Using their massive chests they continued to fight, but the hero's arrows flew into their necks and severed their heads, which danced in the air before they hit the ground.

As if they were a herd of tuskers who had been decimated by an enraged lion, Surpanakha ran, a female elephant making good her escape, to tell Khara all that had happened.

When that cruel demon heard that his trusty henchmen, whom even Siva could never tackle, had been worsted and killed, and by a mere man, his rage boiled over. 'Summon the rakshasa horde,' he ordered, and in an instant a kettledrum was mounted on an elephant and they made a din that would have frightened a lion in its den.

The chariots gathered like unending dark clouds,

terrifying both the gods in heaven and the nagas in the world below. The earth Adisesha bore on his head tottered, contorting in pain, as if the mountains of all the seven worlds had come as one to sit on her.

A group of tigers? A rack of clouds? A herd of elephants? A range of hills? A pride of lions, perhaps? The multitude of veteran warriors moved as one. Those who took the trouble to count said there were as many as sixty lakh in each section, and of such sections there were fourteen!

That flood of an army headed for Rama, guided once again by that rakshasi, who led them all to their doom, like a disease that takes a man to his death.

The heaps of dust came first; trees and bushes crashed; *yalis* and lions ran around bewildered, signalling to the heroes that an army of considerable might was upon them. Rama donned his quiver, put on his armour, girt his sword and picked up his bow.

'Need I tell you, lion heart, that were even heaven and earth to come together, I would single-handedly finish them off? Leave this battle to me and allow me to shrug off the sloth eroding my shoulders,' said the younger warrior. But Rama wouldn't consent.

Knowing the strength of those hill-like shoulders and loath to disobey him, Lakshmana folded his palms worshipfully and stood aside, even while Sita's tears soaked the earth.

The frightening Khara galloped forth on his golden chariot, driving the sun away. To his assembled army he said: 'I shall myself vanquish this man in a one to one combat and don the garland of victory.'

A learned rakshasa called Akamba tried to warn him: 'Hero of heroes! It is good to be fierce in battle. But let me tell you of the bad omen I see. Rumbling clouds are shedding blood.

'Around your flag, raucous flocks of crows attack each other and fall down dead. Flies buzz around the edges of swords. And look at the halo round the sun; observe how the left eyes of our soldiers throb.

'The horses nod; jackals and dogs howl. Elephants are breaking their own tusks. The earth shakes while heaven thunders and the quarters burn. Our chaplets stink like meat gone bad.

'Forgive me for bringing these things to your notice, but these omen are unpropitious. It would be unwise in the extreme to dismiss him as a mere man. Despite your considerable preparations, you may not get the better of him.'

Hearing the augur speak thus, Khara laughed and the worlds trembled. 'These shoulders that have ground down the gods now swell at the prospect of war. Should they be fearing a mere man?'

The battle joined.

Their spears were sundered; sundered their axes. Their swords were sundered; sundered their clubs. Their *bhindis* were sundered and sundered their arrows. Their lances were sundered and so were their shafts.

To the despair of counters, one, ten, hundred, thousand, a crore of Rama's arrows flew precisely to their targets, killing the enemies and making a heap of those whose bodies had been shot through.

Rushing forth like moving mountains, like clouds battered by lightning, those rakshasas, their eyes darting fire, rained all kinds of deadly weapons. Breaking them all into bits and pieces, scattering them in every direction, burdening the earth and filling the forest, Rama heaped up a hill of black bodies and red hair.

Headless torsos danced and elephants bathed in the red blood. Delighted ravens ate their fill. Heaven staggered under the load of new arrivals. For, having been killed by Rama's shower of arrows, those fiery-eyed rakshasas became immortal.

The gods celebrated that the night-stalkers were now forever dead! The huge waves that rose in the sea of blood provided the devils a bathing tank, in which the lungs of the killed became its lotuses, their entrails its flotsam and their chariots its sand dunes.

Heads lay scattered; eyes that had once spat fire were also scattered; scattered were the elephants, like so many hills on earth; shafts were scattered as if they were showers from Rama's bow. Lives flew from bodies as if they were sparks scattered from a forge.

Except for the army chieftains, all those opposing Rama had been felled and bathed in a sea of blood. Those chiefs now looked around and saw none with a head on his shoulders. Gnashing their teeth in wrath, they rushed at Rama in their swift chariots.

In the wink of an eye, he destroyed with his arrows those fourteen chariots. Their perch destroyed, the charioteers descended, bows in their hands and fire in their eyes, and showered an unceasing spray of thunderous arrows.

Those arrows and the fourteen bows that had dispatched them, he destroyed with ease. Their bows lost, the enraged chieftains seized mountainous rocks, and rising high, hurled them, as if they were sparks from the sun.

Brows lowered and bow bent, all-knowing and all-powerful Rama let go fourteen leaf-shaped arrows and brought down to earth both the rocks and the heads!

When the army chiefs died thus, many more rakshasas with fiery eyes advanced upon Rama from above and below. Even the gods fled, afraid that the weapons hurled and cut to bits by Rama might sink the earth. All the worlds drowned in panic and the guardian elephants shut their eyes in fear.

The chief of that army was Trisiras, a three-headed hero with a helmet of gold. Resembling the Destroyer's trident, he discharged a shower of arrows. With him in their midst, the noisy army felt rejuvenated and roared like the sea at Dissolution.

Against him, like a lone lamp in a great darkness, stood the lone bowman, whose only rival was himself.

Rama marshalled his arrows and took on the army group by group. Their heads were severed and so were their legs, shoulders and thighs. Swords and axes fell off their hands and their umbrellas bit the dust.

Flags, horses and chariots all went down crashing.

Elephants in musth, huge and high, fell like hilltops struck by lightning. Those beheaded, not knowing they were headless, continued to shoot their hot and fierce arrows! And others, rising up to the skies, flung their weapons in thunderous torrent.

Armoured torsos, shield in hand, were a strange sight. They swayed like hill-shaped, headless nymphs, dancing in a wild frenzy. The river of blood that was let loose, produced a sea with a new complexion. Flywhisks and white umbrellas took the place of foam, elephants of sharks, and saddles of merchant ships carrying jewels.

Though those arrows shattered his army and made heads roll, enraged Trisiras did not yield. He flew his chariot out of the mire, ascended the sky and roared from his high perch.

From his chariot up above, he scattered a series of fiery arrows to cover the sacred form of that prince, son of the king who bore witness to truth. Rama, in turn, cut down those shafts with his fearsome arrows and, with fourteen bright missiles of his own, destroyed the rakshasa's chariot and its driver.

Even as the gods watched, he followed it up with matchless arrows, sharp and golden. They severed two of Trisiras' crowned heads, which fell and rolled on the ground. Though his chariot was lost and lost was his name, 'three-headed', the rakshasa did not cease. He rained from the sky a shower of arrows as from a dark cloud.

Like a rising wind clearing the sky of its vapours, Rama's arrows cut down the bow from which came that rain of arrows. Trisiras lost his weapon but not his murderous rage or the brightness of his face. Intact were his reserves of strength and his thunderous boast. Whirling his hands like a windmill, he pelted stones.

With him battling thus from the sky, fury unabated, one man magically multiplying into two hundred, Rama first deprived the rakshasa of his two legs and then his shoulders. Legless, handless, teeth flashing from within his stinking and cavernous mouth, he rushed as though to gobble up the prince. For once merciless, Rama sliced away in an instant the remaining head with a sharp arrow.

As soon as that mountain, Trisiras, kissed the earth, the remaining rakshasas fled, despite Dushana's efforts to stop them. He raged: 'Has any rakshasa ever fled before sharp-speared Indra or the deathless Trinity? Did you, you fearful cowards, learn from the gods this trick of fleeing?

'So many of you, and you flee from one man; armed with sword, you rush for safety. Where to? To the embrace of your women, large-eyed and full-breasted?

'Your bloodshot eyes having turned milky white, you wish to show your wedded wives the wounds in your back caused by scratches from trees or those in your chest caused by the foeman's arrows?

'Could there be grief greater than this, that this enemy, a mere man, should show skills that surpass those of the immortals? He not only cuts off the nose of your chieftain's sister, but also brands the word "cowards" on your broad backs?

'Are you the same horde who once deprived the gods of their swords and waged courageous wars with them? Are you now planning to become traders in pearls or have your weapons turned into ploughshares?

'Stay awhile,' he said, 'and see for yourself the strength of my long bow.' With his army's morale thus restored, he stepped forth to confront Rama.

All those men, along with their weapons, were cut down; elephants with long tusks were cut down. A forest of flags was felled when those chariots, swift as the wind, were cut down; the necks of horses were sliced off, as if they were stalks of red rice gathered by peasants at harvest time.

The eagle-feathered arrows remained stuck in their bodies; the crescent-shaped arrows chopped off their heads; blazing shafts pierced their armours and rent their treacherous hearts.

Brushing aside the arrows discharged by Dushana and destroying all those who stood beside him, Rama dried up, as if in sport, the vast sea of rakshasa might.

The red flood of rakshasa blood, dragged along with it the uprooted trees and hills. The terrible arrows that Rama shot pursued the rakshasas, as they ran in every direction, found their targets and made them roll on the ground.

The corpses of those sinners lay in heaps that stretched long and high, defying counting. Enraged, Dushana drove his chariot over dead elephants and horses and over crowned heads that had separated from their torsos.

Admiring, Rama saw the fearless Dushana approach, saw how he stood, bow in hand and immovable as a mountain. 'Well, well', he thought, appreciating the sight of him, even as the other let loose three arrows.

The gods flinched in fright as they hit the band that Rama wore on his forehead. But nothing daunted, Rama taunted, 'Counter this if you can,' and let fly an arrow that cost Dushana his head.

With his brother beheaded and the rakshasa army in disarray, Khara was like a pedigree elephant whose tusks had been smashed. 'I will finish him now with a single shaft,' he swore, and drew the string right up to his shoulder. That strong bow broke at once with a noise like thunder.

Frightened and anguished, the gods watched in dismay, realizing that the raincloud had no other bow and cried, 'Our strength is gone,' fearing for their very safety.

Not in the least perturbed, Rama remembered Vishnu's bow, won from Parsurama, now in Varuna's safe keeping. The rain god, realizing at once that Rama needed the bow, gave it to him.

The moment he grasped that bow in his left hand and bent it with his right, the entire rakshasa race felt a-throbbing on the left sides of their bodies. Even as their shoulders and eyes twitched, he released with a speed that terrified Death himself, a hundred shafts that reduced Khara's chariot to powder.

His chariot gone, but not his courage, Khara rose swiftly to the sky with a roar and rained from there arrows aimed at the shoulders of the handsome prince who stood majestic like Mandara. Warding off those arrows with ease, Rama cut down with a sharp shaft the right arm of Khara.

Immediately, Khara flung with the remaining left limb a huge pestle that Lakshmana's elder brother countered with a fearful and shining shaft. The rakshasa, furious now like a serpent with fangs pulled out, picked up a tree and rushed to attack Rama, who sent a rare shaft in reply.

Rama's arrows took that sinning hand, head, and, finally, his life. Ravana's sins had indeed caught up with him. He'd lost Khara, his right hand as it were. The many boons he had won from the gods, his magical powers and his enviable might, all of which had lent him the arrogance to sin with disdain in all the seven worlds, had been of no avail.

Up rose the gods in acclamation, singing, dancing and showering flowers. And the spotless one stood bright, like the sun that had dispelled a mist. Rama returned to his hermitage and his brother and wife bathed his feet with tears, washing away the blood and dirt of battle.

Ravana's sister beat her belly and clasping Khara's night-dark body, rolled around in despair in the river of blood.

'I fell in love and it cost me my nose but not my life. Instead, my words have cost you your days and life. Oh, my cruel and destructive ways!' she wailed.

As if hell-bent on the destruction of the rakshasa race, she flew like a tornado that confounded the world and reached the city of Lanka.

SURPANAKHA'S STRATAGEM

(We will now travel to Ravana's city that had the wide sea for its moat, the place where Surpanakha had repaired to, still bent on vengeance. In the magnificent hall of audience devised by Maya, the divine architect, Ravana sat in state, adding lustre to an already lustrous setting. The hall was filled with potentates from the seven worlds, all waiting in trepidation to hear what the king of rakshasas might have to say about the death of Khara.

Vidyadharas and siddhas, unagas and kinnaras waited with bated breath. Tumburu, half-man, half-horse, a master of music, was singing Ravana's praise and his accompanist was Narada, no less, with his vina. While the one who wanders at will in the three worlds was thus occupied, Varuna, lord of the shark-filled seas and

*provider of rain ensured that rain poured in Lanka not in torrents
but softly, as from a sprinkler, so that the clothes of the lovely women
of Lanka were not drenched. Vayu, the god of wind, took care that
pollen from flowers wafted away before they fell to the ground, lest
they hurt the lovely feet of Ravana's damsels. Brahaspati, the guru
of the gods, and Sukra, the preceptor of the asuras, ushered in Indra
and the other gods to their assigned seats. Yama, the timekeeper,
his mouth covered in humility with a piece of cloth, announced
the hours with a beat of the drum. Divine damsels like Urvasi and
Rambha, their slender waists weighed down by the weight of their
breasts, danced for the delight of Ravana's preoccupied eyes.)*

Into this court ran Surpanakha, minus nose and ears,
breasts streaming blood, making a din louder than thunder.
Like a rain-bearing cloud that bursts upon reaching a hill, she
fell at the feet of the king and rolled around.

Darkness eclipsed the three worlds; Sesha drew in
his numerous heads; the hills trembled; the sun grew dim;
guardian elephants fled; gods went into hiding.

Shoulders rising, eyes darting fire, fumes issuing from
mouth, his many brows shot up to the tops of his foreheads as
the worlds stood stupefied; gods didn't seem to know what
to do.

All of them, with Yama at the head, stood petrified,
thinking, 'Surely, our end has come.' Earthlings trembled,
sighed, moved restively, dumbstruck.

His lips curled and smoke issued from his cavernous
mouths. His many moustaches trembled and caught fire
from his furious sighs. Sharp teeth flashing like lightning
through a cloud, he boomed thunderously, 'Who has done
this deed?'

'Two who have come to the forest, but rule the earth,'
she said. 'Beautiful like Manmatha,' she added as an
afterthought. 'Men who cannot be rivalled by any on earth
or heaven, though made only of flesh and blood. Their
swords did this.'

When he heard that those who had defaced her were
men, his laughter spread in all directions. His eyes spat fire.

'Weakling! It can't be. Don't lie. Do not fear and speak the truth,' he urged.

Their bodies are gems, like Manmatha's; their might can subdue Meru. What need to speak of it now? They can, in a trice, destroy the seven worlds with their bows.

'Respectful to the sages, their faces are like the moon; their eyes are like fragrant lotuses, likewise their feet and hands; their tapas is unending—who can equal them?

'Bark clad; anklets on their feet; bowmen who wear the sacred string; well-versed in the vedas, they don't deem you worth even dust. Their quivers are inexhaustible, as is their learning.

'How strange to see not one but two such Manmathas in a single world! Could there be a hero stronger than they? Who on earth, Brother, can rival them? Either can equal the three gods put together.

'Sages set on lofty paths have told them how much they fear the oppression and harassment of the rakshasas. And these two heroes have taken it upon themselves to exterminate the race that wants to conquer the entire world.

'They are the sons of a king called Dasaratha who ruled the world and won fame for his good and just reign; commanded by their own father, these blameless men now dwell in the forest. Their names are Rama and Lakshmana,' she finished.

'Mere men have slit the lovely nose of my ambrosial sister and yet continue to live! And I, sword in hand, just look on shamelessly,' fumed Ravana.

'Through victory of sheer might I won this kingdom: is this all that I have to show for it? After what has happened, were even the heads of all the heroes in the world to be sliced off, can my lost honour ever return?

'My mind! Why do you totter at the thought of the disgrace that pierces my body? Don't faint. What is your grief? Haven't we ten heads and many shoulders to bear this blow?'

Thus sneering, he questioned with fire in his eyes: 'Couldn't Khara and his men, the fear of that forest, sweep away with their swords these two men who fought without the aid of an army?'

At this, Surpanakha resumed beating her belly, lamenting: 'Alas! Khara and his bull-like men did confront him with their rattling army. But with a single bow and in just an hour, invincible Rama sent them to heaven!'

'What was your fault,' he asked at length, 'that made them cut off your ears and nose?'

'The fount of my dire fate,' she said grimly, 'is one who is beyond compare. She lives with him. Her form is such that the goddess of beauty herself would be unfit to be her maid. Her name is Sita.

'Her body is of burnished gold, her breasts a pair of golden urns. Her toes and fingers are pure red coral and her feet are soft as silk-cotton. The earth is blest that her feet fall on it.

'To say that her forehead resembles a bow, her eyes spears, teeth pearls, lips coral is to merely play around with words. If one were to liken paddy to grass, would it be a fitting description?

'Search in heaven where your enemies reside, or in the Naga world that lies beneath, or in our own land girdled by the sea, you will not find one such as her.

'Indra has his Sachi, and Siva his Uma; Vishnu too has his Lakshmi; you too should have your Sita.

'One has his beloved by his side; the other bears his prize on his chest; the third keeps his on his tongue. Should you, great hero, acquire this lovely woman with lightning for a waist, where on your person would you place her?

'Once you win that beauty with a charming lisp, you'll devote you life to pleasing her and give away to her all your huge wealth. In commending this peerless one to you, lord, I am doing you a favour, though not to the wives who now live with you!

'Sita has not come from the womb of any woman on heaven or earth. If the milky ocean gave Lakshmi, the Earth, not to be outdone, gave Sita.

'Take Sita, the doe with fragrant locks and narrow waist,

and enjoy her; and with the might of your arms get me Rama for my pleasure. Manmatha will rejoice, and the world laud your feat.

'Since everything is ordained by Fate, even those who have many penances to their credit have to wait to get what is due to them. It will come only when so destined. Good fortune awaits, grasp what it has in store with your twenty hands.

'When I attempted to spirit her away to bring her to you, Rama's brother intervened and cut my nose off with his sword. So doing, he has cut off my happiness too! I therefore decided to tell you everything and then give up my life,' she concluded.

All at once his finer feelings, even anger on his sister's behalf, deserted him, the way blessings do a sinner. Just as one flame merges with another, love and longing took sole possession of him.

He forgot Khara, his sister's nose, his own dishonour and the boons he'd won. The only thing he remembered were the words spoken in praise of that maiden, Sita.

When thoughts of her had so consumed his mind, how could he separate the two? Were he to cast it off, would he be able to find another mind as efficient?

Even before the abduction that was to come, Lanka's lord had thus imprisoned Sita in his heart. And that heart, like butter in the sun, began to melt.

Like a secret vice that overtakes a fool, his sinful past, his destiny that was also to be Lanka's disaster, drew near, making Ravana's senses fall prey to the disease of lustful love.

The king whose mighty chest had broken the tusks of earth-bearing elephants, now wilted as Kama's arrows bored through him like weevils through a tree.

When the seasonal northern breeze entered his heart through the holes Kama had pierced, he raged, 'What season is this?' Whereupon late winter departed in fright and spring wafted in instead!

When even the winter that freezes trees and mountains

turned into a scorching flame, why talk of spring or summer? What potion for those who have swallowed the venom called love?

The heat within him born of love reached deep, tormenting him. Summer seemed an added sore, making him rage, 'What season now? Winter was better than this. Bring it back, quick,' he ordered his slaves.

But even when that season returned, his shoulders burned. 'This is no winter, early or late!' he yelled angrily. 'Throw all the seasons out.' All seasons then departed.

Shorn of them, the world became like heaven eternal, where Time, hearts of yogis that have no attachments, can never be measured. Still Ravana continued to pine with unrequited love.

He then commanded his attendants to bring him the cooling Moon at once. They brought him, trembling in fear. Glaring daggers at his servants, he said, 'I asked for the cool Moon that soothes. How dare you bring the fiery Sun instead?'

The frightened servants pleaded, 'Lord, do we ever disobey you? It is indeed the Moon before you. The red-rayed Sun won't come but in his chariot.' And he who had never felt till now, the hopeless longing brought on by thoughts of a woman, was disconsolate.

His frenzied imagination came up with the vision of the perfect woman that haunted him. When darkness fell, he summoned his sister, wanting to know whether the vision he had conjured up measured up to that woman she had seen.

When that treacherous and cruel rakshasi entered, he asked, 'Look now, a sword-eyed peacock stood before me. Is that the Sita you spoke about?'

And Surpanakha, haunted by her own vision, replied, 'Eyes red lotuses, mouth a red fruit, huge shoulders and long arms, garland on his broad chest, a veritable jade mountain: that must be the bowman Rama.'

'You fool, I saw a woman's form, and you describe a man not thought of by me. How strange that both of us, skilled in witchcraft, should be falling victims to mere humans!'

'Your thought pursuing nothing else,' she said, 'you see

only her wherever you look.' Ravana concurred, 'So be it. But how is it that you see none but Rama everywhere?' And she replied, 'I can't ever forget him from the day he did this to me.'

'Yes, yes, I understand that,' he said impatiently, 'but what hope for me, my life and limbs withered?' And she replied, 'You are the emperor of this world. Why should *you* feel helpless and forlorn? Go forth and seize that dark-tressed woman.'

When she departed, the rakshasa, racked by lust unassuaged, tried in vain to slake his thirst through other diversions. Finally, his mind thrown in utter confusion, he got into his chariot and went to Maricha who, senses well under control, was in deep meditation.

MARICHA'S DEATH

On seeing Ravana, Maricha was perturbed and frightened but welcomed him with due respect and asked, 'How is it that you, a king who makes even Indra and Yama quake, have deigned to come to my sad abode, as if you were a poor and ordinary man?' And Ravana replied:

'I have taken as much as I can bear and am tired. My greatness, glory and honour are gone. What I tell you today will make even the gods jeer at me.

'Two strong men have with their swords cut off your niece's nose. What greater disgrace for your kin and mine? Is it not a blot on our entire race? A single man has exterminated all our indignant kinsmen who, unable to bear this insult, waged a war against him. How come that your own hands lay sweetly idle, while your nephews were thus being killed?

'My anger has not cooled; I am shamed but I refuse to fight those who are beneath me. With your help, I shall take their woman away and be avenged. It is for this I have come.'

The rakshasa's words fell like molten lead in his ears. Clapping his hands over his ears, Maricha let out an exclamation of disgust. At first his mind was all bewilde but soon he grew calm and said in wrath:

'O king, you are a fool seeking thus your end. This decision of yours, I know, is not really yours but Fate's. Though unpleasant, I must speak the truth. It cannot hurt the seeker of advice.

'With your own hands you set fire to your heads and fasted for countless years. If you lose the boons obtained at the cost of such great pain, will you ever get them back?

'O king who knows all the vedas, will you throw away the fruits of a lifetime's penance by pursuing the vicious course you now propose?

'You know that justice destroys those who by fraud take another man's land or take by force somebody else's wife. Which tyrant, given to such excesses, has survived righteous wrath?

'Leave aside the shame and sin of it all. The king of heaven himself came to grief because of Ahalya. Countless Indras have since met the same fate! So will you, if you persist with this folly.

'What you suggest will never, never happen; and even if it should, Rama, the world's protector, with his deadly arrows is sure to destroy not only you and your might, but your entire kin and race. Have you forgotten what happened to Khara? Dead, dead, all of them, all slain by Rama's arrows.

'When I think of the arrow that destroyed my mother and my brother, my manhood melts, my heart trembles. Even thinking of Rama and his brother fills me with foreboding.

'That all things that move are impermanent is a truth you are well aware of. Don't think of mean revenge. Pay heed to my advice, and you will thrive in greatness, forever.'

Eyes belching fire, brows climbing, Ravana said, 'You say that I, who lifted on my palm Siva's mountain, am inferior to a puny man?

'You have given no thought to what has happened. You have mocked, unafraid, at my feelings and extolled those who have excavated my sister's face. This terrible crime I have borne, sir, with patience.'

Lest he offend that terrible tyrant even more, Maricha said, more in sorrow than in anger, 'Your anger will harm not me as much as you and your kin. True, you hefted that mountain. But what about that mountain who picked up Siva's bow, strung it, and broke it in a trice?

'You know nothing and will never learn. When doughty Rama strings his bow, many lives of ours will be lost for sure. In your ignorance you think this Sita a woman. She is not. She is our sins that are catching up with us!

'My heart tolls—if you do this, neither you nor your kinsmen will survive. My soul is afraid, but you don't care. If one, not knowing better, insists on drinking venom, will it be right for the other, witnessing the folly next, to say "go ahead"?

'The divine weapons that Kausika bequeathed him are at Rama's command, waiting for but a word from that bowman. Impossible to counter, innumerable to count, they will destroy in a second all the worlds starting from the one where Siva resides.

'You are demented with the poison of love and have spoken wickedly. Such thoughts are ruinous. As an uncle and a tribal chief, I advise you to desist.'

Despising him for such considered advice, the rakshasa chief said, 'You have spoken in terror of one who killed your mother. It is my mistake for thinking of you as one who can oppose a warrior.

'Are Dasaratha's sons any match for one such as I? I have made the eight elephants flee and hide, caused the gods to leave their stations and set fire to heaven. I am now sole emperor of all the worlds. You do not think my strength adequate to deal with mere men?

'I now have the three worlds under me. What is sweeter than to be challenged? Obey my orders. You, a minister, cannot disregard the duty I have laid on you.

'Should you refuse, I will cut you down with my sword and do what I please. I won't desist. If you wish to live, stop giving me this hateful advice and do my bidding.'

When the rakshasa said this, Maricha thought, 'Isn't it true that the proud will perish?' and said, 'I told you the truth for your own good, not out of fear for myself. Doesn't good look bad when ruin is close at hand? Tell me, flippant one, what I should do.'

Anger appeased, Ravana embraced Maricha and said, 'O valiant one, isn't it better to be killed by Rama's arrow than by Kama's? Get me Sita, who has made the south wind my foe!'

Maricha replied, 'Once I went with two other rakshasas to Dandaka to try and erase my shame. Those other two were shot and killed and I retreated in fright. What would you have me do now?'

The rakshasa king promised, 'I will kill the one who killed your mother. You do well to ask me what you should do. We must carry Sita away by deceit.'

'No need to say more,' Maricha replied. 'It is mean, not virtuous, to take a queen by deceit. Win her in war and add to your glory.'

Ravana laughed, 'Do I need an army to win against him? Won't the sword in my hand be enough to slay them? If they die, she too will die in grief. Hence the need for deceit.'

'Before he can touch her,' Maricha thought, 'his own heads will fall in battle. I have tried in vain to advice him. Alas, my plan has failed. Strange are the ways of Fate.'

Aloud he said, 'Tell me what witchcraft I should employ.' Ravana said at once, 'Turn into a golden stag and rouse the greed of that golden maiden.' Agreeing to this plan, Maricha left to do his bidding, while the demon-king took another path.

(*Not by choice but forced by the sword, Maricha who'd once tasted the might of Rama's bow, went in the guise of a deer to lure guileless Sita to her fate. He had survived that distant day at the yaga and escaped from Panchavati as well. He had been living in constant fear ever since. And now for the third time, fate had decreed that he should become Rama's target.*)

In the form of a golden deer, unrivalled in beauty on earth or in heaven, he went to the place where she, a golden doe herself, would yearn for it.

Desire surging within them, all the antlered deer in the forest were lured by his golden form and followed him blindly, like those who pursue prostitutes, tricky and flighty and untouched by love.

Slender waist straining, there was Sita, plucking flowers with her fair hand, white as conch, hand, itself an unplucked flower!

Just like those about to suffer ill luck see in their dream things unheard of, so Sita, destined for pangs never suffered before, saw now in real life a thing never seen before!

She didn't realize that this marvel was a trick; she only coveted it for its beauty; all this because Ravana's days were numbered. It was time Dharma was reinstated on earth.

As it stood before her crescent-browed, a strong desire to possess it flooded her mind. Saying, 'I will ask him to catch it,' she hastened to Rama. She said, excitedly, 'I saw a stag of the purest gold, most beautiful to behold, ears stiff, legs set with rubies, shining bright.'

That such a stag could not possibly be of this world did not occur to our lord! Hearing it described thus by his wife, even he, the father of Brahma, began to desire it! 'Golden maiden, let's see it,' said Rama, who could never refuse her anything.

Lakshmana, guessing his intent, cautioned: 'A body of gold, legs, ears and tail of gems, and yet it leaps! How extraordinary! This is a trick, lord. We must not assume this suspicious creature to be for real.'

'On what basis do you say this? Haven't we all heard of strange wonders? Do you not know of the seven swans whose bodies are made of gold? Who can lay down a law or limit for what is possible and what is not?

'Even the learned do not know the true nature of this fleeting world with its crores of denizens. What then, young prince, is impossible?'

'While you two stand about talking this way, the stag will have gone!' wailed Sita. Deeply moved, Rama said, 'Show him to me.' His unhappy brother trailed after them.

Rama stood gazing raptly at the deer, which stared back

at them, like Fate inescapable. For once, not exercising his sharp brain, he said, 'It is beautiful.'

What to make of that? Did he not leave his serpent-bed to grant the gods their wish? Could that boon go waste?

'Look at it, brother. What other creature can vie with its beauty? Its rival can only be itself. Teeth like pearls, and a body of gold spotted with silver!

'O bowman skilled in archery and the vedas! What man or woman who sets eyes upon this deer will not fall in love with it? Even things that crawl and fly will rush enamoured to it, their hearts melting, as moths do towards the flame.'

But the younger brother was sceptical, convinced that something was amiss and said, 'If it is indeed a deer of gold, what good is it to us? Let us get away.'

Before the words were out, the beauteous one said to Rama, 'If, my lord, you catch it quickly, we can take it back to Ayodhya with us. It is such a rare thing to play with.'

When Sita of the wasp-waist said this, Rama promised that he would indeed catch it. Lakshmana, clear-sighted as ever, continued his attempt to convince them otherwise. 'Brother, you will discover soon enough that this is a treacherous trick of the wicked rakshasas.'

'If a trick, it will die by my shaft,' said the saviour of the gods. 'Our debt to the sages will be paid. If true, it will be caught. Tell me, which of these two sounds wrong?'

'We don't know who is behind this,' persisted Lakshmana, 'and we do not know the reason behind it; nor exactly what it is. It will not credit us to pursue this hasty decision.

'Anyway, no matter how many wicked minds there are behind this plot, let me go and dispose of them with my fell arrows. Or allow me to catch that deer and bring it here.'

Driven by fate, the swan-girl sulked. Normally parrot-like and sweet, her words now were tearful and harsh. 'My lord, you won't get it for me?' she cried out, and went into the hut in a temper.

On seeing her peeved, the Protector said, 'Lakshmana, I shall myself catch this deer and get back quick. Stay here and guard Sita.'

'I suspect, my lord, it is the same Maricha,' said Lakshmana, 'one of the three who attempted to disrupt the yaga and got away. You yourself will see this yet.' But resigned, respecting Rama's decision, he stood guard over Sita.

Rama gave no thought to his brother's wise advice. He saw only the sulks on that beautiful face and taking his bow and arrows, departed.

The golden deer trod softly at first, and then, as if frightened, leapt. Ears stretched, heels reaching the chest, it shot up, teaching wind and mind one or two things about speed.

Rama stretched the foot that had once spanned all three worlds. Was there another world for that foot to measure? He followed that deer wherever it went, filling every inch of space, as if revealing his true self.

It would climb a hill; leap for the clouds; speed away if he got too close; and if he paused, come teasingly close; pretending to hover there, it would flee the minute he made a move, like the love of women who sell their charms, showing their fondness for money, not men.

'Its form is one, but it acts like another,' thought Rama. 'My brother was right. A careful probe wouldn't have led to this. A rakshasa's trick has made me a fool.'

'He won't catch me now,' thought that sorcerer, gauging his mind. 'He will only kill me and send me to heaven with his shaft.' He leapt to the sky to get away, but Rama took a shaft, red and irresistible as his discus, and commanded, 'Go wherever he goes and kill him.'

That long and sharp shaft in the form of a leaf, pierced the heart of that impostor. In a voice that reached the quarters and beyond, he cried out for help, and crashed to the ground like a hill.

When that monster in his true form fell to the ground, Rama thought, 'My brother who said, "Things are not how they seem" was right. Though born after me, he was wiser and I am a reckless, unheeding fool.'

He stood looking long and hard at the form of the

wretch whose yell had reached the horizon and saw too late that it was Maricha, the same rakshasa who had tried to ruin the sage's yaga.

'When my shaft pierced him,' he thought in grief, 'the wretch, using his witchcraft, called out in my voice; my poor wife, her eyes in flood, will wilt in sorrow.

'He could not have come here just to die. Someone else must have plotted this. Only harm will result from this cry. Before that happens, I should return.' He began to hurry back to the hermitage.

RAVANA'S PLAN

When that grievous cry from Maricha's cavernous throat reached her ears, Sita fell down, a koel dropping from a tree, beat her stomach and fainted away.

'Like a fool I asked him to catch me that deer and have now destroyed the very reason for my existence,' said she, a sprig cut down, a snake struck by lightning.

'My virtuous and spotless husband has fallen a victim to rakshasa witchcraft and you, his younger brother, unmoving, continue to stand before me?' She raged at Lakshmana.

'How can you say such things? Is there in this world a stronger man than Rama? You speak like a woman,' the wise one said, trying to make her understand.

'Earth, water, wind, sky and fire, all collapse at his mere frown. Who do you think that dark lotus-eyed one is? Why plunge yourself in needless misery?

'Will Rama, even if cowed down by a rakshasa, appeal for help from someone else? That will be the day! Were it to happen, would not the world itself turn upside down? All life, from Brahma down, will collapse.

'Why say anything further? The bow strung by Siva who reduced three cities to ashes and stunned heaven and earth, broke in Rama's hands. Could there be greater strength than that?

'If the Protector himself is in danger as you seem to fear, all the three worlds would have ended; the gods, the sages and everyone righteous, would have fallen, including Dharma himself.

'But why go on and on? Rama must have brought the rakshasa down with his shaft. And it is that wicked one who would have called out in the raincloud's voice as he collapsed. Don't worry. Stay quiet,' he said firmly.

At that, anger boiling and heart afire, she said severely, 'Your staying put here is most improper. There are those who would give up their lives for him after a mere day's acquaintance. But you hear with your own ears his cry and stand unaffected. Why should I waste time talking? I shall throw myself in the fire at once and end my life right here.'

'If I stay here, she will set fire to herself. If I go in search of Rama, disaster is sure to ensue. What should I do to end this dilemma?

'Rather than stay here and cause her death, I'll leave it to Dharma to protect her. Should anything untoward happen, the eagle chief who keeps guard will cope.'

He put out the fire she had prepared and fell at her feet. Sensing the disaster to come, he said, 'You overrule the king's command by asking me to go, leaving you alone. But I shall obey.' And he left.

Treacherous Ravana, who had been waiting for exactly such a moment, appeared in a sanyasi's guise, carrying in his hand the three-pronged staff that symbolized conquest over the three deadly foes.

Thin, as if he had been fasting long, tired as if after a long journey, he approached the hut, chanting the vedas in a voice so sweet, that it seemed to come from a vina.

Treading the ground with circumspection, as if walking on flowers or fire, legs and hands trembling as if old age had paralysed them, back bent like a tortoise shell, chest bearing the sacred thread, rosary of lotus buds in hand, he appeared in a guise that would have fooled even the gods.

He stood at the entrance to the hut, stuttering and stammering, 'Is there anyone inside?' And she, thinking him to be an ascetic engaged in penance, said in a honey-sweet voice, 'Please enter,' and duly welcomed him, and extended all courtesies.

How shall we describe the state of his mind when he heard that koel voice and saw her form, more divine than a nymph's? His hero's shoulders drooped. 'Even the three and a half crore years my tapas has procured me,' he told himself, 'will not suffice to experience the joy this woman's love will give me.

'While she rules the three worlds, the gods, asuras and their wives shall be at her beck and call and I myself will be her willing servitor. If her face, filled with sorrow, can be so bright, what will it be like when she smiles? I'll give my kingdom away to my sister who found her for me.'

Even as such wicked thoughts raced through his head and desire surged within him like a river in spate, she welcomed him and bade him sit. Placing his three-pronged rod beside him, the impostor sat on the proffered seat.

Hills and trees shivered; birds went dumb; beasts were thrown into fright; snakes slunk away, their hoods shrinking, as they sensed that tyrant's dreadful intention.

'What is this place? Which sage dwells here? Who are you?' questioned that great pretender, and she, large-eyed, thinking him a guileless stranger, began to speak.

'This is the abode of Dasaratha's eldest son who has come to live in the forest as directed by his noble mother. His brother, Lakshmana, too has come with him to this wilderness. You must surely have heard of Rama?'

'I have heard of him, though not met him. Been once to the land washed by the Ganga. And whose daughter are you, lovely lady, who spend your precious days in a forest?'

Said Sita, spotlessly chaste, 'I am the elder daughter of Janaka, whose only gods are sages like you. My name is Janaki and I am Kakutsa's wife.' Guilelessly, she queried: 'O wise one seeking salvation, where have you come from?'

And he, full of guile, replied, 'There is a king of kings, truly the Indra of Indras; born in the family of Brahma and well-versed in all the vedas. Words cannot describe his greatness. His might is such that he once tore up by the roots Siva's mountain and made slaves of the gods of heaven.

'His home is Lanka, a jewel set in the sea, the best place

in this world, better than Indra's kingdom in heaven. Gods work in his courtyard, and heavenly maidens work as slaves in his palace.

'Gentle and righteous, he is widely read, equable and handsome enough to make Kama ache. He is great as the Trinity worshipped by all.

'Lovely women in all the worlds pine for his love, their hearts aflame, but he doesn't care for any of them. He yearns only for the affections of one maiden who has charmed him.

'I had planned only to stay a little while in the city ruled by this great king. But as it happens, I prolonged my visit to that great land and have just arrived here.' He spun a story, pursuing his plot.

'How is it,' she asked, 'that you, who might think your own body a hindrance to salvation, spent so much time with the rakshasas, who respect neither the vedas nor the brahmins and feed on living creatures?

'You did not stay in forests with other sages, nor thought of living in the cities of good men, preferring instead the company of sinners. What made you do such a thing?'

The sinner replied, 'Lovely lady, you err in thinking that rakshasas are wicked and cruel. They are no worse than the gods. They treat us well too.'

Not aware that rakshasas could assume any form they wished and not suspecting any evil, she said, 'Surely, mingling with sinners is not right for those wedded to virtue.'

Not wanting to attract suspicion, he at once changed track. 'For those who live in these three worlds, what other sensible course than to fall in line with the powerful?'

Innocent, she said, 'Ere the great one ends his penance here, the rakshasas who tread the evil path, will all be destroyed and the world rid of its misery.'

Hearing such words from a doe, he replied, amused, 'Carp-eyed one, to say that men will destroy the rakshasas is like saying a hare will kill the elephants or a stag a pride of lions.'

'You have perhaps not heard,' she said, 'what happened to red-haired Virada or Khara and his vast army.' The very thought of those battles made her eyes fill up.

'Don't you realize that all the rakshasas of Lanka will be killed within a day by that great lion? Can evil ever triumph over good?'

Her voice, sweeter than honey mixed with nectar, was enough to make him swell in delight. But his pride was hurt at being told that mere men were mightier than his race. His rage roused, he hissed,

'If you say that a man overcame those bowless creatures, you will witness for yourself tomorrow how Ravana's mere breath blows away your red-cotton hero!

'Whether it is uprooting Meru or breaking down the sky, stirring up the ocean or putting out the fire in its belly, why, even such a feat as lifting the earth . . . which of these, poor chatterbox, do you think, is beyond Ravana's might?'

It was then she realized that this was no ascetic. But still perplexed, she wondered about his real identity. A cobra infuriated, he rose and revealed his true self.

At that moment her agony knew no bounds. How to describe her anguish? She had no words to say. There was nothing she could do. She was like one who had been visited by Death.

'Unaware of my prowess which has made slaves of gods, you say that men, mere worms, are stronger than I. I spare you, because of your sex. Else, I would have gobbled you up, though after that deed, I may well have died.

'Fear not, dear swan! I shall wear you as a crown on my head which, till now has never bowed to any. All the apsaras will be your slaves, and I myself, the ruler of the fourteen worlds, will be at your command.'

She shut her ears tight. 'How dare you talk like this,' she cried, 'to Rama's wedded wife? As if a dog should drag away the oblation meant for the gods?

'Are you asking me to sacrifice my honour, that I may now save my life, which is no more than a drop of water on a blade of grass? If you want to save *your* life, run away and hide yourself before Rama, the wielder of the fierce bow, comes back to his hut.'

The wicked rakshasa laughed, 'If your husband's arrow

should touch the chest that has broken the tusks of elephants, it would hurt no more than a flower thrown at a mountain.

'O nymph more beautiful than all others, I am well-nigh dead for the love that surges within me. Give me my life and take your rightful place as the queen of all heavenly maids,' pleaded the one whose shoulders alone were mightier than the mountains that bear the world.

To her shock, he fell at her feet and she, patience personified, screamed, 'O my lord, O Lakshmana!' as if a sword had plunged into her.

Remembering the curse upon his head if he ever touched an unwilling woman, the sinner hefted with his shoulders the earth on which the hut stood. He took it to his vahana, a flying chariot that hovered overhead, and resolved to fly to Lanka, hut and all.

Borne away thus, she wilted like a burnt sprig, and prayed to Dharma to protect her. In her distraction, she appealed to all living things to inform Rama of the disaster that had befallen her.

'O hills and trees, peacocks and koels, stags and doe, tuskers and cows, seek him whose strength never ebbs and tell him of my fate.

'Clouds, groves and gods of the forest, surely you know where my husband is. Tell him of my plight and save me. It will do you no credit to stand mutely by, when I am being dishonoured thus.

'Won't you, Rama and Lakshmana, turn up with a rain of arrows to destroy the rakshasas, root and branch? Bharata and Satrughna spotless, how will you ever bear this shame?

'O Godavari, cool and sinuous! A mother to all those pure of mind, won't you at least run and tell that astute man about my sorry state? O mountain pools and lions in caves! You will surely laugh uproariously, when the twenty hands and ten heads which uprooted me are blown to bits?'

She said all this and more, praying she should escape that wicked rakshasa. Meanwhile, that demon whose days were numbered, laughed, clapping his hands, 'O lovely one, you think that these mere men will kill me and rescue you? By all means, let them try if they can!'

Defiant, she said, 'By conjuring up a stag through witchcraft, you have invited your death. Entering his house like a thief, you have taken me away. If you have any wish to save yourself, stop your chariot right here!

'When you heard that all your clan were swiftly slain and your sister's breasts and nose were cut by mere men, why didn't you fight the two responsible for those deeds instead of trying this dirty trick? Are you not a shameless coward?'

'Listen, woman,' he said, irritated, 'if I should indulge in a fight with men, poor and paltry, it will be an insult to the shoulders that heaved up Siva's hill. Trickery will yield better results.'

The fair one said mockingly, 'It is a shame to unsheathe your sword; and a sin to fight your family foe. The thing to do is to cheat and abduct! What strange values the rakshasas have!'

JATAYU'S DEATH

At that moment appeared before Ravana's chariot the king of eagles, who said in a thunderous voice, 'Stop! Where are you going?'

Beak like lightning, eyes flashing fire, looking like the golden Meru emerging from the sky, his two wings churned up a storm, as if the tempest of Dissolution was upon them. Mountains knocked mountains in the tornado thus created, filling the earth with dust.

Trees stooped down and clouds drifted higher in fright. All the hooded serpents, thinking it was Garuda who had come, went into hiding. Elephants, *yalis* and other beasts, trees and bushes and stones were all dislodged by the sweep of those powerful wings. It seemed as if the forest and the sky had changed places.

Throat pink, legs and head scarlet, body huge like Mount Kailasa, the king of eagles swooped to the rescue, his two protective wings spread far and wide, resolving to destroy that aerial chariot.

'You are abducting the wife of a great man. But where will you go if I eclipse the sky and all directions?' Even as he was telling Sita not to fear, he noticed that Ravana hadn't touched her. Relieved, restraining his wrath, he addressed himself to the evil rakshasa:

'You are lost, reduced to ashes your life, and those of your kin. What is this you have started? Give up the lady, and you may yet save yourself.

'Rash adventurer! You have committed a grave error. Whom do you think you are stealing? She is the mother of all the world! Thoughtless fool! Save yourself. Haven't you heard how your kinsmen were all killed by Rama and how Death, in a rare experience, feasted full on them?

'You wish to tackle with balls of mud an angry tusker come to kill you. Don't you know that deadly venom is sure to kill, even if eaten in ignorance? The fourteen worlds and Indra himself, the Trinity and Death themselves, are but deer before a tiger, when it comes to fighting that bowman.

'This monstrous deed unprecedented, will lead to your ruin, here on earth, and also in the hell that lies beyond. What good do you think it will bring you? These men are not one of a thousand gods but *the* God, first and primordial.

'What inconceivable madness has made you err like this? The boon you have secured from Siva and all your other skills and crafts put together, will avail you nothing once he, Truth in person, releases those deadly shafts.'

Eyes darting fire and lips curled in contempt, the rakshasa king said, 'Stop. Show me quickly the ones you are talking about. Eagle, get away from here if you wish to avoid my arrow that will pierce and leave a hole in your chest. One may sooner hope to get back the water sucked in by a hot plate of iron than take this sweet girl from me.'

Looking at that swan who quaked in fear at what Ravana said, the eagle consoled, 'Don't despair, daughter, because the prince isn't here. This rakshasa's bones I shall break right now.

'Let not your tears, like pearls, fall on your breast and be scattered. You shall see today his ten heads on a platter of palm leaves offered to the gods of the ten directions he claims to have conquered.'

Intending to knock down the row of heads with his sword-sharp beak, he flapped his wings making an ominous noise. He then seized Ravana's flag that had the vina on it and snapped it in two, much to the delight of the gods.

Eyes red as molten wax, the rakshasa who had never encountered such impudence, lowered his brows and bent his mountainous bow, letting lose a shower of shafts.

Some of those the eagle-king brushed away with his wings; some his strong talons broke. Some he powdered to bits with his beak. Not even Death would have dared to defy Lanka's king in this fashion.

Striking again with his discus-sharp beak at Ravana's ten heads, as if he were Garuda attacking a hydra-headed serpent, he plucked away his earrings. And even as the other bent his bow on his broad chest to retaliate, he flew into the sky.

Roaring, the rakshasa shot fourteen shafts and when they went astray, shot some more. The frightened gods sighed, 'Alas! Dead is valiant Jatayu.' The king of eagles rose high, blood oozing from his wounds, as if the cloud that had gorged on Khara's blood was raining it back on earth.

Heaving an impatient sigh, Jatayu hopped along Ravana's twenty shoulders, pecking, digging his claws, landing blows with his wings and snapping the armour on his chest.

The infuriated rakshasa shot a hundred arrows at the eagle's broad chest, even as the gods watched, frightened and stunned. But the bird-king seized with his beak Ravana's bow and the crowds in heaven cheered aloud.

Pulling out of his mouth the bow of one who had made Indra flee, Jatayu snapped it in two. And enraged Ravana, threw a spear, deadly as the arrow that Siva had let lose on Tripura.

The eagle-king took that trident on his chest, saying, 'Don't think I cannot withstand it.' The denizens of heaven slapped each other's shoulders and laughed aloud in glee!

Like an indigent seeking a prostitute's love, a guest in an unwelcoming household, a woman wooing a steadfast ascetic, the trident returned empty-handed. Before Ravana could lay his hands on another weapon, Jatayu plucked off the charioteer's head and flung it on the face of the evil one, so besotted with love for that chaste lady.

Seeing how inexhaustible his opponent was, Ravana chose now his well-used club of gold and smote Jatayu till the eagle-king collapsed like a hill.

When he fell, Ravana raised the chariot to the sky and sped away faster than eye could follow. Even as it rose, the gentle Sita quivered in terror.

Recovering from the deadly blows, Jatayu called to Sita, 'Don't cry, don't fear, dear swan.' To Ravana, 'Where are you fleeing to!' he roared, and fell on the vahana.

He seized Ravana's club and flung it away and attacked with his beak the sixteen horses that drew the chariot, till he had killed them all. Even Death threw up his hands in amazement.

After he destroyed that chariot, he seized Ravana's quiver with his talons and beat his wings against Ravana's chest, pecking away at his shoulders. Weakened, Ravana fainted away and the eagle-king jeered: 'Is this then your famed might?'

Ravana recovered quickly, but with no more missiles left to discharge, said, 'Enough is enough.' He drew from its sheath his sword that never failed and struck Jatayu. Not so much because his strength had failed him, as because that divine sword could not fail, and also because Fate had thus ordained his end, valiant Jatayu collapsed like a mountain felled by Indra.

He sprawled on the ground, wings spread wide apart; the gods fled; the sages wailed, and Sita, bewildered as a trapped doe, sighed and grew faint. With no one else left to come to her aid, she was a creeper bereft of support.

'This good creature,' she lamented, 'who came to my rescue has been defeated. Must this hound from hell triumph? Will sin alone win? Are the vedas false, after all? Is virtue to be found nowhere?

'O brother, whom to my lasting shame I sent away, come

here that you may see for yourself the state of this touchstone of truth and virtue,' she sobbed, distracted. 'I have maintained my chastity. But even so, ill-fated, I have brought disgrace upon my bowman husband,' she wailed.

The rakshasa saw her desperate loneliness and the condition of that wingless bird. Reassured that there was no one to stop him now, he hefted on his shoulders the earth he had uprooted along with Sita, and rose to the sky.

Because of the speed with which that tyrant took to the sky, the chaste lady, her eyes and mind all in a whirl, swooned and lay on the floor of the hut he held aloft.

The eagle-king, his numbing pain a little lessened, looked thoughtfully at the sky and seeing Ravana go, said sadly, 'My sons have not come. Fate has denied me the honour of helping my daughter-in-law. The fence around Dharma has been broken. What further evil now waits in store?

'If Fate was on their side, could such a thing have happened to her? I am unable to understand this. Is this all Kaikeyi's doing?

'The evil rakshasa could never have won in an open fight with Rama. Hence it was he took to cheating and witchcraft. My son will destroy root and branch the rakshasa clan and avenge himself. The tyrant dare not touch her against her will, thanks to Brahma's curse.'

Crestfallen, Jatayu told himself, 'Poor thing, she will be thrown in prison. But though my wings have failed me, her guardian chastity will not.'

His lovely wings weakened with loss of blood, his shame at not having been able to help Sita, and thoughts of his great love for Dasaratha's two sons, combined to plunge him into slumber.

Once up in the sky, Ravana quickly took Sita away to Lanka. There he imprisoned her in a shisham grove, guarded well by evil rakshasis.

Let's now turn to Lakshmana, harshly commanded by Sita to bring news of that prince gone in search of the elusive deer. Distressed at leaving Sita unprotected, he ran swift as a boat on the sea. Soon he came upon Rama and his eyes rejoiced as much as his heart did.

Rama too set eyes on him the same instant, mind troubled by thoughts of what Sita might have made of that loud cry let out by Maricha in his dying moments.

'Misled by the false cry, foolish Sita must have harshly ordered him to come after me, making him break my clear command asking him to stay back—just the way I, urged by her, went after that deceitful deer, disregarding his wise advice.'

Even as he was wondering how it would all end, young Lakshmana fell at his feet. He raised him and clasped him close to his chest and asked, 'What has brought you here?' Lakshmana explained, 'When that unearthly cry arose, she wilted like a broken sprig.

'I told her it was a false cry but she wouldn't listen to me. Said, "Don't stand here, go and find out." Refusing to pay heed to my reassuring words that no might on earth can possibly fell you, she was sunk in rage, disgust and despair and spoke wildly of many things.

"If you don't go, I'll fall into a fire," she said. I was afraid that she would suspect treachery and kill herself, to prevent which sin, I did as she bade.'

Rama said brokenly, 'It now seems her death is certain. Alas, that her troubled heart had but heeded your wise advice! Unprotected, she's in danger. Those bent on taking her away have planned this trick.

'Your coming away is no fault of yours, meant as it was to appease the fear in her perturbed mind. You are absolved of blame. When you, mind unclouded, advised me against rushing out in pursuit of a phantom deer, I, deluded, didn't listen to you. Alas! Disaster has now struck.

'What use to stand around wailing, wasting time? Until we find her safe in the hermitage, we'll have no peace.' With the speed of an arrow discharged from a bow, they reached the hut, where the golden maiden had been left alone.

They didn't see either the hut or Sita, all decked with flowers from the grove. Rama was shattered, like a soul unable to find its body. He felt like a miser who, having buried all his wealth in the ground, discovers that a thief had taken the pot away.

The earth whirled and the mountains whirled, as if the world had turned into a kaleidoscope—sages, seven seas, sky, vedas, the eyes of Brahma, the sun and the moon—they all whirled.

Lakshmana thought in terror, 'Will he now curse Dharma itself? Or will his wrath target the gods or the sages, the very foundation of all virtue? Where will it all end?

'With him thus upset, will this be the end of all creation? Of Brahma and many precious things? Of lofty beings descending and creatures low ascending?'

Recovering quickly, Lakshmana said, 'Here is the print of a chariot wheel and evidence of earth having been dug up. To brood like weaklings is pointless. She could not have been carried far. Let us chase them, whoever they are.'

'Yes,' said Rama, 'that's our only course.' They followed the chariot's trail a long way, over the mountains and the trees it had damaged.

When the tracks on the ground came to an abrupt end, Rama, tortured as if with a spear asked, 'What now?'

Ever practical, Lakshmana urged him, 'That chariot seems to have headed south. Those shoulders of yours, brother, have never shunned war. Nor is the sky too far for your arrow. Come, we mustn't just stand and mope.'

In that direction they went for two *yojanas*, and came across a broken flagstaff with the symbol of a vina, huge as a hill uprooted by a typhoon.

They guessed at once that a great battle had taken place at that spot. The flag had been rent to pieces as if by a sharp beak and the great prince understood at once what had happened.

In a choked voice, eyes brimming with tears, he said, 'Brother, it is plain for all to see that it is our father Jatayu who has broken this flag. Alone, frail, and of years uncounted, he must have fought with all his might. We must find out what's happened to him.'

Struck with wonder, Lakshmana said, 'What unshakeable strength in one so old! Let's go and look for him. He may yet be fighting the enemy. Might even have rescued her. No use just standing here surmising.'

They went like a whirlwind sweeping the earth and soon came upon the remains of a great bow. Said Rama amazed, 'This bow, Lakshmana, is huge as the mount that the devas churned the ocean with. In shape and colour, it resembles the moon. Remarkable the strength of the one who broke it.'

They went quite some distance before coming upon the remains of a huge trident and two quivers full of arrows. Still further they found a mail studded, it seemed, with all the stars in the sky, putting the forest quite literally, in the shade.

They then saw the mangled corpses of Ravana's horses and his charioteer and threw up their hands in astonishment at the heaps of earrings and priceless jewels strewn on the ground. It seemed as if the sun and the planets had abandoned heaven and crashed down to earth, with the yuga having ended!

'So many epaulettes! Such a heap of brilliant earrings! So many crowns! Lakshmana, our father Jatayu, old and alone, must have been attacked by numerous bands of leonine foes!'

To this, Sumitra's lion-cub replied, 'So many heads and shoulders! Surely, this long-drawn battle must have involved Ravana.'

Then it was that Rama saw, his heart and eyes discharging fire, Jatayu lying in a pool of blood, like Mount Mandara afloat in the sea. His lotus eyes shedding tears, the spotless one fell on the chest of his second father. It seemed as if a dark cloud had descended on the white mountain of flame-red Siva.

He did not breathe for close to twenty minutes. Fearing he had become unconscious, Lakshmana sprinkled some water on him, whereupon he opened his eyes and said:

'Alas! Destiny has cast me for Death! Who other before me has killed his fathers? One has already gone, and now you! Both because of me.

'It is I who should have died. But I have a vow to redeem. I must bring to an end the woes of the harried sages. Hence it is that I continue to bear my life that bodes ill for others. Oh! How I loathe this meaningless life!

'You came to the rescue of my wife abducted by a rakshasa and, for your pains, have been slain. The killer is still alive and so am I! With my big bow and quiverful of arrows, I stand like a tall tree immobile!

'Who is there that can beat me in words alone? You, whose only weapons were your wings and teeth, were killed by one armed to the teeth, all for the sake of my wife. And here I am, weapons and all, and impotent. Who says I am not a valiant hero!'

And so he ranted and raved and wept. Both he and his brother grew faint. Meantime, the bird-king, a little recovered, sighed deeply and looked at them.

Sighting the valiant princes, and not aware of what had happened, the eagle-king was filled with joy, as if he'd regained his wings, his life and all the seven worlds.

'I am relinquishing my life today, so useless and so blameworthy. Yet I am lucky to see you two once again. Come,' he said.

With the beak that had dented the rakshasa's crowned heads, he drew them close and breathed deeply of the scent of their hair, again and again.

'My heart told me something was afoot when I saw what had happened. I did not think that both of you could have left that peacock, Arundhati, alone.'

The younger prince then narrated all that had happened from the moment the deer had shown itself. Jatayu listened, heart melting. Wanting to console his distraught sons, he said:

'Who can control the unpredictable? Fate decides the joys and sorrows of our wretched lives and we have to accept them. When grief comes, it is folly to brood over it. Remember, omnipotent Fate took away a head from Brahma, the Creator, himself.

'Can our frail bodies prevent us from being visited by joy or sorrow? Didn't Siva who destroyed Tripura, beg for alms, skull in hand, because pitiless Fate ordained it thus?

'That flower of the sky, the sun with its fierce rays, is swallowed and spat out by a fearful serpent every now and

again. The moon that spreads soft radiance, is fated to wax
and wane by turn.

'Lovely children! Disasters come and go, as decided by
fate inexorable. Can't you not recall what Indra suffered,
when cursed by his own learned guru?

'The same Indra, armed with thunder, was disgraced
time and again by Sambara, the mighty and mean rakshasa.
And it was your mighty father who wiped out that shame.

'Like a mother, you've fed the vultures with the flesh
of the foes you've overcome. Now go forth and destroy
the treacherous ones who have caused pain and sorrow to
Dharma and the gods, by separating you from your gracious
and soft-spoken wife.

'I fought with all my strength that rakshasa king who
abducted her along with the ground she stood on. Alas, I was
struck by the sword that was Siva's boon to him.'

These words had hardly reached Rama's ears when his
red eyes shed blood and he sighed fire. His brows rose, earth
split and hills everywhere were rent in two.

The earth whirled; so did the sea, the wind, the sun, the
moon and heaven. Even Brahma in his lofty abode whirled,
revealing Rama as all-powerful!

When the whole world shaken to its core, quaked at the
thought of where Rama's wrath would fall, he laughed like a
roaring fire, and said in accents of thunder:

'You shall all witness how this very moment I destroy all
the worlds and all the gods that watched unmoved, when a
brazen bully carried off a frail and helpless woman.

'Stars shall drop dead, the sun become mere dust and
fire will spread across the broad sky above. Earth, water,
wind and other elements will meet their end and the gods
themselves be banished.

'This very instant, behold the seven worlds multiplied by
seven perishing, like drops of water on a hot surface. Nothing
will survive my wrath!'

Immediately the sun sank behind Meru; the tuskers
of the quarters fled in fear. Even doughty Lakshmana was
frightened.

Thereupon the eagle-king said gently, 'Patience, Rama, patience. Please don't forget you have tasks before you. Gods and sages hope to win their war against Ravana and his ilk through you. Can you, in your anger and grief, let them down?

'In that land enclosed by the sea, they now live as slaves of rakshasas. But for the nectar that Vishnu gave them, they wouldn't even be alive now.

'Leaving frail Sita unprotected, you went after a phantom deer. With Fate playing its hand at will, who can be blamed? Neither you nor they.

'So don't be wroth. Stop sorrowing for her, the one as chaste as Arundhati. Fulfil the gods' hopes and wipe away all evil from the face of the earth,' said the stout-hearted king of eagles, now set on his journey to the feet of God.

Rama took this advice to heart, as though it were from Dasaratha himself. 'Why be angry?' he said to himself, 'the thing to do is to destroy the rakshasa race.'

Turning to Jatayu, he said, 'When you yourself have asked me to calm down, can I do anything else? Tell me father, which way did the evil rakshasa go?' But, enfeebled and spent, the bird-king did not reply, for his life had departed.

IN SEARCH OF SITA

Disconsolate Rama, racked by guilt, blamed himself for losing Sita and for the death of Jatayu, his other father, and talked wildly of giving up his life. Lakshmana, ever practical and focused, counselled, 'Victorious prince! Has anything ever happened in the world that has not been decreed by Fate?

'Why brood on the past? First destroy the rakshasas, and then lament to your heart's content. Let alone recovering Sita, don't you want to avenge your father's murderer?'

Confusion cleared and apathy gone, Rama returned to the task on hand. They made a pyre with heaps of *akhil*, sandalwood, *kusa* grass and flowers, bathed and decked the body of the eagle-king.

Reverently they placed him on the pyre and set fire, as the rules ordained, first to the head and then to the rest of the body. His distress lessened and desire for revenge taking over, Rama was calmer now.

The cremation over, he had his ritual bath, looking like a cloud dipping itself in water, and completed the other rites. At the end of that long day; the sun, both Rama's and Jatayu's progenitor, plunged into the western sea. It was as though he too was taking a ritual bath for his dead descendant.

Heartbroken Rama, remembered every little detail of his happier days with Sita. His mind darkened by shame and sorrow, and his heart tossed between disgrace and desire, he said bitterly to himself, 'What use is this great bow I carry?

'They said that I was destined to guard the world and protect the gods and the sages. I could not even protect my wedded wife!'

The ever-loyal Lakshmana then gently told his grieving brother, 'We are still making no real effort to find Sita.' An abashed Rama said, 'You are right, let us take the route that Ravana took.'

(Then began their arduous journey, through many greenwood forests, and across many hills and rivers. They walked many miles with no success and finally arrived at a cool grove haunted by birds. Parched with thirst, Rama asked Lakshmana to fetch some water and he immediately took off in search of a stream. There a rakshasi named Ayomukhi saw him and fell instantly in love with him.)

'I would sooner clasp him tight than make a meal of him, as I usually do when I see a human being,' she told herself. 'If he spurns my advances, I'll take him to my cave and force my will on him.'

With snakes for bangles, tigers for necklaces, and strong lions for dangling earrings, she stood before him. Lakshmana guessed at once that this was another like the one he had disfigured, but politely asked who she was.

She answered, 'I am Ayomukhi and I am in love with

you.' Furious, Lakshmana said, 'If you utter those words again, my sharp shaft will cut you to pieces.' Nothing daunted and not angered either, she said, 'Lord, if you will take charge of my life, I shall deem it as having begun just today. If it is water you want, say the word, I shall bring it from the Ganga.'

'Get away,' he commanded in fury, 'before I slice off your ears and nose.' Convinced that words would not work against him, she used magic to bewitch and carry him away. Stunned at first, Lakshmana recovered soon enough from the spell cast on him and promptly cut off her nose and ears.

The scream she let out as she fell resounded through the forests and the hills and reached Rama's anxious ears. Worried and perplexed about what might be delaying Lakshmana, he began to blame himself for sending him off alone.

Addressing his absent brother, he wailed, 'Sinner that I am, I have survived the death of my father, separation from my mothers and then lost my golden wife. But I shall surely die, if you, my eyes in the darkness of my life, do not return.'

Then he saw Lakshmana, who bounded back, shouting reassuringly, 'I am back, I am back, don't you grieve, don't you grieve.' His eyes, streaming a fountain of tears, Rama felt like a cow that had thought its calf lost forever, but finding it returning safe and sound, spurted milk involuntarily from its heavy udders.

Lakshmana told him what had transpired. Still without water and parched, Rama took recourse to the Varunastra, the water-giving arrow, to quench his thirst.

The two heroes then travelled many, many miles into the Dandaka forest in search of Sita. They then reached the forest of Kabandha, a headless monster known for his insatiable appetite. He would put into his capacious stomach any living thing within the reach of his hands.

Creatures small and big, from ant to elephant, lived in mortal fear of him. When he saw those two warriors unafraid, he asked, 'Who are you two, destined to die at my hands?' Their imperturbability annoyed him and he attempted to grab them. Reacting quickly, the two heroes hacked his shoulders with a quick swish of their swords.

And wonder of wonders! The monster's body fell on the ground and there stood the beautiful form of a denizen of heaven. He bowed low to the brothers and said in ecstasy, 'O Primordial One! You have lifted my curse. I am Danu, a gandharva, forced by a curse to assume the form of a monster. Your touch has restored me to my former self.'

He then fell at Rama's feet and asked him what had brought him to Dandaka and was told the whole story. He then said, 'Though you two are invincible bowmen, you could still do with some help in looking for the peerless one.

'Seek out Sabari, more tender than a mother, and she will guide you to the deer-faced hill, Rishyamukhi. Befriend the gold-hued son of the sun, Sugriva, and with his help, seek out Sita.'

He bowed and disappeared into the air and the brothers took the path advised by him. Passing many hills and forests, they reached the Matanga Ashrama by nightfall. And there they met Sabari.

SABARI

It was a place of quiet grace and a dense grove of *karpaka* trees famous for fulfilling every wish that one sought. Rama then saw Sabari, who had spent countless years meditating, on him alone. Eyes brimming, he asked gently, 'Mother, are you well?'

'Welcome,' she said, her voice shaking. 'Blessed am I and my penance has been rewarded. Having seen you, I shall be reborn no more. I was told this by none other than Siva and Brahma.

"The time has come," they told me, "for your flawless penance to end. Rama will come one of these days. Welcome him and entertain him. Then you must join us." '

She plied them with fruits and nuts, which they ate with zest and joy, even as she looked on lovingly. 'My good deeds have borne fruit today,' she said, eyes streaming tears of joy.

Then, that pure woman full of love for Rama, invoked her yogic powers to cast off her mortal body and obtained release as promised by the gods. Astonished beyond all measure, the heroes took the way showed by her.

Leaving behind the cool forests, they arrived on the banks of Pampa. A serene river full of grace, it was as though the sins of those who'd bathed in it had drifted downstream and left behind a cool, clear and cleansing river.

KISHKINDA KANDAM

HANUMAN

(Pampa was clear as crystal but gave no solace to Rama whose mind was full of Sita. Everything, the stream, the birds and the beasts, the trees and the flowers, reminded him of Sita. Overwhelmed with grief, he addressed all of them, begging for news of her. 'Have you, O cruel and heartless stream, nothing at all to tell me of the whereabouts of Sita?' Hearing his heartfelt cry, the flowers drooped, and so did the leaves on the trees. Parrots ceased chattering and peacocks stopped dancing. The koel didn't sing and the elephant didn't trumpet. As the day wore into night, the earth slept, and so did the mountains and streams, but not the two brothers who had once taken their ease on the milky ocean.

When day dawned, the two sons of Kosala resumed their quest for the lovely doe they had lost, traversing through many thick groves and high hills. At last they reached the hill where Sabari had long resided.

Sighting them from afar, Sugriva, king of the monkeys, who happened to be there by chance was frightened, thinking they were his foes sent by his brother, Vali. He ran to Hanuman, his friend, trusted servant and counsellor, and asked for advice.)

'Great son of the wind,' he said, 'please find out if these two men, bows in hand, looking exactly like two blue mountains, have not been sent by our enemy, Vali.'

Assuming the form of a student, Anjana's son approached those dark mountains in ascetic garb but with bows in hand. Puzzled at the contrast, he too wondered who they were and why they were here.

'Some grief seems to haunt them. They don't seem to be gods, only men. They are endowed with virtue and goodness. Something precious they seem to have lost and seek it here in these hills.'

Looking hard at them he, whose greatness was unrivalled, felt his heart melt with love, as though he was about to renew a former bond.

Righteous Hanuman presented himself as they drew closer and said, 'May god attend you!' To which Rama replied, 'Where do you come from? Who are you?'

'I serve the Sun's son, who lives on this hill. He saw you approach, and slightly alarmed, sent me to find out who you were,' said he, the fame resting on his shoulders enough to dwarf a mountain.

When Hanuman spoke those words, the prince realized that here was one, incomparable, the very embodiment of valour, wisdom and learning.

Addressing Lakshmana, he said, 'My bowman-brother! Doesn't his speech reveal his great knowledge and wisdom, as if there is no part of the vedic sea he hasn't plumbed? Who do you think is this lord of language?

'Is he Brahma? Siva? Who is he? I can see that he is much more than a mere brahmachari-scholar. His greatness, it is obvious, is the very linchpin of this world.'

And to Hanuman, he said, 'Where does that righteous one, the king of monkeys, reside? Lead us to him.' Said Hanuman, 'O heroes, it is his good fortune that has brought you here. My lord's prayers have at last been answered.

'Merciless Vali, the son of Indra, has in a rage driven his brother to exile on this hill. I am his only companion. And he lives in constant terror of that vengeful brother of his.

'One undertakes penances and austerities to get from the gods the gifts that one desires. But is there ever a gift more precious than giving refuge to those in flight from a fell enemy, dreadful as Death?

'To ask you to protect us would be an insult, since you, the primal guardian, save without being asked. To one sorely afflicted, what greater succour than you?'

At Hanuman's request, Lakshmana then narrated the story of their exile and their subsequent loss of Sita. Deeply moved, the monkey fell at Rama's feet. At this sudden gesture, a shocked Rama said,

'How can you commit such sacrilege! A brahmin-brahmachari falling at my feet, a mere kshatriya? How could you ever do such a thing?' Hanuman, high-shouldered, replied, 'Lotus-eyed one! I'm just a monkey.'

And to the amazement of the two brothers, in front of their eyes he grew till he filled the sky, higher than anything in the vedas. Even Meru, the golden mountain, could not rival those massive shoulders.

When even he, the bearer of the discus, the lotus-eyed lord who had measured the three worlds with his feet, was unable to see Hanuman's face or his glittering earrings, for that's how high he had risen, how can I, a mere poet, describe the form of Sun's devoted disciple?

Astonished, Rama told his brother, 'By all that is wonderful, this is the Supreme Lord himself in the form of a mere monkey, dazzling as the ever-fresh vedas.'

His heart gladdened, a smiling Rama said to his younger brother, 'This is indeed a happy augury. Our sorrows behind, only pure joy lies ahead. A king who has such a servant is indeed blessed.'

And that lion of a monkey said, 'Please wait here, victorious ones, I shall bring him here in a trice,' and took leave of them.

A FRIENDSHIP FORGED

'Saved am I, saved are my kin and the world,' thought the one with shoulders mighty as the Mandara. Dwelling long on virtuous Rama's grace, he approached his despondent king.

He reported to Sugriva, 'Lord, we've crossed the troubled seas. The one who has arrived will prove the death of garlanded Vali.' Having made this announcement, he danced like Siva who had swallowed the venom that rose from the great churning.

'They are the sons of Dasaratha, that great king who brought the whole world under his rule. Handsome and wise, they can help you regain your lost kingdom with ease.

'That senseless king of the rakshasas, has through witchcraft seized the elder's wife and they have come in search of her. Thanks to the fruits of your penance and your abiding virtue, they have come to seek your friendship.

'Wise one, come and meet them. They will give you all the help you need. Our inveterate foe Vali is about to meet his end,' said the apt counsellor.

Delighted, Sugriva replied, 'My friend, good as gold, with you as counsellor, there is nothing I can't achieve.' And so the two of them went to Rama.

The Sun's son saw that jade mountain, whose face was like the moon, his ears unadorned, and his eyes like cool lotuses abloom in a rain-cloud.

Rama, without sin, and Sugriva, the king of monkeys, came together like the sun and the moon on a new moon day, as if to dispel demonic darkness and establish Dharma on earth.

'The great tapaswini, Sabari, engaged in faultless penance, told us that you were here. We thought you might help us. And you, in turn, can depend on us for whatever little we can do for you,' promised Rama.

Sugriva told them his sorry tale, 'My elder brother, his mighty fist raised in rage, chased me all over the world and I sought refuge in this hill. My life I've saved, but not my kingdom. Now I seek your aid. Please help me.'

Looking at the distressed monkey-king with deep compassion, Rama replied, 'Let the joys and sorrows of those bygone days remain in the past. I will help you ensure your future, and share everything with you.

'Need I say more? In heaven or on earth, whoever is your foe is my foe; your friend, even if evil, is my friend; your kin, my kin; my loved ones, yours; you are my greatest friend,' said he.

The monkey horde celebrated and Hanuman trembled with joy. The heaven showered flowers and the clouds rained their joy. Rama's stirring words of eternal friendship rang truer than the vedas.

(The four of them then reached a lovely grove thick with sandal and akhil trees, crystal rocks and limpid pools, where lilies

bloomed and heavenly apsaras sported on swings. Resting awhile in these lovely surroundings, they talked of various things while feasting on delicious fruits, roots and nuts. After a while, Rama asked tentatively, 'Are you too parted from your wife, the prop of a virtuous householder?' While Sugriva himself was hesitant to talk, Hanuman spoke, 'Noble lord, it is a long story. Please listen to it with patience.' He then recounted the story of Vali, Sugriva's brother.)

'Through the grace of the trident-bearer who lives on the mountain, Vali obtained his boundless strength. When gods and demons were churning the ocean, the Mandara hill, used as the churner, lost its shape. Serpent Vasuki, the churning rope, began to spit fire. Then it was that valiant Vali appeared on the scene, and by himself completed the churning.

'He has the strength of all the elements—earth, water, fire and air. Were he to leap from Chakravala, that great mountain that encircles the world, he could easily jump across the seas and land here.

'When he faces an enemy in combat, half the foe's strength becomes his, by virtue of a boon he has secured from Siva, to whom he offers obeisance every day.

'Generous lord, because of that enviable might, even Death is afraid to take away a monkey without his leave. The wind cannot overtake him, nor Skanda's spear pierce his chest. Should he choose to take a stride, Meru will rock. Should he stand to his full height, his huge shoulders will displace the clouds and the sky.

'On one occasion, justifying his name and great reputation, he bound with his tail Ravana, twenty shoulders and all, and dragged him along behind him. Was there then a land where Ravana's blood did not flood the streets?

'Those days, with him as ruler, Sugriva here was his trusted deputy. Then one day, our great enemy, an asura, assailed us with his flashing fangs. What forgiveness for such rashness? Enraged at the impudence of the foolish challenger, Vali chased him all over the world.

'Unable to cope with his vengeful onslaught and

convinced he couldn't save his life, no matter where he sought shelter on earth, the asura hid himself in the depths of a cave.

'Enraged Vali said to Sugriva, "He shall not escape me, the mean coward. I'll bring him out soon. Meanwhile, guard this place." He then plunged into the cave.

'Obsessed with that fugitive challenger, for fourteen seasons Vali searched every corner of that cavern. And his brother, grieved and confused, waited in vain for his return.

'Though we knew his state of mind, we beseeched him, "You must do your duty and take over the kingship." To which he replied, sore of heart, that it would be wrong and totally improper for him to do so.

'He said, "I'll instead go into that cave, search for my brother and kill his killer, failing which, be killed myself." He then got ready to storm that hideout. But urged by the monkeys, his ministers prevented him from going in.

'Swallowing his sorrow and setting aside his scruples, going strictly by the code laid down by the great lawmakers, he agreed to be crowned king. Sugriva did not usurp the throne. It was our doing.

'Then, lest Vali should emerge from the cave, we closed its exit, heaping massive rocks round its mouth. Having thus secured it, we returned to our hill with the Sun's son.

'Meanwhile, valiant Vali had killed his foe. Drunk with victory, he hurried back to the mouth of the cave and called for his brother but got no answer.

"Well indeed has my younger brother kept his guard over me!" he thought bitterly. With a swish of his tail, he smashed the rocks that covered the opening. Some pieces of shattered rock flew to the blue sky, others to the sea.

'In a towering rage enough to frighten even the most fearless, he climbed atop our high hill. Sugriva, always just and without guilt, came out and fell at his feet. Bowing, he said, "My noble brother, anguished at your long absence, I sorely wished to seek you out.

"But your people wouldn't agree and insisted it was my duty to rule over them. Not daring to disobey, I took on the mantle of kingship. Doughty one, forgive kindly my shameless deed."

'His mind befuddled with rage, Vali indulged in a tirade, long and cruel. With those hands he had once used to churn the sea, he pummelled Sugriva and filled him with the deepest fear. The rest of us could only watch in terror.

'In pain and distress, Sugriva leapt across the seven seas and the world beyond. But, his rage unappeased, Vali chased him. His fury incandescent, he seized Sugriva by the scruff of his neck and smashed his face.

'Finally, dexterous Sugriva managed somehow to escape to this safe haven. Because of an ancient curse, this hill is out of bounds for Vali, and Sugriva is safe as long as he is here. Even Yama cannot capture him.

'Gracious lord, along with his kingship, Sugriva lost Tara, his wedded wife, to Vali who'd long coveted her. This is the whole story.'

Hearing this sorry tale, Rama's lips quivered in anger. His large eyes becoming a livid red, he turned to Sugriva and said, 'Wise one, even if the fourteen worlds should come to his aid and try to stop me, a shaft from my bow is all it will take to give you back your kingdom and your wife. Please show me where he is.'

His joy a sea of roaring waves, Sugriva felt like one long drowned in grief sighting at last the shore. But though he felt in his bones that Vali's days were numbered now, he still had some doubts.

He consulted Hanuman and other advisers, wise and learned. Hanuman spoke first: 'Dearest lord, I know what is on your mind. You have lingering doubts whether these heroes really have what it takes to kill Vali. Listen carefully to what I've to say.

'Marks of the conch and the discus adorn his hands and feet. In all the seven worlds, only one bears these signs. That red-eyed bowman is Vishnu incarnate, come to re-establish Dharma on earth.

'Vayu, my father, had told me once, "Son, become the slave of the father of Brahma. That will prove your greatest blessing and mine." This Rama here, my lord, is that very same Vishnu.

'I'll tell you why. When I asked my father, "How will I know him?" He replied, "Whenever there is trouble, when all that is true and just is challenged, then he will come to redeem Dharma. The minute you see him you will feel an overwhelming love." And so it was! My bones melted when I saw him. What more can I say?

'However, if you wish to test his might, there's a way. Ask him to shoot his arrow through those trees that stand before us, seven in a row.'

Reassured, Sugriva warmly embraced matchless Maruti. Returning to Rama, he said, 'There's something I should like to say. Please come this way.'

THE MARAMARAS

(*The monkey-king led the brothers to those seven trees that rose so tall as to make the very space around seem insignificant. He said, 'If your unfailing arrow can bring down even one of these, the anguish in my heart will be quelled.'*

The lord of the gods heard the request and guessed shrewdly the reason for it. Smiling serenely, he strung his bow with his strong hands and aimed for those trees not easy to measure.)

Unchanging even when the yugas changed, upright even when the world went under, they stood, as if the seven mountains that bear this world had all come together to stand in a row.

Their lower trunks were broad enough to please even the moon and the sun, were they to seek a place to rest and do penance.

The reason why, despite racing around the world all day, the horses yoked to the sun's chariot never seem to tire, is, we think, because from time to time, they probably stop to enjoy the cool shade of those seven magnificent trees.

So tall were they that the planets and the stars seemed to be the flowers that bloomed on their branches and the dark spot on the moon the shadow cast by their leaves.

Taller than Meru they were, their tops reaching the outer

sphere, where Vishnu placed his foot when he measured the universe. Their cores were hard as the hearts of those two mutual foes—the monkey brothers. And their deep roots went down and through the world-bearer Sesha's shining hood.

Rama looked hard at all those trees. Eager to use a faultless arrow, he twanged his bow and rendered deaf the distant sky and all the quarters, filling the gods with fears unknown.

As they fled in terror, they wondered whether the end of the world had arrived. Only Lakshmana, no stranger to his brother's prowess, stood beside him, calm and unperturbed.

That shaft of Rama's pierced the seven trees and the seven worlds in an instant. Then, not finding anything else to penetrate, came back to him in a flash. The seven seas, the seven heavens, the seven hills, the seven sages, the seven horses of the sun, and the seven maids—all of them trembled, wondering if they too were that arrow's target.

A thoroughly abashed Sugriva fell at Rama's feet: 'You are the earth, the sky and all, Brahma on his lotus, Vishnu on the sea and the good Dharma who destroys sins. You created the worlds in the distant past and have now come to save me, a dog.

'The good deeds of my past have brought you to me. With you by my side, no feat is impossible now. O king of kings, you are like a mother to me, and I shall now be the slave of your slave.'

The monkeys danced and sang, ran hither and thither, the toddy of joy depriving them of their senses. 'We have at last found Vali's death,' rejoiced those who had drooped long and could at last feel their shoulders rise.

DUNDUBHI

(*Convinced of Rama's invincible strength, Sugriva swore eternal friendship and they moved on. On the way, they came upon the body of a rakshasa, huge as a hill. Rama wanted to know the history behind that curious sight. It was an interesting tale that Sugriva told.*

A fiery rakshasa, Dundubhi by name, was so filled with pride

over his invincible strength that he once went to Mahavishnu,
resting on his serpent-bed in the milky ocean and challenged him
to a fight. In sport, the dark one declared that he was no match for
the rakshasa and suggested his taking on a mightier hero, the lord
of Kailasa.

Siva, in turn, played along with the demon's pride and sent
him to fight the 'much stronger' Indra, king of the gods. Indra too
refused to meet the challenge, claiming that the only foe worthy of
his steel was Vali, king of the monkeys. And so it was that the two-
horned demon challenged Vali to a fight.)

It was a memorable battle. Whirling around so fast that
none was able to tell them apart, they fell and rose as one.
Gods and demons hovered in the distance, so great their
fright.

Vali plucked out the two horns on the head of the asura and
smote him hard. He then aimed a blow at his head that threw
him on the ground, blood streaming from his cave-like mouth.

Picking up the prone body of the demon, Vali twirled it
around as if it were a mere flywhisk and hurled it beyond the
clouds, the sun and the planets. The asura's soul left his body,
but his stinking corpse fell here.

Said Sugriva, 'This then is the story of this rotting
mountain of a dead demon. But there is a sequel that has
turned out to be a blessing in disguise for me.

'The carcass happened to fall on the hermitage of Sage
Matanga. Offended by the desecration of his ashrama, the
infuriated sage cursed Vali that his head would burst to pieces
if he ever came anywhere near this hill. That has made this a
safe haven for me.'

Rama was amazed at the story and instructed Lakshmana
to get rid of the putrefying corpse. Lakshmana did so with a
mere flip of his toe, sending the body hurling all the way to
the land of Brahma, never to return.

THE JEWELS SEEN

(Reaching the grove that was now Rama's abode, Sugriva told
another story which proved to be of great interest to Rama in his

quest for Sita. Some time earlier, when they had all been sitting
around there and idly chattering, as is the wont of monkeys, Sugriva
heard a scream from the sky and saw a shower of jewels. 'We still
have them with us. It may be your wife's. You might wish to see
them.' Excited and filled with eager anticipation, Rama inspected
the jewels when they were brought.)

How can a mere poet describe the joy mingled with deep
distress that Rama then felt! He was at once wax melting
in fire and a man drunk with the elixir of life. Crying and
laughing at the same time, Rama was tormented by memories
of shared moments, even as hopes of finding Sita revived.

Then Hanuman said, bowing low, 'Lord! I have a plan
that I would, if I may, like to submit to you. Blessed by Siva
with magical powers of various kinds, Ravana can reach any
world in a trice and depart when done with it.

'Therefore, as of now, we do not know where Sita is,
whether in heaven or on earth, or where the Nagas live. We
have therefore to look high and low to locate her.

'Once our oppressor, Vali, is killed and the son of the Sun
crowned king, we could gather our entire force and mount an
expedition to look for her.

'But to go from place to place would take endless years.
Therefore, the monkey horde, numbering seventy brigades,
should be deployed all at once in different directions, to flush
the world like the ultimate flood.

'They are loyal and capable and will heft up the world or
drink up the sea, if commanded to do so. This would be the
best way to go about our task.' Rama agreed, saying, 'Lead
me then to Vali.'

THE KILLING OF VALI

The heroes left those hills, covered ten leagues and more, and
reached Vali's abode. They then paused to decide what to do
next.

Said Rama in ringing tones, 'Call out to pestilent Vali to
come forth and fight you. That will be the time to attack.'

At this, the Sun's son produced a blood-curdling noise

that frightened the seas, shamed the skies, made earthlings sweat, sent gods into panic and swallowed the entire universe that God Himself had once swallowed.

'Come out Vali, and fight me! I shall kill you!' cried Sugriva, curling his lips in a fearsome snarl, slapping his thighs and thumping his shoulders challengingly. His thunderous defiance, resembling the trumpeting of a frenzied elephant, assailed the sleeping Vali's leonine ears and set his left side trembling.

Wondering about the source of his brother's new-found courage, he laughed and that sound made the fourteen worlds flee in fear. His mocking, 'I am coming, I am coming!' was heard in all the quarters. As he rose, his jewelled crown pierced the skies and knocked down the stars huddling around the moon.

The typhoon set in motion by his movement uprooted the hills, and hurtled them through space. Sparks from his skin hit the walls of the world. Death shut his eyes and the gods shivered anxiously.

Sensing danger, his wife, Tara, of lovely bamboo-like shoulders, intervened. Her long tresses were set aflame by the fire from Vali's eyes.

'O peacock from the hills,' said he, 'do not try to dissuade me. The life of that one who dares to challenge me, I'll drink down in a gulp, as if it were nectar and come back soon.'

Whereupon she said, 'Lord, Sugriva is no more than what he was. If having so long avoided you, he now throws defiance in your face, it can't be that he has grown stronger or been born again with greater courage. Deep in my guts I feel some great power has come his way.'

'Listen, woman,' said impatient Vali, 'even if the three worlds should get together and oppose me, they will lose and perish utterly. Don't you know my valorous past, or have you forgotten it?

'With the mountain Mandara for churner, the endless Vasuki for rope, Vishnu for supporting stone and the moon for pillar, Indra and the asuras churned away from either end.

'When, powerless to move the mountain, they turned to me, with my bare hands I helped produce ambrosia from the ocean, as if I was churning butter out of curd.

'My peacock, my koel, O my lovely bird, can anyone forget that feat of mine? Is it possible to count the gods and demons who opposed me and were beaten? Even Death trembles at my name. Anyone who dares to help my foe, by that very act, proves himself a fool.

'And one more thing, beauteous peacock. Even if someone were to dare to confront me, relying on his strength or the might of boons received, one half of all his strength will be mine, by virtue of Siva's gift to me.

'How then can anyone dare do so? Don't you worry, my lovely wife,' he told her boastfully. 'Lord,' said she, not quite reassured, 'I've been told by people well-disposed towards us that a certain Rama has befriended him and come to kill you.'

'Sinner!' he shouted in rage, 'What is it you have spoken in your womanly ignorance! Don't you know that he is here on earth to show the way of Dharma to all those trapped in the dreadful legacy of their past lives and are clamouring for release?

'How can you believe such slanderous tales about that generous soul who, having obtained the world to rule, gave it away at his stepmother's bidding to her son? Even were all the worlds to attack him, whose aid would he need but his own bow's? Will he, who is without a rival, deign to make friends with a mean monkey?

'Stop worrying, and wait. Before you can blink, I'll drink up that presumptuous monkey's life, break the bones of all his companions and be back.' And she, the one with fragrant tresses, dared not say anything more.

Anticipation of the forthcoming battle swelling his shoulders high like a pair of hills, Vali came to where Sugriva stood, like the sun rising on the eastern hill. He saw his roaring brother and let out an answering roar. The heavens broke into a sweat and it started pouring. The noise spread around the world like thunder.

On seeing Vali in battle array, Rama turned to his brother and said admiringly, 'Look at him Lakshmana! Forget the gods and demons, what sea, what cloud, what air, what fire can stand up to him?'

The younger one told his generous brother, 'To kill his brother, Sugriva has brought a more than ordinary Lord of Death. This will be no mere battle of the monkeys. It is a thought that makes my mind go blank.'

Troubled in mind, he continued: 'Will it be wisdom to trust one who let down Dharma, betrayed trust and is now ready to kill his own brother? How faithful will he prove to others?'

'Listen, child,' said the noble one, 'is the mad code of animals worth pondering over? Even among humans, how many younger brothers can you name, that are as noble as our Bharata? Or you, lovely-shouldered one!'

'It is true that in this world the good are few and the bad many. From friends we take what we can get, not weigh their faults.'

While the two heroes were talking thus, Sugriva and Vali tore into each other, clashing like hills, two lions fighting for their lives. Now preparing to pounce, now circling each other, they set the world awhirl as if it were a potter's wheel gone mad. Shoulder rubbing shoulder, foot trampling foot, they were making it hard for old mother earth to bear them.

It was as if two planets were at war. Onlookers watched stunned. Were the two fighting in the sky or could it be that they were on earth, dancing within their own eyeballs! The heat engendered by that fierce tussle set aflame the world and ran across the sky like lightning.

The sparks that flew turned their white skin red, like a forest of dry grass that had caught fire. Strong men both, born to one mother, they were like Sunda and Upasunda fighting for the nymph Tillotama, whom Brahma had created from sesame seeds.

Never having seen two seas at war, or the split halves of Mount Meru colliding or two parts of righteous anger battling each other, we are unable to find a simile to aptly describe the event.

As the ferocious battle wore on, strong Vali, whose arms reached his knees and whose hands were armed with long deadly nails, seemed to be getting the better of his brother.

Depressed, Sugriva approached Rama who consoled him, 'Don't despair. Keep fighting. I could not make you out in battle, so alike you two looked. Wear a garland of wild flowers and go forth with complete confidence.'

Wearing now a garland that shone like stars, Sugriva let out a roar that would have shamed a tiger, and rushed forth. Even Vali stood shaken for a moment, puzzled by this new Sugriva.

However, swiftly recovering, he turned more ferocious. His laughter of derision sent Death scurrying. He resumed his fight with even greater vigour, boxing, clawing, kicking.

Blood oozing from ears and eyes and gasping for breath, Sugriva turned in Rama's direction. Taking advantage of his momentary distraction, Vali struck a vicious blow that threw Sugriva to the ground. Lifting him up by his middle and neck, he was about to fling him down.

It was then that Rama took aim and shot his deadly shaft. Like a needle passing through a ripe banana, that arrow went through the chest of one known to have the strength of the four elements.

Bewildered Vali crashed to the ground, like Meru uprooted by the winds of Dissolution. He loosened his hold on Sugriva, but did not let go of that fierce shaft. 'I'll break down the sky,' he said, rising, 'set the quarters awhirl in a trice.'

Even as he promised a million retributions, he wondered who could have shot the deadly arrow. 'The gods? Would they have dared? Who else? Vishnu's discus? Siva's trident? Indra's thunderbolt? A rishi's curse?' he puzzled, racked with pain.

He attempted to pull out with his teeth the missile that was so torturing him. 'This is just an arrow, nothing more. With my two hands, my tail and sturdy legs, I shall pluck it out and find out who it was that sent it.'

With a mental strength that equalled his body's, Vali

plucked the arrow out. All who witnessed this remarkable feat, be they gods, demons or others, were elated. Who in this world does not admire a hero?

The blood that flowed out of that wound flooded the forests, the mountains and the seas. It would be an insult to compare it to the inundation of the sea at the time of Dissolution. Not even then would the seas have been flooded thus.

When he saw the stream of blood gushing forth from the hero's mountainous chest, Sugriva, still bound by brotherly ties, shed copious tears and fell on the ground weeping.

He who could have broken the Meru, attempted in vain to break the arrow that had struck him. Wondering why, he scanned the name engraved on it.

He saw with his own eyes the name of Rama, that primordial mantra, the supreme balm, not only for all the ills one suffers in this life but also for the afflictions in the next seven births.

Like a mighty tusker trapped in a deep pit, Vali felt helpless and beaten. Even so, he laughed aloud and said jeeringly, 'This then is the great hero who never ever forsook the path of Truth!

'Is this then the supreme Dharma? Is this the behaviour of one come down to exemplify right conduct? What would happen to lesser mortals, if the lofty forsake virtue's path?'

Vali then saw with bloodshot eyes the lord who appeared before him, a blue raincloud with bow in hand. All fire and contempt, he said, 'O son of that pure king who died for the sake of truth and honour, how can you be Bharata's elder and do what you have done?

'Does evil, forbidden to others, cease to be one if committed by you, who claim to be eternally on the side of Dharma? You whose ancestors were the very epitome of virtue and valour, rulers like none other, not only in this but in all the three worlds, how could you, as if you'd momentarily forgotten all this, shake thus the foundations of the world?

'Maybe losing Sita has so shaken your soul that you have

ceased to be yourself! Does Manu's code prescribe that the punitive fine for a wrong committed by a rakshasa can be extracted from another race?

'What fault have you found in me? O fount of grace, has Kaliyuga dawned for monkeys alone? Are virtue and honour meant only for the low? Can great ones do wrong with impunity?

'O hero incomparable! You gave away the crown your father gave you to your younger brother. That was indeed noble of you. But here in the forest, you have done another noble deed—gifting *my* crown to my younger brother! Who can excel you in such deeds?

'Hero is as hero does. If you, the lord of righteousness, can do what you have done to me, how can you be wroth with Lanka's lord?

'I was no enemy of yours. My body was no burden to your land. Why then a deed so ignoble, an arrow from a place of hiding! Is this virtue, valour or something else?

'Not heroic; not prescribed; not allied to virtue or truth; how then to describe this deed of yours that lacks every sanction in the book?

'The dark stain on the moon you perhaps deemed unfair; so you thought it only right that the sun should have one too. Hence this act that will forever be a blot on your race.

'O man of might, you have reduced to nothing the codes and fine traditions of your race. Virtue ignored, you've destroyed not Vali's life, but Dharma's frontiers.

'Perhaps with your wife abducted, the bow in your hand seemed a burden. Finding no other target, you used it to shoot an unarmed man from a place of hiding. What disgrace!'

(Thus spoke Vali, enraged and anguished. Unruffled by his passionate invective, Rama replied thus:)

'When you did not return as promised, Sugriva had wanted to follow you into that cave you had disappeared into. But the elders of your tribe stopped him and said, "You must now become our king." Sugriva demurred, saying "Your advice is all wrong. I'll sooner kill that foe who has killed my brother or die in the effort rather than rule."

'The army chiefs and ministers and all other elders present insisted: "What's happened has happened. You can't change it. You must rule," and made that innocent wear the crown.

'He rejoiced when you returned safe, saying, "My father, here is your kingdom that was forced on me," and explained how he had come to wear your crown.

'But you, enraged, though aware he was faultless, showed no mercy and determined to kill him. His pleas and extenuations fell on deaf ears.

'Though he had his share of supporters, he, fearing defeat, waged no war and put his hands up in surrender. Yet, stubborn and unbending, you made him flee from place to place.

'Only because he made his home in that golden mountain, off bounds to you because of Sage Matanga's curse, you could not capture him.

'Mercy, high birth, valour, learning—should they not take pride in guarding the chastity of another's wife? For men of wisdom and knowledge, the arrogance of power that makes one oppress the weak and the meek, is no sign of valour but of its defeat.

'You never had any use for virtue; never gave a thought to the fruits of your actions. Had you done so, would you have so meanly coveted his dear wife and made her your own?

'For these reasons and also because he is now my great friend, I resolved to kill you. My aim is to save the oppressed and the weak, even if total strangers to me.'

Vali retorted, 'All that you have called unbecoming is quite natural to us. Brahma has not imposed on us the code of chastity that truthful women of your race follow. He has left us in our natural state.

'For us, there is no vedic marriage. Our tradition is simply to follow our natural instincts. I'm entirely guiltless.'

Rama countered that expert speaker's arguments thus: 'Being the son of a god of renown, you surely know the ways of Dharma. Do the base urges of the body determine Dharma or is it the discerning mind that does so? How then can you wilfully err and then defend yourself on specious grounds?

'Was he too only an animal who, caught and dragged by a crocodile, invoked the lord with the conch and thus got released and gained salvation?

'Wasn't he too only an eagle who, his mind trained in the way of virtue, came to the rescue of distressed Sita and lost his life in the fight that ensued and, released from earth, gained salvation?

'You are not just any beast incapable of seeing the difference between good and bad. Your own words reveal that no aspect of virtue is unknown to you. Why then such base behaviour?

'Even men, the so-called higher kind, if they can't distinguish right from wrong, are only beasts. In the same fashion the beasts that follow Manu's laws are as good as gods.

'Because of your devotion to Siva, that conqueror of Yama, you acquired the united might of the four elements created by Vishnu.

'Sages given to penance and pleasing the gods have sometimes been guilty of sin. Similarly, many low-born sinners have trodden the hard path of virtue. That being so, only he is high who acts high and he is low who acts low. Knowing all this, you thought nothing of becoming an adulterer.'

The monkey-king heard all this and said, 'Let all this be as it may. But how is it that you avoided fighting me in the open and aimed your arrow from a hidden place, like a base and cruel hunter?'

To which Lakshmana made reply:

'Your brother approached him first and sought refuge, and was promised, "I'll send that sinner to his death." Thus did Sugriva sally forth to fight you, Rama by his side.

'Had you seen Rama, you too might have sought his protection, thereby putting him in a dilemma. That was why he chose to hide himself.'

The monkey-king absorbed these words and reflected

deeply on them. He knew in his heart of hearts that Rama wouldn't, even when sorely distressed, do anything against Dharma.

Never small of mind, valiant Vali said with deep reverence, 'Forgive me, my lord, you are Dharma's very incarnation. How can one like me understand your far-sighted righteousness?

'O rare balm for earthly afflictions, ever generous with your boons, regard me as a thoughtless monkey. Ignore whatever I, a dog, have said.

'With a sharp shaft, well aimed, you've opened the eyes of this dying cur. You are all: the first; the all; sin and virtue; foe and friend; and all else that remains.

'All persons and things on earth are you, all seasons and their fruits are you. Like the flower and its fragrance, you are inseparable and yet, alone, aloof, and all by yourself.

'I've seen you, Dharma Affirmative. There's none left for me to see anymore. My sins from birth have been punished and absolved by you.

'O king whose greatness rips the sky, my brother with his monkey ways brought you here to get me killed. He has thus obtained a worthless kingdom. In exchange, I have been given a precious kingdom in the land of salvation. What greater gift could he have given me?

'Gracious father! There is something that I, a wretched monkey, beg of you: should my brother, mind led astray in a drunken state, commit evil, do not in wrath discharge on him, as you did on me, your deadly shaft.

'One more request have I to make. Should your brothers ever try to jeer at him for causing his elder brother's death, please forbid them. You had promised to fulfil his want. What took place thereafter is but the wages of sin, which none can ever escape.

'My only regret, victorious lord, is that I can't now bring wicked Ravana tied to my tail as a gift for you and thus show a bit of my monkey trick. Alas! What use crying over the past? But one comfort remains. What I couldn't do for you, Hanuman here can do just as well.

'Consider Hanuman, emperor, as the very bow in your beautiful hand and my brother as your brother. There is none else in this wide world as good as his monkeys to help you look for and restore your lovely wife to you.'

He then stretched out his hand to his brother, embraced him and said, 'Dear one, don't grieve for me. I've something to tell you which you should take to heart.

'This Rama with his chastening bow has come here to establish Dharma. Never ever forget this. There is nothing you can't achieve, when fate itself has come to help you.

'With his friendship, you've gained both this world and the one that lies beyond. All that remains now is for you to carry on your head the lord's command with wholehearted devotion.

'Do not burst with the pride of kingship and ever insult or provoke him to anger. Try and guess his thoughts, anticipate his wishes and carry them out meticulously.'

Having advised his aching brother thus, he turned again to Rama, 'Son of the emperor, he and all his subjects are your servants.' Raising his hands he put them on his head, and looking at his brother said, 'Bring your son here quickly.'

Shining like the moon in bloom came Angada, who in his young life had never known what distress was. Now he saw with his own eyes his beloved father lying, not on a bed of flowers but in a vast red sea of blood.

He shed blood-curdled tears at the sight of the full moon fallen on the earth and collapsed on his father's body like a star from the sky. Crying as if his heart would break, he said,

'Father mine, Father mine, you never wronged anyone in thought or deed. How dared Death come to take your life? With you gone, who's left to look him in the eye?

'Alas, fear must now have fled from the heart of that Ravana, whose heart thrummed like a funeral drum every time he thought of your tail! Was there ever one mightier than you? You gave the gods the ambrosia which has made them all immortal but you yourself lie dying now.'

When he heard this from the heartbroken Angada, Vali said, heart melting like wax in fire, 'Grieve no more, my beloved son,' and embraced him tight. 'This death that Rama has given me is no calamity but the fruit of my good deeds.

'Understand carefully, birth and death are predestined. As a result of my penance, God in person has given me release. Grow up son, and don't grieve in vain.

'Bow always to that reality come down to us with a bow in hand, the one we perceive with our senses, a balm to birth's ills and desire's fruit.

'Don't for a moment, my bejewelled son, think of him as my destroyer. Your life should be his to command. If he has to wage a war, help him. Carry on your head the feet of one who judges us only by karma. May you live eternally.'

Turning to his saviour, he said, 'O pure one who will not show yourself to those whose hearts are not pure, I commend to your feet, this, my son, a terror to rakshasas, and in all his actions without guilt.'

When Angada bowed low at his feet, the lotus-eyed one gave to him a sword of gold and said, 'This is yours to bear always.' The gods cheered and Vali left for the abode of the blessed ones.

As his hand loosened its grip, the swift shaft rose and dipped itself in the holy sea, and even as the gods showered flowers, returned triumphant to Rama's quiver. Vali ascended to heaven and Rama too left with Sugriva and Angada

On hearing the news of Vali's glorious death, Tara rushed to the site, her eyes a flood of tears as she fell upon that hero's body. Heartbroken, she rolled on his broad chest, her breasts and snake-like tresses turning saffron with Vali's noble blood. She looked like a streak of lightning on a sky red with the rays of the rising sun.

She sobbed, wailed and melted. Head held between her two hands, she drooped; then pushed back her curls, lamenting loud the loss of her beloved husband.

'My life, my heart, my king! I nestled so long in your hill-like shoulders and never knew any sorrow. But now this sea of grief I'd never dreamt of is to be my fate.

'Of one thought and mind we were, will you not be filled with disdain that my sorrow has not killed me yet? O vengeful Fate, when life is gone, how much longer should the body live?

'Does Death not know he is immortal because of the nectar you gave him? Or is he just a mean ingrate, unmindful of your great kindness?

'How can you stay in one place like this—you who would flit from place to place, worshipping Siva thrice a day, with fresh flowers and deep devotion?

'O king! Instead of a bed of flowers you now lie on bare ground. You see me cry my heart out and yet there's no word of comfort from you. What, alas, is my fault?

'O godly one who never told a lie! Here I am, sunk in despair, while you have gone to blissful heaven. Was it then a lie you uttered when you said, "You are my very life?"

'O warrior, if it was indeed true that I was ever in your heart, I too should have fallen to that shaft. And if you were ever in my heart, you should now be living beside me. No, no. We never were part of each other.

'Did those in heaven welcome you with love, gratitude and fresh flowers, saying, "Father, we are all alive today, because of the nectar you gave us?"

'If only that Rama, who aimed his shaft from a place of hiding, had asked you in so many words, "Give me all you have," wouldn't you, who gave ambrosia to the gods, have given him even your life?

'I told you but you wouldn't heed my words. "He'll never do anything wrong," you said, and recklessly went to meet your brother. Now you've gone, you, who could have outlasted the Deluge. When shall I see you again?

'Even Meru would have been pulverized by your chest. How can an arrow aimed against it pierce it to death? I won't believe it. It is a trick of the gods or this is not Vali.

'My son, you saw before your eyes how all our lives have been ruined by one brother fighting another, under whose shadow he gained his fame. The bowman, a sovereign balm for all, has done an unworthy deed. That a man is known by his deeds is nothing but empty words.'

(*Thus did Tara wail, inconsolable. Anguished Hanuman took charge and sent her with her maids to her palace, Vali's obsequies*

were performed according to the scriptures and Rama was informed
of all that had happened after he left the scene. Finally, the sun that
destroys all darkness and sin sank behind the western hill, leaving
the sky resembling the face of the dead monkey chief himself. His
mind full of Sita, Rama tried unsuccessfully to cross the sea of the
night.)

SUGRIVA'S CORONATION

(The sun dawned the next day, exultant at the prospect of witnessing
his son Sugriva's coronation and opened up the lotuses as if to let
Lakshmi emerge to bless the start of the new rule with her fabulous
wealth. Rama, the abode of grace, then asked Lakshmana to place
the crown with due ceremony on Sugriva's head. With Hanuman's
assistance, waters from all the sacred rivers had been brought.
Sugriva was duly crowned with sages taking on the mantle of
priests, brahmins showering blessings, and the gods raining flowers
from above.

The newly crowned monarch of the monkeys then fell at Rama's
feet and sought his blessings. Rama embraced him warmly and gave
sound advice on the art of kingship.)

'Go forth, my friend,' he said, 'and rule wisely with
assistance from truthful counsellors and loyal army chiefs
devoid of sin. Get the best out of everyone, by understanding
their nature.

'Show even your enemies a pleasant face and a sweet
tongue. You have wealth that even gods might envy—use it
well and wisely. Be generous and don't covet the wealth of
another.

'Desist from hurting the weak. This I say from experience.
As a boy, I thoughtlessly struck hunchback Mantara,
Kaikeyei's loyal maid, with mud pellets from a sling and am
paying for that sin in this life itself.

'Think of yourself not as a king but as a loving mother,
but deal sternly with all evil-doers. The wise will approve of
all I have said. So keep it all in your mind and rule well. Come
to me after the rains with your sea of an army.'

Overwhelmed, Sugriva fell at Rama's feet and said,

'Victorious one! We took refuge at your feet and earned your grace. How can we now bear separation from you? Come and stay with us, till it is time to go searching for Sita.'

Rama heard him out and said with a smile, 'It will not be proper for one in my state to live in a palace. And should I stay with you, all your time will be spent looking after my comforts, causing you to neglect your kingly duties.

'On my father's order, I undertook to spend fourteen years as a self-denying forester. The world will scoff at me, if I were to break my promises and agree to live in a city with you and that too, without Sita.

'Wouldn't they think of me as a profligate, bent on pleasure and spending time in royal delights with his friend, while his wife languishes in captivity? So go forth to your kingly duties and come to me after four months, to aid me in my search for Sita.'

Hanuman, the wise, then said, 'It is your command and we obey.'

(Then they left for Kishkinda, the capital of the monkey kingdom. Once there, the Sun's son bowed to Tara as to his mother and began his benign rule. He made Angada his deputy and with Hanuman as his guide and philosopher, he was now the undisputed monarch of all he surveyed.

As for Rama, followed by his shadow-like brother, he repaired to the sky-high, stream-fed mount of Matanga and lived in the hut lovingly built by Lakshmana.)

THE RAINY SEASON

As if commanded by heaven's king, the sun hastened from the north to the south, as if it were a scout sent in advance to look for Sita. And then the rains came.

The clouds in the sky looked like collyrium that had been collected when smoke rose from the lamp whose base was the earth, the sea its oil, mount Meru its wick, and the sun its flame. The sky grew dark as the neck of Siva, when he drank the dreadful poison that rose out of the milky ocean as it was being churned.

The huge black clouds that had drunk up avidly the sea's water, looked as if they were pregnant with elephants. The wind blew this way and that, constant to none, like a prostitute who changed her lovers at whim, her heart set only on money.

The great clouds collided against one another again and again, thundering as if they were elephants clashing and trumpeting their anger at each other in the sky. Dry branches of flower-bearing trees blossomed at the amorous touch of the rains, like the faces of wives at the sight of their husbands returning home after a long absence, laden with wealth.

The countryside was aflame with colours and abuzz with insects. Red and white *kandals* and blue *kuvalais* charmed. Beetles and chafers of different colours hummed around, looking like rings on the fingers of mother earth, whose hands stretched out in wonderment at the rainy season outstripping the spring in splendour. The streams of the *punnai* forests flowed like copious milk from mother earth's ample breasts.

Swans rejoiced in the now full streams, as though they were men, long parted from their lovers, mad with joy at rejoining them. The deer were delighted yet dumb with fright at the sometimes-fearsome look of the new season.

Against the backdrop of the dark sky, the storks in flight appeared to be a garland of pearls around the neck of Mahavishnu himself. The cranes flying in close formation looked like his upper cloth.

The drumbeats of the colliding clouds and the sweet music of a thousand humming bees made the peacocks sway like dancers on a stage.

Bees gathered honey from the new blooms, as if they were voluptuaries versed in the art of love, stroking and enjoying the flowers in different ways, as though each was a different type of woman.

Or should I compare them to poets garnering rasas, in order to compose the ideal play; as prescribed in Bharata's *Natya Shastra*?

(*But while the whole world was vibrant with new life, Rama alone was desolate.*

Everything seemed to conspire against him. His memories of joyous days with Sita during the rains devastated him. When the lovely monsoon can shake even the firmness of sages by teasing them with thoughts of love, is it any wonder that Rama, who had tasted the sweetness of Sita, should pine so? Thus distressed and distracted, he addressed all the joyous beings around him, the dancing peacocks and the fluttering creepers, the blossoms and the frolicking deer, wondering how they could so heartlessly rejoice when he was plumbing the depths of despair.

Watching him breaking his heart thus with idle lamentations, his brother said to him.)

'Great one, how can you so far forget yourself as to behave like one lost and helpless? These sad months of waiting and inaction will soon be over. Let the rain abate.

'We have discovered Hanuman's worth. We have been promised the assistance of the vast monkey army to search and find our lost treasure. Why then, this unmanly despair?

'A fight with the rakshasas was, in any case, preordained. When the sages approached you in distress, you promised them you would rid the world of these crafty and cruel creatures.

'By a stroke of luck, we now have an excuse to do so. Who, if not you, can vanquish them? Is it right that you should now give way to despair?'

Recovering his poise somewhat, Rama went through the motions of carrying out his daily duties, but not for long. The season wore on, and as one disease follows another, the late rains came and Rama fell once again into despondency.

The large tanks filled; the waves rose; koels became scarce, hills grew cold and quarters disappeared from sight. *Anrils* clasped each other in ecstasy but those separated pined for each other. The sea flowed full and the moon lost its heat. The time of the day could not be told, nor day from night, except by the water clock.

Sparrows slept with their mates in nests lit by glow-worms. Parrots, defeated by peacock-women in their attempts at speech, hid themselves in paddy packs. Pearls defeated by the sheen of the teeth of the selfsame women, hid themselves in the seas.

The *punnai* buds blossomed, as if they were gold unloosed from saris where they had earlier been hid. Shivering swans took refuge under the leaves of sandalwood trees, warmed by the smoke that arose at dawn and at dusk from vedic fires.

Female monkeys went into caves to escape from the chill, while the male ones bore the cold stoically, self-absorbed, like yogis practising breath control. Maidens, slender of waist, joined their mates in bed, even as smoke from burnt *akhils* dimmed the light in the room. Hunters slept with their women in huts of wooden logs.

Whenever darkness descended during the gloomy rain-soaked weather, heroic Rama brooded on the memory of Janaki's lovely smile. In deep despair, he told Lakshmana, 'Brother, a dark cloud of a rakshasa with flashing teeth torments Sita there, and here, the thought of it tortures me. I am steeped in sorrow, unable to forget her.

'When the sky lightens and the clouds thunder, I cower like a serpent. It will take ages for us to discover where the rakshasa has hid her. Janaka's words spoken in front of the fire, "This hand is yours to hold and cherish," I have falsified. Truth will not stay with one thus fated. It is better I die.

'My pure and fiery shafts sleep in my quiver, and my shoulders, sky-high, rest idle. The deeds I've accomplished since entering the forest will provoke the derisive laughter of heaven and earth.'

To the despondent words of the hero tormented by love and guilt, Lakshmana, the wise, replied, 'The rainy season is about to end and the days of waiting are over. The time to trace the thief's whereabouts is almost upon us. With the help of our allies, if we choose the right time, plan our search carefully and proceed, how can victory elude us?

'Brother, great bowman! Shed this unmanly despair and stand up. We have on hand the unfinished task of redeeming the promise to the sages, for which Ravana has, by stealing mother Sita, unwittingly provided the excuse.'

(Rama realized the truth and wisdom of his noble brother's exhortations and once again shook himself free of despondency.

Even as he wondered if the rains would ever cease, the season thinned out and ended.)

The exhausted clouds turned white, like the generous souls who give away all they have to supplicants and turn pale with shame when they have no more to give. The blackness of monsoon melted away, just as a man attached to the material world is rid of darkness, when the wisdom of detachment dawns on him.

As the drums fall silent when fighting ceases, the roll of thunder ceased. Lightning sheathed its swords. The moon revealed itself in all its beauty, like the bright face of a danseuse when curtains are drawn. Swans fluttered in the sky, as if to announce that the time had come to resume the search for Sita.

KISHKINDA

As the season bade farewell, Rama told Lakshmana, 'O stalwart, the king has not come as promised. With the crown securely on his head, he is perhaps idling his time away in new-found pleasures. What do we do now? He has got his lost kingdom and forgotten about the help he received.

'He has neglected virtue, not to mention our love. It is no sin to kill an ingrate who cuts the cord of friendship and destroys faith.

'Go you forth and find out what is on his mind. Tell him on my authority that the bow I had lifted to vanquish the wicked and re-establish Dharma on earth is still with me.'

Thus commanded, the younger one set off at once, quiver on his shoulder, bow in his hand. The monkeys that saw him trembled, as though he were Death in person. They ran as one to Vali's son and spluttered: 'The younger brother is approaching our city, all speed and simmering wrath.'

Guessing the prince's intention, Angada went to his father's palace. Sugriva lay on a bed strewn with petals, feet on the lap of young women with budding breasts and long tresses.

Sated with pleasure, he was like an honoured guest who

has had his fill. Drunk with the powers of the great wealth he had got with the help of those two wise men, he lay stretched out like a silver hill atop a golden mountain.

As he lay thus lost in pleasure, Tara's son, that ferocious cub, woke him up and said, 'Listen, Father, Rama's brother has come here, wroth. What do you intend to do?'

Sodden with toddy, drowning in bliss, and half asleep, Sugriva's besotted mind failed to register these words. Unable to wake him and not knowing what to do, Angada went to seek the help of Hanuman, virtuous and wise.

Accompanied by him and the fierce army chiefs, they sought the advice of Tara, Sugriva's wife and Angada's mother. Infuriated, she said, 'You ingrates, after such conduct, what forgiveness?

'You took no heed of my warnings that you should get ready to go to Rama's aid. Now you have made yourselves the target of his wrath. Will he, who bent his bow to make Vali a prey to Yama, wait at your doorstep?

'His wife lost, this hero, greater than all the gods, is shattered, while you make love to your wives, unconcerned. You have proved yourselves treacherous and ungrateful, pleasure-seeking profligates. Don't you dare think you can oppose him and survive.'

Even as she was speaking thus, Lakshmana arrived at the gate. A group of foolish monkeys tried to shut and bolt it with iron bars. Seeking to prevent his entry, they heaped boulders in front of the entrance and told each other, 'Should Lakshmana enter, we'll frighten him and beat him up.'

Lips curled in anger, Lakshmana kicked the gate open in an instant. Touched by that divine foot, the gate and the wall of the fortress crumbled. The terrified monkeys stood still, panic writ large on their faces.

Lakshmana walked into the golden streets of the city, now without walls, looking for the errant Sugriva. On witnessing such fury, those huddled around Tara were stricken with terror.

'Go away, all of you,' she said in disgust. 'I will meet the hero and clear his mind of any misapprehension,' and went forward, accompanied by her flower-decked maids.

Even as he strode into the palace, he saw Tara, she of the fragrant tresses, surrounded by maids with thin waists and young breasts. Looking like an army of peacocks with flashing jewels for swords, anklets and bracelets for war alarms, their brows the flags of war, the women's battalion surrounded him.

Confronted by this unusual army, wrath was subdued. Too shy to look at the women, chaste Lakshmana turned his face away and stood like a young and bashful bridegroom confronted by women in-laws. Then long-eyed Tara spoke nervously:

'Son, blessed are we that you walked all the way to our humble abode. Our past deeds can no longer bind us and we are saved. However, watching you enter in wrath, but not knowing why, the army here is struck with terror. Could you please tell me what brings you here?'

His rage subdued, the hero wondered who this could be. Raising his face and looking at her, a full moon in daytime, he was reminded of his own mother as he last saw her. Just like her, Tara too was unadorned by the sacred thread that women with husbands should always wear.

She wore no jewels, flowers or kumkum. There was no sandal-paste on her breasts. A single cloth covered her. 'How like my two mothers she looks,' he thought, and his eyes filled with tears and depression seized his heart.

Shaking himself free of gloom, he explained to her the reason for his visit. 'The Sun's son has forgotten the promise he made to Rama that he and his army would seek out his wife. I've been sent by him to find out what's happened.'

Tactful as ever, Tara replied soothingly, 'Noble son, don't be angry. When small men err, is it not the duty of the large-hearted to forgive?

'Sugriva hasn't been idle either, though he didn't show up at the appointed time as promised. He has sent a thousand crore messengers all over the world, and is waiting for news from them. They should be here any moment.

'Aren't you also to blame for his thoughtless ways of

heedless pleasure? It was you who restored to him the wealth he'd lost. If in the coming battle to get back that golden maiden he does not give up his life, he would indeed be a despicable worm.'

Hearing Tara's tactful words, Lakshmana was a little abashed. While he stood indecisively, his wrath turned away by Tara's gentle words, sturdy-shouldered Hanuman approached him and touched his feet.

Lakshmana, loving even in anger, looked at him and said, 'Even you, son of Vayu, so learned and wise, have forgot the past?' To which wise Hanuman replied, 'Noble prince, listen to me with some patience.

'One can forgive many things in this world, even matricide and patricide, killing of a teacher or a god-like brahmin, a cow or a child, or a lovely woman. The one unforgivable thing is base ingratitude. Should Sugriva break his word to you, he will never live down the infamy.

'Was it not through me, lord, that immortal friendship between the two of you and our monkey king was forged? Should that break, it would only prove our stupidity.

'As Tara said, the monkey-king has not forgotten his promise. He has sent his men to gather his army and is awaiting their return. Please forgive any lapse on our part and come and meet your brother Sugriva.'

On hearing Hanuman's soothing words, Lakshmana's wrath, already half-doused, vanished totally. Sugriva had not disobeyed with deliberate intent; sudden wealth had turned his head and roused his starved lust.

Nevertheless, he warned Hanuman, 'Listen to me, son of Vayu, I saw with my own eyes how angry Rama was at all this delay. He was even prepared to kill Sugriva as punishment for his ingratitude.

'It was all I could do to pacify him. Else the three worlds would have gone up in flames, the gods would have died, and Dharma itself would have perished.

'This delay on the part of Sugriva has prolonged the life of the rakshasas. It has hurt the gods, added to the woes of the sages, multiplied the sins in this world and, last but not least, made one not easily given to anger, furious.'

Hanuman bowed and said, 'Broad-shouldered one, don't let past wrongs weigh you down. Dharma as witness, we shall keep our word or else die.'

Angada was sent to inform Sugriva of Lakshmana's impending arrival. When he reached his father's palace, he bowed and clasped Sugriva's feet and said 'Rama's brother, the doughty Lakshmana, is at the door, raging more than an angry sea.'

Befuddled, Sugriva said in puzzlement, 'We have done no wrong! Why should he be angry?' Patient Angada replied, 'Father! He is angry because you did not go to them on the appointed day.

'Made proud by your wealth, you killed gratitude and proved yourself untrustworthy. But wise Hanuman has calmed him down with earnest prayers and he has left us alive.'

Truly rattled, Sugriva said in panic, 'If those two should get angry, who in heaven or earth can face them? Why did you not inform me earlier?'

Angada said calmly, 'I did tell you, Father, but you were too drunk to take notice. I then sought Hanuman's help and he has pacified the prince and brought him here. Get ready quickly to meet him.'

'O God,' wailed Sugriva, 'what a mean and ungrateful wretch I am! Who has received such help as I from Rama? And yet drink made me forget the great sorrow they hoped to bring to an end through me. I shrink at seeing him, Son.' Collecting himself, he told Angada, 'You go ahead and welcome him with due ceremony. I shall follow soon.'

'Where is your king?' asked Lakshmana when Angada touched his feet. The prince assured him, 'O lion-like hero, the blessed Sugriva is waiting at the victory gate of the palace to welcome you.'

The king of monkeys soon made his appearance in full regalia, surrounded by maidens whose bracelets tinkled as they scattered scented powder, waved flags and flourished flywhisks, one of them was holding an umbrella white as the full moon over Sugriva.

At Sugriva's appearance, full of pomp and ceremony, Lakshmana's anger rose. Bound by Dharma, he controlled himself and the two embraced each other and entered together the palace of gold. Once inside, the monkey-king took Lakshmana to a golden throne and asked him to be seated.

Neither flattered nor pleased, Lakshmana said, anger rising, 'Deprived of his crown by stone-hearted Kaikeyi, my lord rests on grass out there and you expect me to be seated on a bejewelled, flower-decked throne?

'Don't you know that I eat only the leftovers of the leaves, roots and vegetables eaten by Rama? I desire nothing else. Rather than offering me a throne to sit on, you could have helped us look for Rama's wife as promised.'

Abashed, Sugriva said humbly, 'Enjoying life while Rama grieves, as I have done, is conduct befitting only a monkey. Please forgive me.'

Embracing Lakshmana, now placated, he proceeded along with others to where Rama was. On reaching the hermitage, he flung himself at Rama's feet.

Always quick to forgive, Rama forgot his earlier anger. He reached out his long arms and embraced Sugriva so tightly that Lakshmi, forever dwelling in his heart, winced in pain.

Seating him close, he asked, 'How is your rule? Does your authority prevail, as it should? Are people happy under your generous rule? Is your umbrella keeping the heat away from all?'

When he heard those words, the Sun's son said remorsefully, 'Eternal one! With you as my sun, can such things be difficult for me! Noble one! Through your grace I regained my fortune. And yet, by disobeying you, I have revealed my monkey nature.

'Though I had the means at my disposal, I did not carry out any search for Mother Sita. I was wallowing in carnal pleasures, while you, steeped in sorrow, pined for her.'

Ever compassionate, Rama said, 'How can you say such things, my friend? You are like Bharata to me. Although you have come late, your words reveal your anxiety on my behalf.'

Curious, he asked, 'Where is the wise Hanuman?' Sugriva replied, 'He will be here soon with a huge sea of an army. We'll then decide what should be done.'

THE DISPATCH

When Hanuman arrived, Sugriva turned to him and said, 'O son of the wind, what are you waiting for? Your speed is without match. Go forth and search for Sita in heaven, on earth and in the netherworld.

'In the south is Ravana's great city. The thieving rakshasa is most likely to have taken Sita there. Tara's son and Jambavan will join you in your mission. Two *vellams* of the mighty army will go with you. Who else do we need when we have you? Go forth, great Hanuman, and win more fame.

'Search first in the Vindhya, that mountain with a thousand peaks, so worthy of reverence. If you don't find any sign of Sita there, proceed south towards holy Narmada where even the gods bathe.

'If still unsuccessful, proceed further and reach the Pandu mountain, the one that touches the moon and where the red-rayed lord loves to linger on his journey westward.

'Near that mount flows the sacred river Godavari, the ancient stream down which roll pearls, gold and gems resplendent. Those who bathe in it are assured freedom from human bondage and earthly wanderings.

'Further south is the famous Venkatam, the sacred hill that divides the northern tongues from the southern ones. This holiest of holy places is the abode of the vedas and other scriptures. All your sins leave you when you get there, and with no effort on your part, you can gain salvation.

'But avoid this sacred spot, since you have work to do. Go instead to the well-watered Tondaimandalam with its majestic river, Caveri. Make a thorough search on both the banks of this cool stream, divine and famous.

'In Chola country, all along its streams clear as the minds of those in heaven, there are many sages engaged in austerities, oblivious to all except the feet of the lord. Go past them all quickly and remember that the idle achieve nothing.

'Go then through the hilly Chera land lit up with gems and arrive at the Pandya land, the very heart of the Tamil language. In this southern Tamil country, on the Podiya hill is the great sage's Tamil Sangam. You might be reluctant to leave that fount of knowledge but just salute it and go on to golden Tamrabarani.

'Beyond that is the Mahendra mountain, where elephant calves are reared. And there, in front of you, will be the sea. Once there, conduct a search in every direction. Take a month if you need, and come back with news. Now leave at once,' concluded Sugriva.

Hearing these instructions with great satisfaction, Rama took Hanuman aside and said, 'Wise one, let me have a word with you. Should you see her, this is how you can identify her.

'How can I describe her adequately? Whatever I say will sound like stale similes, so beloved of the poets. Yet in Sita's case, they'd be no more than the barest truth.

'Learned poets are wont to compare the instep of a beauteous maiden to the back of a tortoise or some such. It would be an insult to so describe Sita's feet.

'Her thighs are lovelier than banana stalks. Her banded breasts more beautiful than the *chakravahas*. Her waist is the *vanji* creeper. Her middle, as the poets would say, is akin to the hood of Adisesha, or if you prefer, a single wheel of the chariot of the snow-conquering sun.

'A beautiful woman's stomach is often compared by poets to a banana leaf, a painter's palette and such like, all of which are exaggerations. But none describes precisely Sita's perfect stomach with a belly button of such beauty that even the eye-flower bears no comparison. Maybe a water bubble on the Ganga's surface might barely qualify.

'The line on her midriff is my life. If you insist on a simile for it, I can only call it a staff for her spring-like waist, which, if the need arises, can wind itself around it for support.

'Shall I compare her gait with confidence to that of a swan? Her feet to the verse of ancient and practised poets of world renown?

'What of her complexion? The tender mango, gold grown dark, will seem withered in comparison. One look at her and even the lightning will disappear in haste, too shamed to appear again in her presence.

'With whom or what to compare the incomparable! I give up. There is none like her.

'But enough. Once convinced that it is indeed her you have spotted, approach her carefully and tell her these things that crowd my mind.

'When I first went to Mithila with the sage to attend the king's sacrifice, I saw her standing in the maidens' mansion where swans sported.

'Remind her of what she said then: "If the man who broke that mountainous bow is not the one who came with the sage, I'll give up my life."

'Tell her how she appeared to me in the king's assembly, her waist, that mere streak of lightning, carrying the burden of her two breasts.

"Are you, my precious one, indeed determined to come with me and suffer hardships in an unknown forest? Having given me so much happiness, are you now set on giving me sorrow and pain?" I had asked her.

'To which she had replied, "You have lost a kingdom and are going to a forest. In all this, am I your greatest discomfort?" Her large eyes streaming with tears, she had fallen down in a swoon. Remind her of that.

'When we left that large city and even before we had stepped outside the ramparts, she wanted to know whether we had reached the forest. So childlike was she. Remind her of that incident.'

And many such episodes did he narrate to Hanuman. Finally, he said, 'Here is a ring you can show her, to prove you are my messenger. Farewell, wise one.' And Hanuman left with the blessing of that doughty warrior.

(After the son of the wind had left on his southward journey, Sugriva gave thought to the other regions to be scoured. Different search parties set off in different directions and all of them promised solemnly that they would return by the appointed day.

*But leaving aside those that went in these other directions, I shall
stick to describing the adventures of those who went south to the
beautiful Tamil country.)*

GETTING THROUGH A TUNNEL

*(Hanuman and the other stalwarts, all of whom were looking
forward to the prospect of a war, went past the Vindhyas, the
gracious mountain that resembled Siva's bejewelled head, the
sacred Narmada where they came upon buffalo calves in the
water looking rather like dark clouds drinking up the sea, Mount
Hemakuta with its crest of flashing streams and many other
wondrous places. Everywhere they searched diligently for Sita
but in vain. They saw her dark hair in the sand of the river, her
bright face in the lotuses that floated in the pools, her teeth in the
pearls that lay scattered among the hills, but nowhere did they see
all of her together. At Hemakuta they were sure that the fortress
shaped hill was where the evil rakshasa was holding her prisoner.
They scoured it a whole day, frightening the elephants and yalis
that lived there. But nowhere could they find the golden maiden.*

*Finally, they reached a desert tract where water was unknown,
where the sun himself feared to tread. No birds or beasts ever came
there; no grass or flowering tree had ever been found; everything
from without that dared set foot there was turned to dust by that
dreadful desert).*

Senses numbed, feelings crushed, their golden bodies
tortured with sweat, they were like worms and boneless
creatures wilting in the fires of hell. Their tongues hung out
and boils erupted on the soles of their feet. So hot was the
ground that when they trod upon it, they leapt up, like sparks
from a stone.

Seeing no shade to rest under, tortured without end, their
souls having almost deserted their bodies, they approached a
long tunnel. 'We cannot go further without dying. This will at
least give some shelter from the heat,' they told themselves,
and entered the dark opening.

Once inside, it was as if they were stuck in a thick ghee
of blackness. It was like a cave where, fearing the sun, all the

darkness in the world had taken refuge.

They could neither move nor even see their own feet. Not knowing what to do, feeling they were about to die, they prayed earnestly to Hanuman to save them.

'Don't despair,' said he, 'hold on to my tail and don't let go.' Groping his way through, hands outstretched, he began to walk fast. His earrings, flashing like intermittent lightning in a dark sky, dispelled the surrounding darkness.

All of a sudden, they came upon a city that shone as if the sun had hid himself there. With *karpaka* trees and lotus pools, golden towers and a strong fortress, it had been fashioned with care by Maya, the architect of the asuras.

In total astonishment, the monkeys thought it must be Ravana's own city and were happy that the end of their quest was at hand. Then Jambavan said, 'That arch thief who has stolen Sita, has contrived an excellent trap for us. How are we ever going to get out of this endless cave?'

Hanuman snapped impatiently, 'Stop these howls of despondency. We are more numerous than the Sagaras, Rama's ancestors who dug up the earth in search of their father's yaga horse and thus gave the sea its name, "Sagara".

'If they could do it, we too can keep going, till we find another opening. Or kill all the wily rakshasas here and escape. Don't despair.'

(*Thus encouraged, they walked further and saw a lady with golden tresses, dazzling bright, in the middle of that city.*)

A resplendent face, a cloth of bark around her middle, waist and breasts stilled at her indrawn breath, red streaked carp-eyes fixed at the tip of her nose, she sat in meditation, her lotus-like hands outstretched on her thighs.

Lust and other inner foes well under control, the very name of desire obliterated, senses reined in by a disciplined mind, she looked like penance personified. Unattached to good or evil, free of all bondage, compassion streaming through her eyes, she inspired awe, even as she filled one's heart with love.

Approaching her, the monkeys wondered if she was

Sita. Agitatedly they asked Hanuman, 'Is she our lady as described to you?' Replied Hanuman somewhat tartly, 'If a necklace of bones can be taken for one of pearls, this could be Sita.'

Meanwhile, that sanyasin became aware of the strangers approaching her. Upset at the interruption, she said, 'You are not of this city. What brings you here? Who are you?'

'We are the servants of righteous Rama,' said Hanuman humbly. 'The treacherous Ravana, the rakshasa king, craftily stole his wife Sita and has hid her somewhere. We are scouring the earth in search of her.'

When she heard this, she rose, eyes streaming with pleasure and compassion. 'Welcome,' she said, 'I could dance with happiness. But where is Rama?'

Hanuman, his mind now at ease and rid of its earlier hostility, narrated the whole story. She heard him out with increasing joy and said, 'My penance has brought me my salvation, at last.' At Hanuman's request, she told them her story.

'Swayamprabha is my name. The four-faced Brahma gave this great city to the stag-faced Maya, as a reward for his penance. That asura was in love with a heavenly apsara, a dear friend of mine. At his pleading, I brought her down from heaven to this tunnel.

'For a long time, the two of them lived here in pleasurable solitude, unconscious of anything else. Because of my great love for her, I stayed on with them for many, many days. Until, searching high and low for the lost apsara, Indra came looking for her and killed Maya in his rage.

'Then, anger mounting, he asked my friend how she had dared desert her post in heaven and come to be where she was and keeping the company she did.

'My wily, red-lipped friend conveyed with eyes rather than words, that I had contrived it all. The blame thus laid on me, she made good her escape. Irate Indra cursed me to stay and guard this place.

'Bowing to the inevitable, I beseeched, "When will this dark doom end?" He replied, "The day Rama's great monkey messengers arrive in this city is when you will be freed."

'O hero, this city has everything you need—food and clothes aplenty, sandal paste, gems of many hues and much else. But I left them all untouched to do penance and conquer my fate.

'This tunnel, lord, is a hundred leagues long. But I know no way to transcend its roof. If you can help, I can save myself. Please think of a way of getting out.' Hanuman assured her he would find a way to help her reach the world of the gods.

Silently he prayed to Rama: 'O great one, you who saved our lives when we were sunk in the sea of darkness, do something to get us out of here.' Smiling and serene, he told everyone, 'Don't be afraid. All will be well.'

The son of the wind then began to expand in size, his bright hands growing like the fangs of the great black boar that raised the world, terrifying those who saw the sight. Rising like a lion, he pushed the top of the tunnel till it got unstuck and rose above the clouds with Hanuman still in it.

Then, emerging from that cavernous structure he had picked up so effortlessly, he threw the whole one hundred and forty leagues of it into the western sea, frightening the gods. That tunnel still remains there, known to all as Tunnel Island.

Freed at last from that dark cave, the monkeys decided their next course of action, while the bright-browed Swayamprabha departed for heaven.

All praise for Hanuman's prowess, the monkeys walked the earth throughout the day. Even as the sun reached the western hill, they crossed the great land over which the southern breeze blows eternal, and reached the Mahendra mountain.

SAMPATI

With waves that touched the sky, the sea seemed to the monkeys to be Lanka herself, extending her hands in welcome and telling them, 'The fawn-eyed nymph is right here with me.'

Having been instructed to meet at Mahendra, that huge army of monkeys that had spread in all eight directions to search for Sita, now came together, looking like a copy of the ocean.

Unable to find the great lady, comely and chaste, they didn't know what to do. Stuttering in shame and confusion, they wailed, 'The deadline is past. We have not sighted her.

'We have indeed carried out Sugriva's orders to search high and low, but have failed to find the lady. What should we do now?

'Should we undertake a penance or swallow a poison without antidote and die?' Greatly concerned for the sorrowing monkeys, Angada, the young prince spoke: 'I have something to say.

"We'll search the entire world under the sky and bring news of Sita," we'd boasted. Now we are shrouded in shame.

'We couldn't do what we promised; nor did we report failure within the time prescribed. What is worse, even now we have no hope of fulfilling our mission. After this, do we deserve to live?

'My father will frown. Our lord Rama will be filled with sorrow. I dare not face them. I would rather die. Please advise me on what I should do.'

'Young prince,' said Jambavan, 'what nonsense are you talking? You will die and we, I suppose, should sit and mourn your death? Or go back home, forgetting you and our love for you, as a thing of the past?'

Vali's son replied, 'Are you suggesting, father, that all the others here die of shame, and I alone return home with news of failure? The world will sneer, "His near and dear gave up their lives to avoid censure, but he himself came back, shameless."'

The king of bears, much perturbed, spoke out of his love for the young prince, 'Only you and your father have any right to be king of your clan. Hence it was that we thought what we did. Can anyone utter the word "death" in connection with a king?'

When he said this, Hanuman replied, 'There is not one place in the three worlds we haven't searched. But is that any reason to give up halfway? It only means that we should look harder and in other places. We must scour again the netherworld and the world above till we locate the golden lady.

'No doubt it is important to keep to the time assigned. But our king will not blame us for exceeding the limit set, if at the end we meet with success. So let us search once again, more diligently.

'If, after that, we die as Jatayu did after putting up a brave fight, we might be worthy of praise. To die now would be shameful.'

(It so happened that Sampati, the king of eagles, was in the vicinity. Upon overhearing that his brother Jatayu was dead, he was stunned with sorrow. Tearfully, he questioned them: 'Is my virtuous brother really dead? Who in this world has a weapon that can kill my mighty brother?')

Decked with jewels that flashed like lightning, dim eyes streaming like rain, heartbroken and crying aloud, he seemed a cloud rumbling on earth. As he drew nearer, many of the monkeys fled in terror.

Eyes blazing, suspicious Hanuman confronted this fearsome vision, saying, 'Crafty rakshasa disguised as an eagle, do you now hope to escape with your life?'

However, on looking closer, he saw that this was no demon but an eagle deeply distressed. Before Hanuman could say anything more, the other asked again. 'Tell me in full, who killed the formidable Jatayu?'

'If you tell me truly who you are, I will tell you all, omitting nothing,' said Hanuman. The eagle-king replied, 'I am the unfortunate, born before the one you just said was dead.'

Plunged in a sea of sorrow, Hanuman said, 'The sword of cruel Ravana was the cause of his death.' On hearing this, Sampati crashed to the ground, like a mountain felled by a dreadful thunder. Sighing deliriously, deep and hot, and his limbs shivering, he sobbed.

O brother of mine, I, with wings burnt and disabled, should have been the one to die. But you, strong as Dasaratha, have gone before me. How strange!' Anguished and heartbroken, almost dying himself, the mighty eagle lamented a long while. Doughty Hanuman tried to console him.

At last, red-eyed with grief, the eagle asked about the reason behind Jatayu's fight with the deathly swordsman. The son of the wind replied, 'Sita, wife of Rama, our lord, and daughter of Janaka, was by the villain's witchcraft separated from her husband.

'Your virtuous brother saw the fell rakshasa abducting her. He attacked him fiercely, smashed that villain's chariot and tore his shoulders. But the demon cut him dead with the sword gifted to him by the God of gods, and that true one lost his life.'

Upon hearing this story, tearful Sampati rejoiced, saying, 'Well done, my dear brother! Losing thus your life in the cause of one born to save us all. O hero, my brother, who died for Rama and his lovely wife, is not really dead. He lives forever, his fame without limit.

'My brother gave up his life out of his love for Dharma personified. But what is Death? For those who achieve such great worth, what greater joy?' He then went to a stream close by, bathed and performed the obsequies.

Returning, he said, 'O heroes, free of sin and ever truthful, you have not plunged me in grief but given me life. You have removed the darkness that clouded my eyes.

'O messengers of Truth! Recite you all the name of Rama so that I too can benefit from the supreme grace of that God.'

(*Curious about what would ensue from the recital of the lord's name, the assembled monkeys obediently chanted the name of that blue-bodied warrior. Miraculously, Sampati's disabled wings became whole and shot forth, bright and new, his body now like a blazing sword in a scabbard. The monkeys were wonderstruck.*)

Astonished and terrified, yet exultant, they blessed the name of the king of gods. Bowing to Sampati, they begged, 'Tell us in full what happened in the past.' And he, much impressed by their love, told them.

'We two, Sampati and Jatayu, kings of bright-feathered eagles, are the sons of Aruna, the Sun's charioteer, who disperses darkness in this sea-girt world.

'Wishing to see heaven high above, we once flew towards the sky and sighted the chariot of the sun. But before we could see it well, the red-rayed god who could burn even fire, flew into a rage at our impertinence.

'Jatayu, flying ahead of me was about to be burnt and screamed for help. I spread my wings and sheltered him from the sun's wrath. He was saved, but my wings that enfolded him got burnt, and though not dead, I fell down to the earth.

'Seeing me fall, the generous god of the sky said in his mercy, "When the monkeys who come searching for Janaka's daughter recite the name of Rama, you will get back your wings."

'Disabled as I was, I ordered my brother to become the king of eagles in my place. Greatly distressed and reluctant at first, but afraid to disobey me, he did become king. This, O monkeys, is my history. But, tell me, what brought you here?'

Speaking many words in praise of Rama, they said, 'Father, we came here believing that the mean Ravana might have carried Sita away in this direction.'

Sampati said, 'Don't worry, I'll tell you all about it. I saw that wicked rakshasa carrying a lovely girl. He has reached Lanka and has immured her in a cruel prison. You will find her there.

'Sea-girt Lanka is a hundred *yojanas* from here. Even Death with his terrible noose is afraid to cast his eyes on it. When in rage, that mean rakshasa is fire to fire itself. You no doubt are men of wondrous valour. But how will you manage to get there?

'You can't, all of you, go to that city. Better it would be for the ablest among you to go to Sita and secretly give Rama's message and come back here. Or you can all go back and tell Rama all that I have told you and leave it to him to decide what must be done.

'I must leave now. Now that they lack a protector, the eagles will be distressed and forlorn. With Jatayu dead, it is now my duty to look after them. Friends, god bless you, and may you do the right thing,' he said and flew away majestically, momentarily hiding the sky.

MAHENDRA

'The bird-king will not tell a lie,' the monkeys concurred. 'Everything is now clear. He has given us new life. Let us consider what is good, and do one of the two things he asked us to.

'We can go to Sugriva and the great bowman and tell them worshipfully what we have heard and our task will be done. If we ourselves seek her out, that will be even more splendid. But who among us can cross the sea?' they wondered.

'One of us, who can, should jump across the sea and cope with those rakshasas, leaving the rest of us to save our lives,' they decided.

Nila and some others declared frankly that they couldn't cross the sea. Vali's son, a blameless warrior, said, 'I can cross the sea but will not have the strength to return.'

Brahma's son, Jambavan said, 'Alas, my luck! When he whom even the vedas cannot find, measured the earth with his foot, I went around him, singing his praise. But my foot knocked against Meru and was hurt.

'Therefore, mighty-shouldered ones, I cannot leap across the sea, negotiate ditches, climb ramparts, cope with the rakshasas, discover Sita and come back here with her.

'But for us to wring our hands and worry over whose help we should seek is a disgrace,' he continued. 'There is no cause for despair. Don't we have one here with us who will bring us name and fame?

'He is the one who went forth first and met Rama. He is tireless, too, in completing any task assigned to him. Hanuman, whose like doesn't exist, but who is too modest and knows not his own strength, is the man for us.'

(He then proceeded to acquaint Vayu's son with his own greatness.)

'Brahma may die, but you are endless. You are learned and a good speaker. You are fierce enough to frighten Death. You can fight like Siva himself. Neither fire, nor water, nor wind can kill you. Divine weapons cannot destroy you. With one leap, you can jump across this world.

'You can grow higher than Meru and contract to less than a drop of rain. You can lift the earth and touch the sun with your hand. You can probe the good and bad and advise wisely. You it was that skilfully planned the death of Vali, out to destroy Dharma.

'You can take on anyone single-handed. With the undiminished might of your shoulders, you can conquer, liberate or kill. When enraged Indra struck you with his bolt, you did not lose even a single hair.

'Even the three worlds are nothing against you. Your heroic shoulders can shrug them away in an instant. Walking before the sun, dispelling darkness, you learnt from him the Sanskrit lore.

'You are just, you are truthful, you never ever think of the joys of sex. You're well read and know the vedas by rote. You are eternal.

'You have given your heart to Rama and therefore know your duty well. If you resolve to do something, I am certain you will do it, whatever the odds.

'You know that virtue alone stands where others fall. Your righteousness and patience are an example to Indra and other gods. You are the only true pandit, capable of deeds both thoughtful and fruitful. You can get what you want when you want it.

'You can be compared only with yourself. Go forth and save our lives and add to your glory. Cross the sea, return with news of Sita and with that deed, make Rama cross the sea of his sorrow. You are the one, the only one, capable of accomplishing this feat,' concluded Jambavan.

Head bowed, the wise one smiled, his lips a red lotus springing from his face. Clasping his hands with respect, he spoke aloud his thoughts.

'Should you say, "Uproot Lanka, and bring it here, or powder those rakshasas and bring back Sita," I can do exactly that. You will see this with your own eyes. Do not have any doubts whatsoever.

'Leaping over the sea a hundred leagues wide, as if it were but a step that Vishnu measured out, I'll destroy all the wretches in Lanka, even if Indra and the other gods should oppose me.

'Anyone among you, had you given it some thought, could have crossed the seven seas, conquered all the worlds and brought Sita back. But since you ask a worthless monkey like me to do this, as if to test me, who in this world can be deemed more lucky than I?

'Were all the seas to gather and drown the world, or the world itself break into pieces, your grace and my lord's command will bear me up like wings. You will see me, Garuda-like, crossing the sea. Wait here without worries while I go to sea-girt Lanka. Quick, give me leave.'

Even before they'd blessed him and bidden goodbye, he'd climbed to the top of the sky's neighbour, Mount Mahendra.

His mind set on leaping over the sea, he assumed a huge form that reached up to the very sky, resembling the lord who measured the world.

Shoulders garlanded and tail encircling his body, Hanuman stood on that mount eager to cross the sea before the sun lit up the sky. Mahendra sank under his weight, just like Mount Mandara, resting on the divine tortoise, had when the sea was churned for ambrosia.

Surrounded by great clouds, their lightning his tinkling anklets, his huge form drew the attention of the gods above. With the Mahendra for his pedestal, he stood like a pillar supporting the world.

SUNDARA KANDAM

THE LEAP ACROSS THE SEA

Then he saw that ancient city, its ramparts and gates, its fragrant groves and jewelled white houses, and its golden streets. Slapping his shoulders, he whooped in triumph, causing the sky and the eight quarters to shiver in fright.

As his feet pressed down upon that blue mountain, snakes rushed out from their havens in the hollows, mouths belching fire, as if vomiting their very entrails. Lions tore out of impermeable caves and were immediately reduced to pulp.

Harsh, raucous cries of terrified birds filled the air as they fled to the sun in an attempt to find a place to hide. As if Dissolution itself was at hand, musty tuskers, dark as clouds, ears flapping madly and trumpeting wildly, clutched the trees in fright.

Sparks flew everywhere, and tigresses with hairless cubs, whose eyes had yet to open, fled hither and thither, looking for sanctuary.

When that mountain spun, like Mandara churning the milk-white sea, ascetics, their penances interrupted, were tossed up to the sky and reached heaven in their earthly bodies.

Even as that bright mountain was powdered to bits, the gods, shielding their terror-stricken wives, looked on. They looked like so many Sivas, embraced by the fearful Parvati, when the sharp-fanged rakshasa seized Kailasa.

Tail aloft, legs bent at the knees, hands outstretched, chest drawn in, neck merging with shoulders that surged in preparation for the feat to come, he rose to the sky, going out of sight in a flash, as if headed for Brahma's world itself.

Impelled by his speed, rocks, trees and various beasts took off with the son of the wind. But unable to keep up with him, they fell into the sea mid-flight. The vast ocean rent in two, unearthing the glittering world of the Nagas. 'Thanks to my penances,' chuckled the hero, 'I have now seen the underworld as well!'

As if portending that the time bought by the ten-headed Ravana through his many boons was nearing an end, Hanuman appeared, to those witnessing this remarkable sight, like the sun hurtling from north to south—a good omen indeed.

As he sped like a tornado, there suddenly loomed before him a hill just risen from the sea; it slid out of that vast ocean, quick like a grain upon polished glass. Nothing daunted, Hanuman wondered for a moment at this development. Thinking, 'This hill bodes no good,' he pushed it aside with contemptuous ease, and rose quickly again into the sky.

Hidden till now, embraced by the sea, the hill now showed itself as a man. Hurt in body and mind, he said reproachfully, 'Father, I am no enemy of yours.

'When Indra's bolt deprived the mountains of their wings, Vayu, out of his love for me, pushed me into the sea to save my life. Doughty hero, you are his beloved son, and I, forever indebted to him, have surfaced out of love for you to let you rest awhile on my golden peak.

'Think of me as one who is more fond of you than your own mother and stay awhile, accept my hospitality O honoured guest, well beloved. Can't I do this little favour for you?'

Deeply moved by this request, Hanuman shot a dazzling smile and said ruefully, 'Forgive me, my friend. I must rush to Lanka on my lord's errand. If I return, your kindness I'll certainly accept.' He then disappeared beyond his sight.

Next, there lay in wait for him a good-hearted woman, Surasa. She had been told by the gods that the mighty force that would rid the three worlds of all their sorrows had finally arrived. She appeared before Hanuman in the guise of a rakshasi in order to test his strength.

Mouth wide open in a ferocious snarl, head touching the

sky, she wanted to appease her hunger. 'Fat monkey, will you kindly be my meat?

'O stalwart, my hunger rages like fire, and you have come to me of your own accord. Step into my fanged mouth, as there is nowhere else you can go.'

Said the wise one, ever compassionate, 'You are a woman and one with gnawing hunger; I'll gladly give you my body, once I've fulfilled my lord's command.'

At this, she threw her head back and laughed aloud, 'I'll kill you this very moment, in plain sight of the seven worlds. This I swear.' Laughing, he challenged, 'I shall enter your mouth for just an instant. Eat me within that moment, if you can.'

The rakshasi stretched her already open mouth wider, enough to contain the seven worlds and still have space to spare. In a trice, the towering Hanuman shrank, making a miniature of himself and leapt into that cavern.

But even before she could heave a breath, he leapt out, chortling. The gods showered flowers and blessed him and he resumed his gigantic form. After seeking the blessings of Surasa, who then revealed her real self and showered more love than a mother on her son, he sped away on his sacred mission.

More adventure awaited the son of Vayu. Angaratara, the great *halahala*, took the shape of an awful black sea, challenging, 'Who dares cross me here?'

Clothed in elephant skin, she stood erect, bared fangs and all. The waves seemed like mere puddles that wet her giant feet. Her humongous mouth agape, she seemed about to swallow the globe.

Realizing there was no way to avoid her and that neither earth nor sky could provide an escape route, Hanuman decided to repeat his earlier feat of walking through the mouth. 'You have blocked my path in the sky. Who are you? Why do you stand here like a barrier?'

'Don't make the mistake of thinking I'm but a woman; even a god who dares approach me will die. Yama himself cannot prevent me from eating anything that catches my fancy.'

So saying, she opened her mouth and the hero obediently leapt in. Dharma wailed and the gods wilted. In a second, he emerged, having clawed out her entrails like a second Narasimha.

'Evil comes in various guises. Against these obstacles created by the rakshasas, I find that my only defence is Rama's name. Nothing else prevails,' Hanuman said thoughtfully.

Then at last, the hero sighted the well-guarded golden summits of Lanka's fortress surrounding groves of dazzling green. He leapt to the top of a coral hill close by. The impact of his landing set that mount tottering, as if it were a well-stocked boat caught unawares in a storm and capsizing.

Looking at the beautiful city, chin cupped in the palm of his hand, he said, 'It is absurd to compare this vision to the city of the gods in heaven. One is evil, the other good. But then, the scriptures say that heaven is in the mind, not at a particular spot. Heaven is where one's desires are fulfilled.'

SCOURING THE CITY

Were those mansions that rose so high as to pierce the clouds and touch the moon, really made of gold set with gems? Or are they a trick of lightning, perhaps mirages unleashed by the sun's rays?

This wondrous city was the creation of Maya, architect of the asuras. To say that it looked fit to be Indra's capital is but to prattle like a fool and reduce its grandeur.

The trees in that city were *karpaka*, the houses gold; gods, enfeebled, worked as slaves, while heavenly apsaras served as maids. No wayward luck, this, but the fruit of single-minded austerities.

And whom should we laud? The architect? That red-eyed rakshasa's unwavering penance? Or was it Brahma's boon that made such splendour possible? Our feeble wit is quite vanquished.

People said that the sun dared not show its face in Lanka for fear of Ravana. The truth, however, was that the towers of that bright city quite bedazzled that blazing star, who, unable to shield his eyes, avoided that route. In every crystal palace and in every cool grove, there were men without a care in the world, with little else to do but drink, sing and dance.

From casks and goblets they drank wine and sipped nectar from ruby lips. Intoxicated with sweet talk and sulky words, they drank still more to shoo those sulks away, and yet more when they banished them.

Wondered Hanuman: 'What should I report to my lord? Should I extol their might or their wealth? Should I speak of their life of ease and pleasure? Or their fierce bowmen, swordsmen, and wrestlers? A word about warriors wielding javelins, clubs and missiles, perhaps?'

His great heart melting, he thought sadly, 'Alas for this city! Its greatness and glory will soon depart. No matter who, no matter what, even-handed Fate deals everyone the same hand. None is stronger than the sum of his deeds.'

Dragging his mind back to the task on hand, he told himself, 'I should be careful lest some rakshasa comes this way,' and made himself small to avoid being noticed.

As he stood on that pleasant hill, the sun sank in the western sea. Darkness descended everywhere, like the sin of one who's acquired wealth through evil means.

Hanuman's thoughts then turned towards the problem of how best to enter well-guarded Lanka. He, who always trod the right path, wondered now if there was a straight road to that crooked place!

He saw that city, which had the sea for its moat, rising above the seven worlds. Its ramparts, wrought of rare gold, looked strong enough to withstand even the flood of Dissolution.

'If the moon and the other planets,' he thought wonderingly, 'do not pass over these walls, it is not because they are afraid of the crafty tyrant. It is simply that the walls are too high!

'It will be difficult to go through the gate; besides, the clever should not take the way prescribed for others. I'll leap over the rampart that even the sun dare not cross,' he decided.

Barring the way stood one, who, eyes unwinking, guarded that city. Glaring at him the way serpent Rahu does the sun, she went forward, swift as thought, and directed, 'Halt!'

Hanuman hailed her, thinking, 'Lucky is this ancient and dreaded city that has her watchful eyes to cover it like a cloak.'

Her eyes darting smoke and fire, she said, 'Rash fool, what are you doing? I'll not expend my rage on vagabonds feeding on roots and vegetables! Desist from leaping across these ramparts daubed with gold and depart in peace!'

The hero who had no likes or dislikes and was ever anxious to do the right thing, controlled his anger and hailed her yet again: 'I came here drawn irresistibly by the grandeur of this golden city. What harm can a poor monkey like me cause?'

Scarce had he spoken when she jeered, 'Who are you, worm, when told to leave, dare stay and bandy words with me? How dare you walk in as you please? Even Siva cannot enter this city without leave.'

He ignored her anger, smiling all the while. 'You grin?' she said, furious. 'Who are you? Who advised you to come here? Why do you wish to lose your life? Run away.' Without losing his temper, Vayu's son replied, 'Not before I've seen this city.'

'Crafty one,' she thought, standing like a rock. 'This is no ordinary monkey. Even the god of death cowers when he sees me. This one laughs as if he were that three-eyed swallower of venom.

'He must be killed,' she thought, 'else this city will be destroyed.' Fire darting from her eyes and her mouth, she flung her trident at him, saying, 'If you win, you enter.'

He seized that trident, darting like lightning. Jaws bared, he bit into it like Garuda attacking a serpent and broke it with his hands, much to the delight of the gods and the terror of the guardian of that city.

When the trident had been powdered and all other weapons used by that fiery woman flung away, she lost her patience and roared like thunder.

With bare hands that had tossed many a hill, she started to beat him till sparks flew. Hanuman, the unbeaten, seized and held her in one hand, ruefully reminding himself, 'She is but a woman. To kill her would be wrong.'

He then struck a gentle blow on her chest, whereupon she crashed to the ground like a mountain struck by lightning. Rising from the sea of blood, she recalled what Brahma had told her and fell at the feet of the noble messenger.

'Noble one, I guard this city on the orders of the Creator. Lankadevi is my name. Because I do my duty with zeal, I lost my head, spoke to you harshly and treated you badly. If you will graciously grant me life, I'll tell you my story.

'When I asked the creator of all things living, how long I should guard this ancient city, he said, 'The day will come when a mighty monkey will pummel you with his bare hands. You will then return to my world. And that will be the end of this beautiful city. His words have come true.

'Need I remind you, virtue will always prevail over vice. The city is all yours. Enter, and do what you wish.' So saying, the erstwhile guardian of that kingdom made her way to heaven.

Having thus crossed the first hurdle, Hanuman bowed to Rama's feet, a vision he always carried in his heart. And leaping over the tall ramparts, he landed in the middle of the city.

Not wishing to draw unwelcome notice, he shrank till he was tiny and walked the streets of Lanka, trying to locate Sita's whereabouts. Like a bee that pauses upon every flower, he searched every corner—mighty palaces, humble huts, elephant sheds, chariot sheds and stables.

The sights he saw amazed him. The sweet fruits of penance could be seen in the way the rakshasas lived. Apsaras, full-breasted and slim of waist, waited on their wives, bathed them in pellucid waters fetched specially for the purpose from rivers in paradise.

In their pleasure domes he saw some rakshasis lolling in bed, listening to slaves play vinas that had strings designed for the seven swaras. Others watched gandharvas dance under canopies of flowers, keeping perfect rhythm. Women with lily-blue eyes sucked from their men's lips the red of the tootulai fruit.

He saw stalwart men who could kill tigers with their bare hands, bristling with joy every time their women kicked them, anklets tinkling.

There were rakshasas drunk, not on wine, but on the nectar sipped from the red lips of their amorous women, more intoxicating than anything the royal cellar could supply, sweeter than anything the pure ocean of milk could provide.

He saw sulking wives fend off their husbands, fiery breasts scorching the sandal paste. Other women languished, resting on their flower-strewn beds like lifeless bodies, watching the path taken by their husbands gone away on some business.

Outdoors, household gods were being worshipped to the tune of many instruments. Bracelets, waistbands and anklets of heavenly apsaras tinkled, as they clapped their hands and shed benedictions.

After scanning with care the faces of numerous yakshinis, rakshasis, naginis and vidyadharis, all of whom looked like so many spotless moons, Hanuman at last came to a palace where Kumbhakarna lay like a mountain in slumber.

In the middle of a vast bed, like a serpent under the spell of a mantra, oblivious to the whole world, slept the mighty rakshasa. Heavenly nymphs massaged his feet, while the moonstone pillars in the hall, responding to their moonlike faces, sprinkled droplets of fragrance on his face.

Looking at him, Hanuman wondered whom he might be. At first he thought he was the wicked Ravana himself. At that thought his eyes, normally so peaceable, darted fire.

On closer look, however, he noticed neither ten heads nor twenty shoulders. The rage that had surged like the northern fire mere moments ago, was doused by the sea of his good sense.

'Whoever he is,' he said to himself, 'his days are numbered.' Hands raised in supplication, the name of Rama on his lips, he moved on in search of Sita.

High and low he looked for her—in towering domes, rows of mansions, dancing houses, theatres and temples, music halls and halls of learning. Huge one moment, tiny the next, atom and mount by turn, the monkey warrior went everywhere and saw everyone except Sita.

At long last, in a *karpaka* grove, on a crystal platform in a coral palace, he came upon Dharma in person, attired in black.

It was the abode of Vibhishana, a good rakshasa, beloved by all. His own true self he saw reflected in the saintly man he saw resting. 'This one is spotless,' he decided, and void of rage, went past him.

Racing faster than his own thoughts, he peered into hundreds of mansions in the course of a single second and scanned many a coral-lipped celestial face, bright like the full moon. Finally, he found himself standing at the gate of the palace where Indra had once been immured.

He who could enter where smoke couldn't, saw in one of the many mansions a boy, six-faced and twelve shouldered like Siva's son, slumbering deep. 'Who is this, a lion in his cave? Rakshasa or the divine Kartikeya? I do not know. Whoever he is, Rama will find in him a tough opponent,' said Hanuman to himself.

'It is foolish to waste further time here,' he told himself, and leaving Indrajit to his dreams, went on to search for Rama's wife in other places.

Leaping in and out of countless mansions belonging to ministers and army chiefs like Aksha and Adikaya and many others of lesser note, he reached at length the middle moat.

Merely describing that water-filled trench as large or huge would be an insult. Even if the whole world were to be dug up till the day of Dissolution, such a deep trench will not result. 'It looks as if fear of that ruthless tyrant has made all the seven seas rush in here to guard the city,' thought Hanuman to himself.

He crossed the moat as easily as he had crossed the roaring sea and reached the middle of the town and roamed its every street.

Leaping across the third moat, he came at last to the golden abode of Ravana. Surrounded by the palaces of his wives, it appeared as a full moon in the midst of innumerable stars.

Upon entering, he saw Maya's daughter Mandodhari, whose face could have shamed the moon itself. 'My quest,' he thought with joy, 'is over at last.' Not having ever seen Sita before, he thought it was she.

'Surely, lust-oppressed Ravana would not have lodged Sita at any palace less than the best in the kingdom.' But on observing Mandodhari, he felt deeply troubled.

There she was, lying in luxurious abandon, attended upon by the best of heavenly maidens. Rambha, Tilottama and Urvasi were at her beck and call—massaging her feet and twirling flywhisks to keep the heat off her, even as music, said to be the food of love, played in the background.

'Surely, this cannot be Janaki?' he reflected in deep despair. 'If this is Sita, wallowing thus in Ravana's luxury, gone forever is Rama's fame and lustre. Can one who has looked on Rama and lost her heart to him, ever turn to some one else?

'No, this is not she. Sita has a human form. This might be a rakshasi or yakshini. No doubt she has some marks of beauty, but her mouth stutters words that betoken ruin. Enough with this doubting, this is not Sita.'

(His mind at rest, he continued with his search. Leaving Mandodhari's palace behind, he reached another, more magnificent. Whose else could it be but Ravana's?)

Always sharp, he noticed now a host of spearmen guarding the palace. A veritable fortress.

On a magnificent bed, a dark form slept, hands and legs outspread. The many heads covered with jewels, looked as awesome as Vishnu, reclining on Sesha in the milky ocean.

A mighty man, he slept like the morning sun on the eastern hill. The dazzling gems on his person lighted up the world, putting an end to that dark creature called night.

Thoughts of Sita tormenting him, Ravana sighed a soul-deep sigh. The breeze that rose to obey the command of flywhisks wielded by apsaras, only served to torment him further.

Hanuman watched in anger and indignation. 'Of what use my strength or fame if I do not show my might today by kicking those crowns off the heads of the one who stole that sword-eyed maid?'

The earth rumbled and the mountains quivered. The corners of their right eyesbrows twitching, rakshasis felt a sudden fear. The quarters trembled and the cloudless sky rumbled.

'Can a rakshasa who abducted that spotless jewel escape with his life after I've seen him? Let me break all his shoulders and kick those ten heads around like so many balls, uncaring of consequences.'

He ground his teeth and kneaded his hands in rage. In a little while, having calmed himself, 'On second thoughts, I should not disobey my master's command. It doesn't make sense to deviate from one's goal. Such recklessness will only breed mischief.

'Let this rage within me die! If they say that a mere monkey destroyed the fence that kept the fair maid captive, it will not credit the hero born to destroy these wicked demons.'

Thus shaking himself free of fantasies of valour, he stood there and pondered, 'Alas, for me. I am yet to find her in this vast city.

'Has he killed her for daring to resist him? Gobbled her up, as is the wont of man-eating rakshasas? Imprisoned her elsewhere? What should I do? I understand nothing. What shall I tell him on returning empty-handed? How will I live down this failure?

'The fruits of my good deeds are exhausted. "The time fixed for return is past and we haven't found her," my friends said. And I, ordering them to stay put, came here, so proud, confident of my ability to succeed where they had failed. How can I survive this shame?

'There is no place I have left unseen in Lanka, whose ramparts extend over seven hundred *yojanas*. But that great lady still eludes me. Must I, who crossed the great sea to get here, now drown in a sea of sorrow?

'Should I seize mighty Ravana with my bare hands and beat him till blood streams out of his mouth and force him to show me where Sita is? Should I burn him, and this town too, till they melt like wax?

'Sampati, the king of eagles, said that he had spotted Sita in Lanka. But his words too have proved false. It is no lie, however, that Ravana seized Rama's wife, with heaven and earth as witness. If it is the last thing I do, I must plunge Lanka into the sea.'

Like omnipresent God, seeming to be everywhere at the same time, Hanuman once again resumed his search, leaving no spot in Lanka uninvestigated.

(Then at last, there appeared within sight of Rama's messenger, now desperate and sick at heart, a bee-haunted garden in the midst of a grove).

SITA SIGHTED

'I shall seek her here,' he said. 'I will find her and my sorrows will end. If I don't succeed, there is nothing I can do except destroy Lanka along with myself.'

As Rama's messenger approached the grove, the gods rejoiced at the imminent discovery of Sita and showered flowers on him. But before we describe further what happened then, something must be said about Ravana's heartbroken captive.

Surrounded by cruel rakshasis, armed and large of build, she seemed like a plant on a stony surface yearning for a drop of water.

A peacock in looks, a koel in voice, a young doe in a den of sharp-toothed tigers, she had ceased, for a long time now, to close her eyes in sleep. With all her thoughts centred on Rama, she sat immobile most of the time, weeping rain.

Tears cascading down her golden breasts, she was the very picture of grief, a symbol of all lovers suffering the pangs of separation.

She knew that nothing would come of fighting fate, but confident that the lord of the vedas would surely come one day to avenge this unpardonable insult handed out to the solar family, she had refrained from killing herself.

Her hair, piled upon her head in a careless knot, had come undone and lay over her cheeks in wisps. With but a single garment to cover her person, she was self-neglect personified. She, who had once stood at the pinnacle of gracious beauty, was now rendered dim in sorrow. She lamented her cruel fate that'd made her lust for that phantom deer.

'Did Lakshmana find his brother? Haven't they discovered my abduction by now? Haven't they located Lanka as yet?'

She tortured herself endlessly, like one who thrusts a burning rod into one's own open wound.

'Perhaps the king of eagles died? Who can now tell them what happened?

'Has my husband abandoned me because of the thoughtless words that I, like a fool, spoke to his brother? Has luck deserted me for ever and ever?' Mouth dry, eyes streaming, her life a-tremble, she asked herself the same questions again and again.

'Who will feed him now?' she worried. 'Who will now look after the visitors who come to the hermitage? Is there an end to my plight?' Questions swamped her, and she stirred not a whit 'even when termites swarmed her seat'.

'Has he decided that the rakshasas, cruel and crafty, would have eaten me and given up hope of finding me? Has his legendary large-heartedness made him forgive the vile thief?' Thus she lamented night and day, now all the same to her.

'Perhaps his mothers and brothers have prevailed upon him to return to Ayodhya. But surely he, the very soul of honour, wouldn't have gone back without completing the term of exile? Has something else happened to the hero?'

She sometimes saw visions of another battle, fierce as the one with Khara, the treacherous sorcerer. Or maybe this time the enemy was different, like cruel Mura whom Krishna killed.

She would recall his lotus face, a painted flower, calm when his father gave him the throne and serene even when he asked him to return it and go away into the forest! She would recall his upright shoulders, when on that most auspicious day, he broke Siva's mountainous bow and claimed her for his own.

Then she thought of that other bow—the one that had, in a little more than an hour, mowed down 14,000 foes, whose might had proved irksome even to the gods.

Lost in a long daydream, she would recall that humble boatman, whom Rama hailed as his friend and brother, thereby binding him to Lakshmana and her.

She would dwell fondly on the day when, taking her soft hand from her father's, Rama had wed her by performing all the appropriate vedic rituals, and the way he'd placed her foot so tenderly on the grinding stone.

She remembered the day when Bharata, his head uncrowned, his hair matted, and shod in clothes of bark, had come to fetch them back from the jungle. Rama had melted at the very sight, as she, her heart broken, was melting now.

She often recalled the day when Rama had laughingly given away all the cows in sight to a greedy Brahmin. Then there was the time when Indra's son, disguised as a crow, had dared to peck at her breast when she was in deep sleep. Infuriated at such impious temerity, he had dispatched a straw that pursued that wily bird to the ends of the earth and punished him. All crows, have since remained squint-eyed forever.

And now here she was, the very same Sita, whose lord had so cherished and protected her, surrounded by cruel rakshasis. By midnight they had all fallen into a drunken stupor, duties forgotten—all except Trijata.

Daughter of noble Vibhishana, Trijata loved Sita as if she were her own daughter. Her only solace during those dark days in captivity, she kept Sita's hopes alive, not allowing her to get overly depressed. 'O pure-minded friend of mine,' Sita confided now, 'I'm confused, I see some good omens.

'The left side of my forehead, brow, eye and shoulders have all been twitching. The wise say that such signs portend good for women. This was the way I felt when my lord first came to Mithila with Sage Viswamitra.

'And—this I'd forgotten to mention to you—when my dear and righteous husband yielded the kingdom to his brother and set out for the unknown forest, it was on my right side that I had felt a great trembling.

'So it was when that wicked demon came to the forest and deceived me. But now, it is my left that trembles. Tell me what I should make of all this?'

'It indeed bodes well, dearest friend,' Trijata said. 'It means that you'll soon join your husband. A golden bee, bewitched by you, sat on your left ear and caused it to twitch, thereby heralding a change in your fortune. Your pallor will soon leave you and your life will change for the better.

'This omen means that your dear husband will soon send you a messenger bearing good tidings. As always, evil will fall and good triumph.

'Chaste one, you never sleep and so have no dreams. But listen to what I dreamt in the wee hours of the morning. Clad in red, oil dripping from his heads, I saw great Ravana in a chariot drawn by sturdy donkeys and ugly devils journeying south, towards Yama's abode.

'His sons, kinsmen and many others went the same way and none returned. You know that dreams that visit you at that hour of the morning always come true.

'The holy fire that Ravana tends with such reverence will be extinguished. A crash will resound from cloudless skies and stars will drop down from on high. While yet night, darkness will seem to be dispelled by a sun cut in half. The *karpaka* garlands worn by men will begin to smell of stale meat.

'The ramparts of Lanka will whirl madly; castles, uprooted, will fly in the air. There will be fire in all directions and buntings will break into brittle pieces. Bright tusks of elephants will be broken. The waters in the sacred pots that brahmins carry, will turn impure and foam like toddy.

'The stars will defy the moon. Blood will rain from the

sky. Clubs, discuses, swords and bows will war among themselves and perish. The auspicious marriage threads that women wear will snap and fall on their breasts, tormenting them by portending calamity.

'I saw queen Mandodhari's hair hanging uncombed and unplaited, catching fire from a lamp. I saw two strong lions lead a herd of beautiful tigers and a peerless peacock into a city without foes.

'Then I saw a soft-voiced lady carrying a lamp of a thousand wicks from the palace of the demon-king to saintly Vibhishana's mansion. Even as she was entering that golden abode, you woke me, and the dream ended,' she concluded. Excited, Sita clasped her hands and said, 'Mother, please, please sleep on and see the rest.'

It was then that Rama's messenger, who had tirelessly been combing Lanka, reached the very spot where Sita had been languishing in captivity. The terrifying rakshasis, cursing themselves for being derelict in duty, sprang out of sleep and approached Sita. Upon seeing the frightening forms confronting her, Sita wilted, struck dumb with fear.

Ten hands and one head, two hands with twenty heads; mountainous breasts that hung downwards. Some inspired terror while others provoked derisive laughter.

Trident, sword, discus, goad, club, spear, dagger were all held in practised hands. They looked horrifying enough to frighten Siva himself!

Vigilant as ever, Rama's envoy slipped past unnoticed and leapt on to a tree. 'Whom are these armed rakshasis, just jolted into wakefulness, supposed to be intimidating? Whom have they surrounded thus?' he mused, perplexed.

And then,

Like a streak of lightning in the middle of dark clouds, he saw among the gruesome creatures, a woman of incomparable beauty, tears streaming from eyes wide as the sea.

'This must be Sita,' he told himself. 'Her faultless features are the same as those described to me by Rama. How could that crafty and cruel rakshasa have stolen his life and hidden it away here?

'I have found what I sought. This is she! Dharma lives after all, and so will I,' he pranced around singing, intoxicated with joy.

'A dust-covered gem is she, a moon in sunlight. Hair untended and body unwashed, chastity well guarded, she is spotless. Can Dharma ever cease to be?

'Which shall I praise? The sturdy arms of Rama or the steadfast mind of this gem among women? Or the greatness of the family of Janaka, that sage among kings? Which shall I celebrate?

'Had that peerless chastity been tarnished, Rama's rage, I had feared, would have risen like a boiling sea and destroyed all creation. The world is saved! Long live the world!

'Will those austere men who perform penance in fire and water, abstaining from all that appeals to the senses, bear comparison to this noble woman, who has protected her virtue against such odds?

'Surrounded by these spiteful and lawless rakshasis, this great lady has been performing her own silent penance. May Dharma eternally guard such women!

'But was it Dharma that guarded her? Or the good deeds of Janaka? Or her own virtue inviolable? O chastity rare! An island of strange contrasts indeed! So much evil, and yet such goodness too.

Day and night I have seen gods slave here, and yet here is one steadfast in virtue despite enduring untold hardship!' Stormy thoughts assailed his mind as he watched, hidden from view by a leafy branch. Soon enough Ravana arrived to lay siege on Sita's chastity.

(Hanuman saw the lust-tormented rakshasa and thought to himself, 'Now I will see for myself what kind of man this Ravana is.' Reciting Rama's sacred name, he moved a little closer. Waving away the entourage of apsaras who had been waiting on him thus far, Ravana went to where Sita, that lamplight to womanhood, sat quivering like a young doe at the approach of a tiger. When with his own eyes he saw her trembling body and soul, even the last lingering doubts vanished. 'Long live Sita!' he thought, 'Long live Rama! Long live the vedas! Long live the brahmins! Long live

Dharma,' he prayed, fervently blessing her, whose name will grow from aeon to aeon.)

Meanwhile, Ravana began: 'Tell me, koel, when will you favour me with your grace?

'I, who haven't felt inferior even to Siva, have abased myself shamelessly before you. Today is gone, tomorrow will go, so you treat me from day to day. Do you intend joining me only after I die completely?

'O golden sprig, so cool and calm, you despise my wealth and fame. Even if your husband escapes alive and goes back to his city with you, what life can you hope for with him, a mere human?

'How is it, O Janaka's daughter, that you, so womanly, beautiful and firm, show not a jot of compassion or even its shadow, generosity?

'Lovely parrot, do you still hope to see him, whose piteous cry you heard when he died in the forest? Give up such vain hopes. Think of the present.

'When good fortune comes chasing you, is it wise to spurn it with contempt? Gods and goddesses of my vast empire will fall at your feet and be your slaves. Can there be greater foolishness than rejecting such felicities?

'Accept me, the ruler of the three worlds, as your slave,' he pleaded, falling at her feet, unmindful of the scandal and shame of such unmanly abasement.

Those words entered her ears like burning skewers and scorched them. Her heart curdled and her eyes spat blood. Goaded past endurance and reckless of consequences, she lashed out at him:

'Merest trash! Hear me out. The words that came out of your foul mouth are not fit to enter chaste ears,' she said angrily. 'Rama's arrows can rip apart the fourteen worlds. Do you want, you reckless fool, to have your ten heads broken and scattered?

'Coward that you are, you dared not face him. You sent a phantom stag, and using witchcraft, came before me disguised as a holy mendicant, when my lord was not there.

'If you wish to save your paltry life, desist. Soon you and

your kind are going to be confronted by your mortal enemy. Your ten heads and all your shoulders will provide a novel target for the great bowman's deadly arrows.

'You were almost defeated by a bird that day. But for the sword Siva gave you, you'd have been dead. Your penance and boons might ward off Yama's bolts but not Rama's arrows.

'The might you won from Brahma will be of little avail when Rama strings his mighty bow. Can darkness ever withstand light?

'You tried to lift a mountain once; but he who resides on it could with his toe crush you and get the better of you. His was the bow my husband's strength broke in two! Strange you didn't hear the thunderous clap of it snapping!

'You boast that you lifted a mountain and displaced the *diggajas*, the elephants of the quarters. The heads you dared not show Lakshmana, now fall at a woman's feet! Shame on them!

'O you fool! When my husband discovers this place you've hidden me in, will the sea and Lanka quench his wrath? You and your kin will shrivel before that towering rage and the entire world will die. This I swear by my virtue, I swear! I swear!

'Do not make the mistake of thinking these two are but men. Recall the fate of Kartavirya, tall as a hill, a terror to the world. He was vanquished by a man, and that victorious one was, in turn, quelled by the one who now is your foe.

'When Rama first entered the forest, distressed sages, including the great Agastya, beseeched him, "These rakshasas are not letting us do our penance in peace. Relieve us, Rama. You alone can do it." This I heard with my own ears.

'Since then he has decimated any number of your kith and kin. Remember Surpanakha's nose and the countless limbs of your horde of cousins?

'Lawless wretch, haven't you heard of how he disposed of that monkey king, who with a thousand hands had seized you and cut down your rock-like shoulders and immured you for long in prison?

'There seems to be no one here to tell you "This is right and that is wrong." In doing what you please, you bring on yourself nothing but destruction and chaos.'

As her long tirade concluded, the rakshasa's twenty eyes blazed and his ten mouths roared like belching mountains. For that instant, wrath vanquished love.

His huge shoulders heaved, eclipsing the four quarters. Eyes darting fire, he told himself, 'I'll tear and eat her up!' As rage and love battled each other, he stepped forward, urged by rage, then stepped backward, conquered by love.

Hanuman, who was watching tensely, said to himself, 'Before this wretch lays his hands on this maiden, chaste as Arundhati, I'll trample on his ten heads, knock him down, plunge Lanka into the sea, and carry that ascetic away on my back.'

Doused by the sea of his love for her, Ravana's rage, fierce as the final fire that would burn the world to cinders, abated after a while.

'I said in my wrath that I would kill you, but I won't. There is some truth in what you said, but listen to me now. There is nothing in this world that I cannot do, if I set my mind to it. My triumphs and defeats in the past were mere sport.

'If on that day, I'd killed the one you deem *your* very life, you too would have died in grief. With you gone, how could I have carried on living? This was what drove me to deception.

'When those two men, who went pursuing the phantom stag you had set you heart upon, learn who it was that took you away, they'll dare not come looking for you.

'Was there even a single god in all the three worlds who, knowing that it was I, their chief, who had spirited you away, did not run away in panic?

'As for the men you speak of with such awe, how can I, who have emerged victor in wars with the Trinity and lesser gods, ever disgrace myself by fighting weaklings given to penance? No, I cannot bring myself to be really angry with those small creatures, mere men with their puny might and small ambitions.

'No, I'll not kill them. Instead, I'll capture them alive and bring them here, as my slaves for your eyes to feast upon.'

Rage suppressed, he looked at his sword and warned grimly, 'I give you two more months to decide. Comply, and you shall live. If not, you die.'

Then, turning to the rakshasi guards, he screamed, 'Through threat or tact, make her see sense and inform me soon of her change of heart. If you fail, every one of you will die.'

So saying, he left. Vengeful rakshasis swooped on Sita, their dark bodies obscuring her, the way Rahu swallows the pure white moon. In frustrated frenzy, they screamed at her, decibels rising.

'Kill her! Kill her!' said one. 'Cut her and gobble her up,' said another. 'The great-grandson of Brahma, no less, well-versed in the thousand branches of the vedas, the wise one who has conquered Fate, has offered you his love. And you dare spurn it!

'Senseless woman, you are like the fool who sets fire to both the house she was born in, and the one she was bequeathed to. You shall die this instant.'

Through all this shouting and screaming, Sita remained calm, recalling the tyrant's last words. 'They dare not touch me now for at least two months,' she thought with relief.

Trijata, who had watched everything quietly till then, spoke up, 'Don't you grieve over all this. Remember my dream and take heart.'

HANUMAN REVEALS HIMSELF

'This is the time to reveal myself, but these fearsome guards are still awake. They are not going to nod off right now just to please me,' mused Hanuman. So he cast a spell that sent them into a deep trance.

Sita, surprised, saw them asleep as never before. Unable to bear her great sorrow, not seeing any way out, she gave vent to her desperate feelings.

'Will he, who resembles the rain cloud, ever come and restore my life? Will I ever again hear the twang of his mighty bow? Tell me O hard and cruel Fate!

'O fragrant winds that so torment me! You have long known that valiant hero. Don't you know how my soul suffers? Can't you tell him how and where I am?

'A thousand pains I've endured only because of my love and faith in you. But, you, Rama, ever self-sufficient, have never known dependency.

'When at your father's command you left for the forest, and I, unable to bear the very thought of life without you, insisted on going with you, you found it in yourself to tell me, "Stay behind. I'll soon be back." Fourteen long years seemed "soon" for you.

'Is it not folly for me to hope, seeing how heartless you are, seeing how you killed the deathless king by doing his unjust bidding, that you will now come to rescue me?

'All my life I have had to deal with troubles and worries in plenty. Death alone can free me from suffering. I've been keeping this wretched life intact in the hope I shall once again see my lord some day. But will he, the purest of the pure, touch me or take me back since I am one who has lived in the land of rakshasas?

'How worthy am I of my birth and breeding that I carry this blot and continue to live? Will this world ever forgive me the fact that it was I who sent my husband after that false stag? And followed up that blunder by berating my brother-in-law and forcing him to follow Rama?

'Those heroes will wipe out the slur cast on their valour by fighting a war with the rakshasas. They might win or lose. But how will I bear the shame of having lived in Lanka in captivity, my chastity forever suspect?

'Should that day ever come when Rama, having destroyed the entire rakshasa race, sets me free from this prison and then says, "You are now unfit to be my wife", what then?

'So,' she concluded, 'the right thing to do is to die. Thanks to my good deeds in my previous birth, those who would have stopped me from ending my life are now fast asleep. No time can be better than this very moment.'

(She moved to the foot of a madhavi tree. Hanuman, who had been observing her watchfully, rightly guessed her intent. Trembling

*at the thought of touching her body even to save her, he made his
presence known. 'Here I am Rama's messenger,' he announced and
appeared before her, bowing low.)*

'Here I am, at Rama's command,' he repeated. 'Countless
others are scouring the world for you. The result of my
penances, O mother, has brought me to your tender feet.

'That hero, sunk in grief, doesn't know you are here.
The fact that the rakshasa race still survives, root and branch
intact, is proof of that.'

Looking at his prostrate form, startled Sita, her heart
aflutter, thought, 'Surely, this is no rakshasa. This is a person
who seems steeped in virtue.

'Whoever he is, demon, god or monkey, and whatever
his purpose, mischief or compassion, he has spoken my lord's
name and thus given me life. Can one ask for more?'

She looked hard at him. 'My heart melts. His words are
not those of a crook with a deceitful heart. The tears from his
eyes soak the earth.' Finally, she asked him, 'Fearless one,
who are you?'

His fair hands at those hushed words he carried to his
head and said, 'Mother! Distracted beyond belief after he lost
you, Rama searched for your high and low. By happenstance,
he befriended Sugriva, chief of the monkeys, son of the Sun.

'His elder brother was Vali, who once tied up the mighty
Ravana with his tail, gleefully leaping by turn in all the eight
directions. His might was such that when the gods sought
his help for churning the sea of nectar, he caught hold of
serpent Vasuki, who proved too large to be used as a rope,
and thinned its girth with his own bare hands.

'It is this Vali that your lord killed with a single shot from
his mighty bow. He then gave the kingdom to Sugriva, his
ally and friend. I, a mere dog, am counsellor to the monkey-
king. Son of the wind am I, and Hanuman is my name.

'Seventy brigades of monkeys, strong enough to lift the
whole world, powerful enough to leap across the seven seas,
are at the service of valiant Rama, waiting for him to but
whisper his orders.

'They have scattered in all directions to look for you—in the seven isles and the seven seas, in the netherworld of the Nagas, in the heavens above, and if all else failed, in the worlds beyond those known—all within the time ascribed.

'I gave your lord the jewels you flung on our hill the day the vile demon carried you off. He advised me to head southward to look for you.

'How can I ever hope to describe the change in his noble visage when I showed him those jewels? Indeed, he looked as if his very life had been saved. Haven't those jewels you once discarded ensured that you can wear them now and forever?

'But let me complete the story. Vali's son, Angada, who commands the southern brigade, sent me to Lanka to continue with the search. And that's how I came to be here,' he concluded.

On hearing this, joy exploded in her wan face and her distressed body and mind bloomed. 'Fate, inexorable as ever, has been kind to me and given me once more a reason to live,' she thought. Eyes streaming, she said 'Tell me, son, how he is faring?'

'There are no words to describe his state. No comparison is adequate, but I'll try to tell you how he looked when I last saw him.'

The words that followed could only have come from one in whose heart the lord resides. His account made Sita almost faint with recalled joy.

'O lady with the gait of a peacock!' he began, 'There are things your dear lord asked me to tell you, if I ever managed to locate your whereabouts.

"Remind her," he commanded me, "of what transpired when I asked her to stay behind and look after my mothers, assuring her that I shall soon be back. 'The forest tracks are hard to tread,' I told her. To which, eyes blazing, she responded by getting ready to leave with me that very instant, clad in the very clothes she was wearing.

"Remind her too of how she sent word to her sisters-in-law through Sumantra, that with Rama beside her, she had no regrets about leaving Ayodhya. Her only sorrow was that she would no longer have her parrots and mynahs with her. Would they kindly look after them for her? she had requested, revealing thus her childlike heart.

"Do not waste time with words", he said, "show her this rare ring on which is carved my name." ' Hanuman opened his palm to reveal a ring that shone bright as the sun.

How can I begin to describe bright-browed Sita's feelings? As those of a dead man come alive? Or, of one dead, stumbling upon the fruits of his lost life? Were they perhaps akin to the emotions of an amnesiac who suddenly regains his memory?

Maybe the joy of a snake finding again its lost gem or of a man getting back a treasure presumed lost, would be more appropriate? Or is it that she felt the unbounded happiness of a barren woman, who finds herself miraculously big with child?

Maybe, the delirium of a blind man regaining sight? Not having experienced any such thrill first-hand, I can do no justice to this moving scene.

She took the ring; placed it first on her breast, then her head and finally her tender eyelids. Like the moon she waxed and waned, joy and sorrow alternating, refreshed one moment, breathing hot sighs of yearning the next.

She breathed deeply of its scent, rubbed it on her breast, wiped her tears and took her fill of it, her eyes staring at it a long while before once again they filled with tears. Swelling with joy, she swallowed hard.

Teeth flashing like pearls, tears from her eyes drenching her breasts, soft voice stuttering, she spoke at last, 'O wonderful man! You've given my life back to me.'

'O auspicious messenger of good tidings, your great deed has given me life. How can I ever repay you? O father and mother! Abode of grace! You have given me heaven right here on earth.

'O heap of virtue! Where are Rama and Lakshmana now? How did he get to know you? And from whom did he get news of me?'

Hanuman dutifully recounted the incidents of the days past. 'On orders from wicked Ravana, Maricha, the deceitful rakshasa, disguised himself as a golden deer and appeared before you. Guileless lady! Urged by both fate and heart, you forced Rama to chase a phantom.

'After a long and futile pursuit, angry Rama shot him down. Even as he was dying, the wily demon raised a piteous cry in Rama's voice that completely deceived you.

"This cry will breed much mischief. I hope my brother doesn't hear it," prayed Rama. But Fate had willed otherwise. Bow in hand and fear in his heart, he ran back towards the hut. Halfway back, he saw Sumitra's son. On his face he read disaster. From his mouth he heard the rest, and both rushed to the hut. Not finding you there, Rama all but died.

'From that moment, mother, your lifeless husband searched for you everywhere. In the deep forests, the broad rivers and steep hills—there wasn't a place he did not look.

'And then he met Jatayu, the eagle-king, who told him of his encounter with Ravana. Hearing the story, Rama's anger blazed like the fire at Dissolution.

'But now I've finally found you! God bless you. My lord is well. And you are alive. With you here and him in the forests, it is as if you are one life rent in two.'

When Rama's humble servant related all this, her heart ached for the harrowing pain Rama had endured because of her. Her bones melted, but even so, despite the monumental grief, her heart rejoiced in having miraculously found what it had thought as forever lost.

Mired in tears of joy and sorrow she had shed, yet eager for more news, she asked, 'Tell me now, happy warrior, how did you cross the endless sea and find me here?'

'In the same manner as those who cross the great ocean of delusion, O mother. By meditating on the golden feet of your lord.'

'Small and slight as you are, I find it impossible to believe that you crossed that enormous sea,' she said, her smile outshining the moon in the sky. 'Was it through some remarkable penance?'

Then, unbelievingly, she saw him grow before her eyes. Palms folded, shoulders shooting higher and higher, head bent as though he was afraid it might hit the sky, he grew taller and taller. 'Where indeed does supreme might reside? In the guardians of the five elements or in the body of the great Hanuman?' Sita thought in wonderment.

The hair on his person, now dotted with stars, sparkled as if he were Mount Meru covered with glow-worms. Sita could not even see his two feet. 'Dead are the rakshasas,' she rejoiced. 'You frighten me. Please shrink back to your old size.'

And head still in the clouds, Hanuman said, 'As you wish, mother,' and assumed a smaller form. Said Sita admiringly, 'O you, swift and fierce as the wind, who have dug up hills and dragged with one hand the divine Adisesha himself, walking over the sea is nothing to you. Why talk of leaping over it?

'Looking at the number of rakshasas Rama would have to vanquish, I was so worried that he had none but his brother to help him. But now, I fear no more. I feel I have regained the life I had deemed lost. What can these rakshasas do to my husband with you beside him?'

Bowing to her, Hanuman said, 'O Arundhati! Mighty chieftains, impossible to count like the grains of sand that layer the shore, are Rama's slaves. I am but a slave of one such slave, only following orders.'

THE CREST JEWEL.

'Is there, O lord, another like her?' wondered Hanuman to himself, 'Lakshmi herself in deepest distress. The thing to do is to carry her off to the lord of all worlds!'

'Mother, please listen to me,' he said. 'What is most important now is that the demon should not kill you. So, I shall at once take you to Rama.

'O golden creeper, give up your sorrow and lay you head on my shoulder. I'll carry you away in a trice to the hill where Rama now waits for news of you, not even stopping to rest along the way.

'Now that I have seen for myself your desperate state, I won't reach Rama empty-handed. Should the rakshasas dare pursue us, I, the invincible one, will finish them off and thus quench my rage.

'Should you ask me, "Will you uproot Lanka itself to rescue me from this prison?" that too I will accomplish with ease, lifting this tiny island with one hand, while pulverizing the foes with the other. This, mother, will require no effort.

'Tell me, O chaste one, were I to return to Rama and tell him, "Your ambrosial wife is in prison, and in great distress with no prospect ever of getting out," will it be becoming of a servant?

'With my shoulders bearing not a scratch and no sign of battle fought, would it befit me to tell him, "Lord, obsessed with thoughts of my own safety, I didn't wish to risk bringing her back?"

'If instead, you wish that I should burn Lanka, kill Ravana, extinguish the rakshasa clan entire and depart in peace, that too I shall do with pleasure.'

To him who stood in front of her, seeming the very soul of docility like a calf before its mother, and yet speaking these defiant words, Sita said in a choked voice, 'Nothing is beyond you, my child. You think only of what you can achieve. But ignorance and a woman's fear make me think thoughts that would never cross your mind.

'When those men set upon you and target you with their arrows, you will find it hard to fight those creatures, intent as you will be on protecting my life. We'll both perish.

'There's another reason why I will have to refuse your gallant offer. Should I consent to what you're proposing, will not my lord's victorious bow get tarnished for ever and ever? How can you, son, think of such a theft of glory? Wouldn't it be like a dog running away with a feast meant for the gods?

'If I had so wished, I could have burnt to cinders Lanka and the whole world with a deadly curse from my angry tongue. I have refrained, only to ensure that the reputation of my Rama's bow remains untarnished.

'Listen, my son, there's one other thing too. You have no doubt conquered your five senses, but you too are male. How can I touch the body of any man except my husband?

'Had that wicked wretch that carried me touched my person, would he have been alive today? He must have known the consequences of such an act. Which is why he dug out the very earth upon which I stood to abduct me.

'Then there's Brahma's curse which protected me. It is said that should the rakshasa king ever violate an unwilling woman, his heads will split and scatter to the far corners of the earth. It is this that has saved my life.

'What you suggest is therefore unthinkable. The best thing would be for you to return to my lord, and tell him all,' she said finally. Convinced by her unimpeachable arguments, the faultless one agreed with her.

'Gracious mother!' said he, bowing low, 'this world that is now darkened by wicked Ravana will soon be rid of him, do not fear. I will go to Rama at once. In the meantime, you must keep alive your spirits. But tell me what message I should convey to my lord in the throes of depression.'

'Keep this one thing in mind, just this one, and tell him exactly what I tell you now: "I shall live for no more than a month." This I swear by him.

'Since my penance will end in a month, if my lord cannot come here by then, ask him to offer obsequies for me in the pure waters of the holy Ganga.

'Tell him humbly that if even the one wife he acquired, by the strength of his mighty bow-breaking arms, is not worthy of rescue, and even if mercy finds no place in his heart, his valorous reputation at least deserves to be vindicated.

'Tell him that I humbly pray that even if I should die in this place, he should bless me with a boon, absolving me of any sin I may have committed in this life, and enable me once more to clasp his hands in my next.

'To see him seated on a burnished throne or riding an elephant, its bells jingling against the backdrop of a noisy crowd of cheering citizens, I, alas, seem not destined.'

Distressed beyond words, Hanuman gently chided her, 'Are you determined to die here? Do you really think that your lord will go back to Ayodhya without you and get crowned king? Indeed! Indeed!

'And do you really think that the one who immured you, so chaste and pure, in this vile and disgusting prison, will get away with it and live in peace, while those two great bowmen slink away? Could anything be more absurd?

'O mother, do you really think that he who swore, even before any of this happened, to kill all rakshasas would suddenly turn a meek sadhu?

'Never quick to anger, but impossible to quench if roused, will his wrath now be doused with anything less than the blood of the vile rakshasas?

'Please bear with your sorrow for a little while more. When Rama hears the good news I am carrying with me, he and the monkey-king will be struck dumb with joy. Upon recovering, they will stir into action. Huge monkeys will bridge the deep sea, and when you hear the noise they make, your heart will be filled with happiness.

'If he doesn't rescue you by the date you have set, he will thenceforth be called Ravana, not Rama, for that sinful lapse and dereliction of duty.'

These reassuring words made Sita's heart leap with joy. Immediately, she directed, 'Great one, get back quickly and may you triumph over all obstacles.

'To convince him that it is indeed me you saw, here are snatches of memories of some shared moments for you to report. They will bring as much joy to him as they have to me.

'Here is an incident that even Lakshmana does not know of. On one occasion, Indra's son, driven by lust, came in the form of a crow and tried to peck at my breast. Angered by this audacious deed, Rama pulled out a blade of grass and sent it after him.

'The frightened crow fled for its life, seeking shelter in all directions. Pursued by that missile, it went first to Brahma and then to Siva, but to no avail. Advised that his refuge could be none but Rama, he came back and fell at his feet.

He forgave him, but his straw-arrow took its token reward in one eye. And that's how all crows came to be squint-eyed.

'Remind him of the day I asked him to suggest a name for my new pet. He said, half teasing, 'Call the parrot Kaikeyi!''

She then unknotted from her garment's end, a jewel that outshone all the lights on heaven and earth combined. Its blinding lustre swallowed all the darkness around them.

It was like the sun on a rack of rain clouds and the delicate pink of her own flawless skin. Almost blinded by its rare effulgence, one began to wonder whether the banned sun had dared to enter the great city. The lotus and the *chakravaha* rejoiced, their hearts open wide. Sunstones shimmered.

'You sought me out and gave me life. This crest-jewel, my dearest possession, long hid in my sari, I give you now as the supreme token,' she said.

He took it and wrapped it carefully in a piece of cloth to prevent loss or damage. Bowing low and weeping a bit, he went around her thrice. And she, the eternal mother, fondly blessed him.

THE GROVE DESTROYED

Prepared to make his way northwards, Hanuman quietly got ready to leave the grove. Not content with the minor triumph of having found Sita, he pondered on something more striking to accomplish.

'What sort of a servant will I be if I don't kill these vermin, throw Lanka into the deep sea, and place that doe at Rama's feet?

'Let me at least destroy this grove. The rakshasas will be roused to fury and attack; that'll give me the chance to match my strength against theirs and destroy them once and for all.'

With this thought, he quickly assumed a form as forbidding as the great boar that hefted the world. He then started crushing the plants in that well-guarded grove under his enormous feet.

Trees collapsed, bent and broken, twisted out of shape. Burnt and scorched, they shattered to bits and scattered in every direction.

Some were dug up and thrown into the wind. Others flew up to heaven, bees and all, causing considerable damage to the gardens of the gods.

The countless trees that Hanuman in his fury had flung into the sky, made it look as though the great Ravana had planted a new grove in the sky! The sandalwood trees he had kicked up caught fire and burned as if they were mere firewood, much to the distress of the god of love.

Trees flung about by Hanuman demolished elephant sheds, stables and chariot houses. The rakshasi guards, awoken rudely, stared frightened at the apparition that stood before them like a mountain. For once respectful, they asked Sita, 'O lady, who is this? Do you know anything about him?'

'How should I know?' she replied, smiling. 'This could be one of your own tricks. Only the wicked understand the deeds of the wicked. How can the good know of your evil ways?

'When I saw that stag, Lakshmana warned me. "This is only rakshasa witchcraft," he said. But deluded fool that I was, I took it for real. For all I know, this one too is one of your creations.'

The terrified rakshasis began to beat their stomachs and breasts, howling loud enough to frighten the earth, the sky and the sea.

In red-hot fury, Hanuman uprooted a shrine tall enough to shame even Mount Meru, and hurled it with all his might at the city of Lanka. Immediately, the houses that reached up to skim the heavens crumbled or caught fire, burning entire neighbourhoods down to ash.

The gods of the seasons guarding that grove deserted their posts in utter panic and rushed to Ravana, their screams renting the air.

Falling at his feet, they said, 'O lord of the universe, a monkey with shoulders huge as the hills, is tearing up and flinging in all directions the trees in the grove we've been guarding with zealous love and care.

'There are no words to describe the havoc wrought by this monkey. It has demolished the entire grove, leaving not a blade of grass untouched. It has uprooted the shrine of gold and flung it high in the sky, destroying a good portion of divine Lanka.'

'A single monkey?' Ravana exclaimed in utter disbelief. His temper on the simmer, he said, 'Trees uprooted and groves destroyed, the well-guarded Chaitya shrine pulled out and hurled, leaving half of Lanka devastated! Shame on you! Even fools dare not carry such tales to me.'

But the gods persisted with their story, 'O king, no ordinary monkey this, please believe us. If one were to assume he was one among the holy Trinity, worshipped by the gods themselves, it might well be no exaggeration.'

Even as Ravana was mulling over this stunning piece of news, he heard a roar that made one wonder whether the cosmos itself had exploded.

THE KINKARAS KILLED

Was it thunder battering a mountain or was Dissolution upon them? Like the echo of the deafening clap made by Siva's bow when it was broken, Hanuman's mighty yell entered Ravana's twenty ears and reverberated in those ten heads adorned with gem-set crowns.

With a smile, and not without some envy, he called for his brigade of kinkaras, 'Do not allow him to escape. Capture him alive and bring him to me.'

With bodies black as hell, carrying countless weapons—tridents, swords, clubs, spears, javelins, cudgels and other deadly missiles, they sped as if they were the sea unleashed.

For them, news of war was sweeter to the ear than honey on the tongue. In battle attire, they were Yama's messengers in the flesh. Proud of their proven prowess in war, they felt aggrieved at being pitted against a herb-eating monkey. But Ravana's orders couldn't be slighted.

'A mere monkey, it would seem, has destroyed our

grove and pulled out the *Chaitya*. Could there be a worse shame?' they roared in wrath.

The sun, upon sighting these fearsome creatures, had already fled in fright. And Hanuman stood as exposed to the enemies as the heaven-kissing Himalayas.

The noise made by the horns, conches and drums of the enemy horde were deafening as monsoon thunder. 'Here he is! Here he is! Here he is! Let's destroy him!' they chanted, rushing forth to seize the wind god's son.

He saw them hurl their deadly missiles and looked around for an appropriate weapon to counter the attack. His eyes fell upon a tall tree, helpfully lying where he had flung it. Welcoming it as a friend in need, he picked it up and smashed it into the rushing hordes.

Shoulders streaming blood like waterfalls on a hill, they scattered in confusion, heads broken and rolling. Others, hands and feet plucked off, lay on the ground in inert mounds. Tying them up with his tail, he whirled it around fast and furious, and let go.

As if out of pity for their loved ones, he tossed away a few kinkaras he had captured, saying, 'Go forth and live in peace.' He even advised some of them to make up their lovers' tiffs!

The wounds inflicted on the shoulders of this brave soldier by the arrows and spears of his enemies were beyond count. Equally innumerable were the kinkaras he had slain that day.

The guards who had watched the proceedings with dismay ran to tell Ravana about the rout of his kinkara army.

Made incoherent by fear and shame, their account of the battle made no sense. But their faces narrated the story their tongues dared not put into words.

Breathing fire and contempt, Ravana asked in mounting fury, 'Did they disobey my orders? Did they die fighting or did they run away, afraid to engage an ape in battle?'

A little angry themselves, they replied, 'O king, they neither disobeyed your orders nor fled the battlefield like cowards. Attacked by a fierce monkey, they perished like the kin of those bearing false witness.'

Ashamed to hear news that diminished him before the gods and not quite able to believe it, he asked incredulously, 'This story you tell me—is it mere hearsay or did you see it with your own eyes?'

'O king, please understand. We stood there and watched the battle with our own eyes. That monkey killed the entire army, wielding but a tree as his weapon. He's still at the spot, roaring defiantly.'

JAMBUMALI KILLED

Ravana then turned to Jambumali standing close, hands clasped in reverence, and said, 'I am putting a troop of horses at your command. Subdue this monkey and bring it to me at the end of a string. That alone can assuage the fire in my anguished heart.'

Jambumali bowed, 'What greater honour than being preferred over countless other rakshasas to fulfil this task?' Eager to prove his mettle, he left, vowing vengeance. With his own army, further strengthened by the might of the troops sent by his father, he went in search of the monkey.

At the head of the formidable force were elephants trumpeting like thunder. Following them were huge chariots with wheels like clouds, horses that flew as if the wind god had been imprisoned in their four legs, and a cavalry of men eager for fight, waiting for just a word from their commander. They bore sharp-edged weapons such as javelins and swords, blunt clubs to deal deadly blows, bright missiles like thunderbolts, burning discuses, bows and arrows, not to mention some more unusual ones like iron staves, nooses and trees. It seemed as if Lanka's entire arsenal had been emptied, to aid the capture of the monkey.

Rama's messenger awaited their arrival at the grove, wondering what was taking them so long. He let out another mighty roar that scattered the clouds and silenced the sea, planted terror in the hearts of the demons and made even gods shiver in fright.

They came then, stumbling over the corpses of their kin, attacking from three sides as directed by Jambumali. He himself was in the lead, galloping ahead on a chariot. Seeing that his wishes were about to come true, Hanuman, who had been waiting at the gate, felt his shoulders swell at the prospect of further success.

He, a one-man army, then made four divisions of his body: his forehead was his chariot, his powerful arms that bristled with hair and his nails, keener than the enemy's sharpest spear, were his right and left flanks, while his sacred buttocks were the troops he held in reserve!

Then began the great fight. The rakshasas, in a frenzy of wrath, let fly thick and fast deadly weapons, bright as the sun's rays. Hanuman seized them with his bare hands, broke them into bits, kneaded them into small balls and threw them into the sea. With his left hand, he destroyed the weapons flung at him, and with his right, killed elephants, broke chariots and knocked down horses.

Those who came up against his might fainted in fear; then rising from their swoon, dazed and confused, they fought him and lost their lives. Those who managed to survive, fled.

Like a king's sceptre, a sage's mind, unbound by deeds good or bad, marauding Hanuman went wherever he wished and found no barrier. As God's servant, enabled by the power of the Almighty, he seemed omnipresent: on earth, in the sky, permeating the eight directions and the eyes and minds of his enemies.

His hordes summarily dispatched to heaven, Jambumali, stood like a second Yama, all alone, eyes shedding fire. And Hanuman, wounded all over, was aglow, a glittering tree in flower. To Jambumali he now spoke, 'You have but a single weapon and a single chariot. It is not proper to kill a person thus enfeebled. So go away.'

'How kind of you,' sneered Jambumali. 'So you think you can kill me?' From his bow, hard as diamond, he shot his arrows, one, ten, hundred and, finally, hundred thousands of them.

Laughing, Hanuman said contemptuously, 'Well, well! With a bow in hand, it shouldn't be difficult to overcome an unarmed monkey.' Pulling out a pillar, he scattered all the arrows Jambumali shot at him.

After a while, tiring of games, Hanuman leapt at Jambumali's chariot, seized his bow and slinging it around the rakshasa's neck, sliced off his head. The demon crumbled to the ground like a felled mountain.

Having witnessed the fall of Jambumali, the guards ran once again to Ravana, terrified of what they had seen with their own eyes, but also fearing the reaction of the king of Lanka when he heard their story.

Upon entering that imposing palace, they stood around, gaping. Unable to utter a word, they could only sob. Ravana encouraged them to speak up. 'Don't be afraid. Tell me what happened.' 'Lord,' they replied trembling, 'All our men are dead, including Jambumali. O what a monkey!'

When Ravana heard this, he rose, letting out a bloodcurdling yell. Eyes shooting blood, he said, 'I will myself catch that vaunted monkey!' At this, his five army chiefs spoke up.

THE FIVE ARMY CHIEFS KILLED

'Should you, O mighty king, undertake to fight with a monkey, wouldn't it be like pitting Garuda against a mosquito? Wouldn't it make Kailasa, that silvery mountain, lose its fear of you?

'Would not the Trinity, who tremble at your very name, who have never dared to fight you until now, curl their lips in a contemptuous smile?

'You have so far sent weaklings who proved themselves unfit even for this trivial job. And now, if you choose to go yourself, it will look as though you've no reliable men around you. Send us instead and we shall return victorious.'

Ravana readily consented. A huge army, vast as the foaming sea, now set forth to conquer the lord's messenger. Fifty thousand chariots drawn by the same number of elephants, twice that many horses and four times that many men, set off down the streets of Lanka, leaving the awestruck citizens gaping in amazement.

The gods who had been witnessing the carnage from their abode in the skies and cheering the son of Vayu, now drowned in a sea of sorrow, fearing the rout of that doughty hero. But Hanuman, unmoved, pledged solemnly, 'These rakshasas too shall die today.'

Standing atop the gateway, bright Vayu's son inflated himself even beyond the skies. Though wonder-struck by this transformation in front of their stunned eyes, the rakshasas sent a shower of arrows to the accompaniment of the beating of kettledrums.

Resenting their arrogance, Hanuman seized an iron post near at hand and flung it at the oncoming missiles and smashed them to bits. Turning to tackle the elephants and horses, he pulled the tusks off the tuskers and used them as implements to break the chariots and kill the horses and soldiers.

And so, this unequal battle, too long to describe here, dragged on interminably, as Hanuman spread death and destruction all round. Finally, he confronted the chiefs— treacherous, thieving rakshasas who had trodden lawless roads all their lives—and killed all five of them.

Fearing that the monkey might kill them too, the guards, messengers of doom, ran to Ravana and gave him the news that scorched his ears 'The army, lord, is finished. We alone escaped, because we did not fight him. With none left to fight now, the monkey is taking his ease.'

AKSHA KUMAR KILLED

Ravana heard them out in rage. Once again, he announced that he would go to the battlefield himself, but Aksha Kumar, his valorous son, fell at his feet and said, 'Let me go instead, Father.'

'This is not the bull ridden by the one with three eyes. Nor the bird, flown by the one who measured the three worlds. Nor is it the snake on which he rests. Why would you want to wage a war with a mean monkey?

'I have already been feeling aggrieved that you sent my brother before me. My hurt feelings will be assuaged somewhat, if you, the one who has conquered the eight quarters, dispatch me now to catch this thing, a forward monkey though it be.

'Even if it is the lidless three-eyed one who has taken the form of a herb-eating monkey, just to shame us in front of the rest of the world, I promise you I'll catch him in a trice and haul him up before you.'

Ravana, looking well-pleased at these words from his valorous son, said, 'Well spoken, my son. Take a swift-horsed chariot and go.' The young hero ascended Indra's chariot drawn by 200 horses, a trophy he had won at war with the king of the devas, and led his army to vanquish the enemy.

Hanuman watched with interest the arrival of this new force being led by a garlanded hero, and wondered, 'Is this Indrajit himself?' Both annoyed and delighted at the prospect of war with Ravana's most illustrious son, he told himself, 'Whoever he is, he has come to fulfil my wishes.'

With Rama's name on his lips, he moved forward to confront the prince. Seeing him, Aksha Kumar burst into derisive laughter and flashed his fangs! 'Is this the paltry thing that destroyed the rakshasa horde?'

The forces surrounded Hanuman, showering upon him a torrent of weapons. The guardians of the quarters broke into a sweat but Hanuman remained his usual tranquil self.

All the missiles discharged by the demons met his rocklike body and were broken. The elephants were killed, the chariots and horses destroyed. The souls of innumerable rakshasas left their bodies.

Then Hanuman engaged Aksha Kumar in single combat. Fourteen arrows the demon shot, all of which were nullified by the monkey. Then the rakshasa shattered Hanuman's club by raining arrows on him. Upon which, the latter leapt on to the rakshasa's chariot, his bare hands his only weapon.

He killed the charioteer with a slash of his hand. The horses met the same fate. The arrows that Aksha shot struck on his chest but he seized the rakshasa's bow with one hand. In the ensuing tug of war the bow broke and the young rakshasa seized his scimitar, and went for Maruti's chest.

Nothing daunted, the great messenger grabbed the new weapon and reduced it to dust.

His weapons gone, Aksha decided to wrestle with Hanuman and caught him in a fierce grip. But the spiky hair on Hanuman's body pierced Aksha's body like a million needles.

Then, binding him with his long tail, Hanuman slapped his cheek so hard that his teeth and the gems from his earrings fell to the ground. He then pummelled the demon till his entrails dropped.

With the blood of the rakshasa for water, the ground for grindstone, his bones for pestle, Hanuman ground his flesh and entrails to a pulp.

Upon hearing of the gory death of her son, Maya's daughter, Mandodhari, came running to the spot. Her eyes filled with tears and her cloud-dark tresses sweeping the ground, she fell on the remains of his body.

THE NOOSE

When the hero who had won his name by his victory over Indra, heard of the death of his brother, he rose in anguish. Heart afire, eyes blazing, he ascended a towering chariot drawn by 1,200 demons and proceeded to his father's palace.

His eyes streaming for his brother, he examined derisively the useless bow in his hand, and said, 'Have the antics of a nomad monkey killed my brother or is it my father's fame that has been destroyed?'

Lamenting long and loud his brothers' death, he fell at his father's feet. Valorous Ravana raised him up by his shoulders and embraced him, sobbing. Then Indrajit, formidable as Death, had his say.

'You never, O king, think of what is right. You take all the wrong steps, get hurt and then lament. Knowing well that this monkey's might was nothing ordinary, you sent rows and rows of men to fight him. It is you, therefore, who have decimated the rakshasa clan.

'If, dear father, not one kinkara escaped alive, and dead are Jambumali, those five strong army chiefs and almost the entire Lankan army, is it not evident that this monkey surpasses the might of Siva, Brahma and Vishnu?

'You defeated the *diggajas*, conquered Siva's Kailasa and the three worlds. And yet you let this monkey show his strength by killing Aksha. If now you say "Let us go and capture him," what else is this but senseless prattle?

'Even so, father, I shall myself catch this monkey in a trice. You will know no further sorrow. Long may you live!' So saying, he departed, to complete a task none had yet accomplished.

Hanuman, flush with triumph, stood majestic as Siva preparing to burn the three worlds, when Indrajit's chariot came into his range of vision, the prince looking like the sun god himself.

'This must be the legendary Indrajit, the one who vanquished Indra. Provoked by my exploits with his kin and countrymen, he has now come himself. *This* will be the decisive battle.'

Then began the battle to end all battles, or so it seemed. In a huge rush, rakshasas, elephants, chariots, horses and all, bore down upon Hanuman. Enraged, Hanuman picked up a *sala* tree to counter the attack.

The fiery shafts that Indrajit shot at Hanuman, by now thoroughly incensed, were burnt and reduced to ashes, even as Ravana's son watched laughing and the gods watched bewildered.

Then there came a stage in the battle when chariots, elephants, horses and men were scattered away and he alone, the hero of heroes, was face to face with Hanuman. Amused yet angry, 'Come on, come on,' he said, inciting Rama's devotee.

He twanged his terrible bow, making Indra cower in remembered horror, frightening the clouds in heaven and causing even Sesha's many heads to twitch.

Unafraid, that doughty messenger slapped his enormous shoulders, making a noise that split the universe and snapped the string of Indrajit's bow.

'Marvellous! There is none in this world to equal you,'

said Indrajit admiringly. 'All the same, this day will be your last on earth!'

'On the contrary, it is *your* time that has come,' Hanuman responded. 'This is the end of your cruelties, the end of your weapons. I carry the message of your demise on my endless shoulders.'

'I will shatter once and for all this arrogance,' Indrajit thought, letting go a flurry of shafts, aiming for his head and chest. The hero, who had inflated himself once again, stretched his long hands and plucked the arrows out of the air. He then returned them to the one who had dispatched them.

He smashed Indrajit's chariot, finishing off the charioteer and those yoked demons. Swift as the whirlwind of Dissolution, doughty Indrajit leapt onto another chariot ready at hand and blanked out the body of Hanuman with numerous arrows, each as terrible as Narayana's discus.

Shaking them off as if they were mere blades of grass, victorious Maruti jumped on the new chariot. He then caught in his powerful hand the bow that in the past had won many a battle and broke it into two.

Before that noise ceased, Indrajit, his rage mounting, took another bow which he had won from Indra and shot from it arrows, over a hundred at a time. Wounded all over, Hanuman paused awhile, though only for a few brief moments.

The gods who had been cheering him were now in anguish. On seeing their sorrowing faces, Hanuman seized a huge tree, and running it over his body, got rid of all the shafts. He then struck at Indrajit's gem-decked crown.

With blood pouring from his head like a waterfall, Indrajit stood stunned, but not for long. Grinding his teeth, he once again dispatched a thousand deadly arrows in quick succession, making it seem like one endless shaft.

Disgusted and angered, Maruti, speeding faster than an arrow from Rama's bow, seized the chariot that carried Indrajit and flung it into the sky. In the twinkling of an eye, the powerful Indrajit hit the ceiling of the world. Blood streaming, flesh torn, he crashed to the ground like a felled tree.

Left without a chariot, powerless to fight, having wandered the air, Indrajit was greatly enraged and perplexed. It was then that he decided to use Brahmastra, the king among weapons.

Making a symbolic offering of flowers and incense, he took in his hand the weapon sacred to the creator himself. That invincible missile he aimed at the shoulder of Maruti, letting go with a resounding twang.

As the world itself shook, that terrible, irresistible astra took the form of the king of serpents. Eyes belching fire in a way that would have frightened Garuda himself, it twined itself round Maruti's shoulders and held him in a deadly grip.

Thus bound by the shaft of Brahma, Hanuman went down like the full moon at the time of Dissolution. Bathed in tears, Dharma followed.

Even as he fell, Hanuman realized that the weapon that brought him to the ground was sacred to Brahma. In profound respect, he shut his eyes and the rakshasa thought, 'Ended at last is his indomitable strength.'

HANUMAN UNBOUND

'Shoot him, cut him, stab him, axe him, pluck his heart out, slice him to bits, grind him to pulp and eat him up. Should he escape, we will all die!' said the rakshasas who thronged the felled hero.

They hissed like so many angry serpents, surrounding him menacingly, as if to kill him. 'Use venomous weapons to finish him off! Plunge his body into the rolling sea. If even that doesn't kill him, set fire to him,' one of them screamed.

'Return to us our fathers, brothers and other elders,' said one lot. 'He must have been sent by the gods above,' thought a few others.

Those among the onlookers, who were not rakshasas, could not hold back their tears. Whether in sympathy for Sita, pity for Hanuman, or for Dharma rendered impotent, it is hard to say.

Willingly did Hanuman go with them, making no attempt

to escape. He thought to himself, 'By my father's grace, my devotion to Rama and the boon given by Siva and several other gods, I can easily shake myself free of this bond. But it is best to submit.

'It would be best to go with them and see Lanka's king for myself. If I see that rakshasa, I can tell him and his counsellors that the result of their past deeds awaits them in the not too distant future.

'I can tell them the story of Vali's death and of the fall of the seven trees; warn them of the might of the monkey army that Rama has at his disposal as a result of his friendship with Sugriva. He might well relent and yield Mithila's daughter to me and I can carry her safely back to my lord.

'Even if my attempts to make him see sense do not work, I shall at least be able to gauge, both by his words and by his face, the state of his mind and the strength of those who support him.

'The thing to do, therefore, is to reach the rakshasa, bring to his attention the might of right. Even if I fail in this mission, I can still kill a good half of his men.'

Surrounded by a sea of soldiers, the prince who had taken Indra captive, took the bull-like hero to the palace of the monarch.

Messengers ran to Ravana to tell him of the great victory. 'Lord, your beloved son has bound with the Brahmastra the enemy monkey.'

Heart soaring with joy on hearing the news, he took off a bright necklace from around his neck and extended it to the messenger. Shoulders swelling with delight, eyes aglow like red lilies in blossom, he told those men, 'Run quickly and tell him to bring me that monkey alive.'

Indrajit did as his father had commanded and took mighty Hanuman to the presence of the one who had earned through his many penances, kingship over creation itself.

Above his throne stood a white umbrella, cool and dazzling, decorated with pearls, a moon to the three worlds, not unlike the snow-covered mountain he himself had once lifted.

There he sat, his shoulders bearing the dent of Vishnu's discus, the scar from the battleaxe of the three-eyed one, and the nail marks of the flower-fingered maiden he had captured. The rack of red hair on his head shot forth in every direction, as if it had a life of its own. Smoke issued from his nostrils—a northern volcano in the south!

There he sat, like the thousand-headed Sesha in state, the lustre of the gems in his crowns enough to dispel even the darkness of hell. The cloth around his waist an evening cloud, on his person a string of pearls white as stars, he sat under that moon, his umbrella, as if darkness itself were holding court.

Each of his ten heads looked in a different direction. One face imbibed honey off a sulking pout, another mouth drank the toddy off a sated one; a third consumed the nectar off a singer's lips, while a fourth ate manna off a dancer's mouth.

Yet another face looked upon the gods under him, another sat in counsel with his three committees. One engaged in plotting sinful plans, even as the other was lost in the memory of the unapproachable maiden who tormented him.

Yet another head schemed to cross the sea of Sita's chastity, and one vain face contemplated his own beauty in the mirror held by handmaidens.

When he saw him, the lord of the eight quarters, Hanuman felt incensed, like Garuda sighting a black serpent. He decided that he would shake off the ties that bound him and spring upon that venomous creature.

'I who spared him when he was asleep to avoid a sin, now see him on a golden throne; why think any further? I shall break his head, rescue that sprig of virtue, and depart.

'What sort of servant would I be if I don't pluck the crowns of a sinner who has cruelly kept Sita in prison here?' For a brief moment, he was really tempted to loosen his bond and leap like a lion at the wicked rakshasa. But wiser counsel prevailed and he changed his mind thinking, 'It won't be proper.

'He is strong, cannot be easily killed; well-entrenched, not easily conquered. To attack him is a waste of time. He won't be able to defeat me, nor can I vanquish him here. Why embark on a hopeless war?

'But one day, darkness personified, he will yield to Rama. Hasn't the great lord himself pledged that "to the delight of all seven worlds, I'll cover the earth with the many heads and sinful hands of this rakshasa?"

'If I waste precious time in fierce combat, the golden maiden, who swore by her husband that she will live no more than a bare month, is sure to lose her sweet life.

'On second thoughts, therefore, war wouldn't be right just yet. I shall just complete my task as an envoy.'

Having made this decision, Vayu's son entered the great enemy's hall, his earlier anger completely controlled.

He who had made even the gods flee, now brought Hanuman to Ravana's presence. Looking at his father who had conquered as many worlds as existed, Indrajit folded his palms in respect and said, 'Here is one in the guise of a monkey, but strong as Siva or Vishnu.'

The sparks from Ravana's eyes singed the hair on Hanuman's body. The smoke issuing from his nostrils coiled around his body, like the snake that held him bound.

Raging like Yama, frightening those around him, he questioned furiously, 'What brought you here? Who are you?

'Are you Vishnu or Indra? Or the bearer of the trident? Or are you Brahma who meditates on his lotus? Or Sesha, fearless and many-headed, who bears the earth upon those heads? Why, keeping your name and your real self secret, have you come here to fight and perish?

'Are you Yama, bent upon dragging all of this city to the land of Death with your noose? Or might you be the same Subrahmanya who once cleaved a cliff? Could you be Agastya, lord of the south? One of the *digpalakas*, perhaps? Or are you a terrible demon some sage produced through a yaga? Or a fearless new god, created by Brahma to destroy Lanka?

'Who are you and what brought you here? Who sent you here? I order you to tell me the truth,' said the mighty king who had destroyed the reputation of the gods.

'I am none of the above,' said Hanuman, 'nor a messenger from any of those weaklings you've mentioned. I run errands for a lotus-eyed bowman who has sent me here to Lanka.

'If you truly want to know who he is, I will tell you. He is the one who has vowed to accomplish a deed that neither the sages nor the gods, not even the great Trinity or any other being alive, can so much as contemplate.

'The might you have accumulated over ages, the fruits of your past penance, your shiny new weapons, the numerous boons you won from the gods, your intentions and inscriptions, all these he will negate with one arrow from his famous bow!

'No god, no demon, no *diggaja* who guards the quarters; neither Siva, Vishnu nor Brahma; no sage either. Just the son of a great emperor.

'Wisdom, the sinless benefit of yagas, and the abiding boons of honest penance, are all on his side. And if you want to know the reason why, it is that this bowman is the one true God, recognized by both the vedas and Dharma.

'I am his slave, Hanuman my name. I am a messenger from Vali's son, Angada, who commands the southern division of the army that has been dispatched to all four directions to look for Sita, the bright-browed wife of the great bowman. I have come here alone.'

Upon hearing this, the lord of Lanka smiled, a flash of lightning in a dark cloud. 'Messenger of Vali's son! How is Vali, that doughty warrior? Is his kingdom flourishing?' Hanuman broke into laughter.

'Fear not, great one! The fierce Vali has left the earth and gone to heaven. He won't come back, nor will his tail! Rama slayed him with a single arrow. Our king now is Sugriva, son of the Sun.'

'What was the need for that arrow to deprive Vali of his sweet life? Where is this Rama? Explain how it comes about that Angada is searching for that man's wife?'

'Our king befriended the lotus-eyed one, who came searching for his wife, and sought his help to rid the world of Vali and put an end to his misery. And Sugriva, in turn, promised to help him look for the wife you had abducted.

'He spent four months with us, and once the rains ceased, the hero directed us to commence the search for Sita. And that is how I came to be here.'

'You have all made yourselves the slaves of one whose arrow killed your matchless chief! How does it reflect on your glory! And how like a woman, that mother earth should approve of such actions!

'What message have you from the one who had his brother slain and made friends with the killer? You say you came as an envoy. Why then did you cause such destruction? Speak without fear, I won't kill you. Tell me the truth.'

Hanuman, that inconceivably sapient soul, pondered over Ravana's words. Thinking good sense might yet prevail, he spoke after some thought, 'My lord Sugriva has asked me to tell you the following:

"You will ruin your life if you continue to ignore Dharma. You have committed a sin for which the punishment is nothing less than death. Even so, if you heed me now, it may not be too late, and you can yet retrieve your life.

"You have lost what you gained through your penance— the control over your senses. You have sinned in your treatment of her who is unshakeably chaste and purer than the fire that tests all purity.

"Your conquest of the gods has made you arrogant, and the fame you once enjoyed is much depleted. You do not seem to understand that sin cannot ever triumph over virtue. The purity you gained through rigorous penance has been erased by your lust for that chaste lady.

"Those who are deluded by unlawful love and leave the path of righteousness can only go from bad to worse. Has anyone who swayed away from virtue ever prospered?

"You may have a million hands and twice five hundred heads, but when confronted by a fierce fire, they will be no better than rags.

"Even the boon you obtained from Siva, by playing music with your nerves for strings, may come to naught. But do not imagine that righteous Rama's shaft will fail.

"Therefore," the son of the Sun told me to tell you, "Save your fortune, family and life by restoring Sita to her husband." '

Ravana, who had been listening attentively, broke into a mocking laugh, 'Well, well, what a lecture from a hill-haunting monkey!

'Anyway, let us set aside for the moment, the monkey's words of wisdom and the lesson about man's good and bad deeds! How come, fellow, that you, an envoy, killed so many of my rakshasas?'

'Since no one would bring me to your presence, I had to destroy the fragrant grove. I killed those who tried to kill me and have now willingly come, without putting up a struggle, to see you.'

Anger blazing at Hanuman's arrogance and his teeth flashing, Ravana ordered, 'Kill him!' But even as Hanuman was being surrounded by those who rushed to obey the king, 'Stop!' cried Vibhishana, the just.

He stood up, folding his palms in obeisance, and addressed Ravana thus: 'O righteous one, it is not correct to get angry with this monkey.' He then proceeded gently to tell his brother some much needed truths.

'You who are so learned in the vedas, who, through your many penances have endeared yourself to the Creator himself, you who have won the throne of Indra, how can one such as you even think of killing one who claims to be but a messenger?

'In this world and others, where the vedas reign supreme, good men in the past have killed even women. But which king has ever killed an envoy?

'To kill an envoy, tactful and efficient, who reaches the enemy's land only to convey a message, who is wedded to truth and calms the wrath that might arise from the message he tenders, is an act which will make us the laughing stock of the world and indelibly tarnish our name.

'Despite being in the right, those heroes didn't kill our sister. They merely disfigured and sent her back to us. If you kill this monkey now, they won't know what he has seen here with his own eyes.'

'Well said, good brother. Though he has harmed us, to kill him would indeed be wrong,' Ravana accepted. Turning to Hanuman he said, 'Go, tell your masters to come here.'

And to his men he ordered, 'Burn his tail up to its root, take him around the city and set him loose beyond the borders.' At this, they all rose and cheered.

But Indrajit, knowing it was not proper to set fire to one bound by the Brahmastra, ordered them to tie his shoulders with hefty ropes instead, which they did with alacrity.

'My enemies themselves have freed me,' thought the messenger gleefully. 'Now I don't have to defy Brahma or virtue. And as for setting my tail on fire, it is as good as a licence to burn the city.'

Like an expert pretending ignorance, like a yogi who knows the world to be a mirage and yet carries on as if it were real and bides his time, Hanuman waited for an opportunity to act. Pretending that the trivial cords around him were too strong for him to shuffle off, he went quietly with his persecutors.

They crossed the king's palace quickly. Then the fierce rakshasas who surrounded him, dipped his long tail in oil and set it on fire. Delighted with this punishment they'd dealt, they roared and roared with triumphant laughter.

Running from street to street and knocking at every door, they exhorted the people to come out and join the fun. 'Come, come and see what we've done to the monkey that destroyed our city and its groves, killed Aksha and the rest, dared to speak to Sita and lecture our great king about the might of mere men.'

As if to spread the news even beyond the confines of the earth, they raised a din, the boom of drumbeats adding to their thundering voices, full of bluster; they danced around the bound Hanuman and gleefully narrated the tale to Sita.

When that tender-hearted lady heard it, she almost lost her life. Perspiring profusely, she shrank into herself, sobbing, and fell down in a swoon. Rising, once again she wept and sighed burning sighs. 'O god of fire, you who are a friend of the wind god, aren't you moved to see him being baited by those worthless rakshasas?

'O *Bhatavagni!* Fire in the belly of the ocean! You, if anyone, know about chastity. If you think me worthy of passing the test, be cool, I beg of you, to Hanuman.'

When he heard these words from her pure lips, the god of fire shrank within himself and, immediately, Hanuman shivered with cold.

The fire in the sky, the three fires of the sages, and the fire that burns in Siva's forehead, that had once consumed the three worlds, all went cold.

The fire on the palm of Brahma cooled, as did the fires in the sky, including the fierce blaze of the sun and the fires of hell!

Hanuman, now bound by love, wondered why the fire that blazed in the mountain of cloth around his tail did not seem to scorch him at all. Guessing that Sita might be the cause, he was rendered speechless with immense joy.

When they reached the city limits, he decided it was time to escape. He folded his two arms bound tight by the ropes, and with a shrug of his shoulders, freed himself from those trifling bonds and rose majestically to the sky. Hundreds of thousands of rakshasas, who had been holding the poles to which he had been tied, lost their hold and fell down dead.

With the remains of the coils hanging around him, he shone in the sky like Garuda bound by snakes. Deciding to burn that city of sin in a feat that would put even Shiva's wrathful burning of Tripura to shame, he let his fiery tail do the work of a torch. Hailing his lord's name, he then reduced the city to a shambles.

The great Lanka, girdled by the sea, was burnt completely in a matter of minutes. On those rare, hard-to-destroy houses of silver, gold and gems of varied hues, the mansions that the divine architect had built so lovingly with his own hands, he leapt by turn, setting them on fire with his tail.

And Agni, long deprived by the dark rakshasas of his sacrificial fire, now fed his raging hunger. It looked as if Death's day had finally dawned!

THE BURNING OF LANKA

That fierce flame caught the royal flag. It clasped in its fiery embrace pillars and walls and completely consumed every house. Screaming, people ran back and forth from their houses as if on a swing: fear drove them away but thoughts of their possessions sent them back, to salvage as much as they could.

Smoke rose high and hid the sky and women wailed and ran about like peacocks in panic. Many lost their way. Screaming women and men tried to recover their singed tresses by pouring water on each other's heads. Their own hair being a livid red, they sometimes found it hard to tell the fire from their locks!

Sacrificial fires in their houses, freed at last from the rakshasa's tyranny, came into their own. Smoke increased with every passing second: it was like Vishnu repeating his feat—beginning as a dwarf and growing gradually gigantic, to measure with his foot all the three worlds.

Elephants scorched by the fire became white, turning into a thousand Iravatas. Frightened buffaloes ran helter-skelter, attempting to seek refuge in the cool sea. But the sea itself was afire. As great tongues of flame fell on it, waves rose like boiling water, scalding the fish to death.

The floors of mansions paved with gold melted and fell, drop by drop, into the sea. Cooled, they were transformed into rods of gold.

The fire spread to the wine parlours and drank up the toddy in huge gulps. Isn't it true that when good men fall into bad company, they too will imitate the deeds of the wicked?

The bees in the groves, mistaking the golden flames for lotus tanks, fell into them and were scorched to death. Gardens of fragrant *akhil* and sandalwood were burnt to cinders in mere seconds. Their plants charred right down to the very roots, all those groves, the pride of Lanka, turned into blackened charcoal yards.

Swans looked no different from crows. The milky ocean of the gods became dark, like the seas on earth and the *diggajas* looked no different from ordinary elephants.

After burning everything in sight, having sucked up the sea and scorched the earth, the leaping flames from Hanuman's incandescent tail entered at last the palace of the king himself. Bewildered apsaras and other beauties didn't know where to flee.

Attacking that seven-storeyed fortress with the speed of a whirlwind, the fire burned it all down. That imposing abode of gold and priceless gems melted like sorry wax.

Ravana and his kin escaped in his gem-studded pushpaka vimana that took to the sky, swift as thought itself.

A second fire blazing his eyes, an enraged Ravana demanded an explanation. 'Is this Dissolution? Or is there some other reason for this catastrophe?'

Some surviving rakhasas wailed and told him, 'Your majesty, this is the work of that monkey whose long tail we set aflame.' Seething, he sneered, 'A mean monkey has set Lanka afire and reduced it to ashes! And Agni, once my humble servant, having gorged himself on my city, dares belch in satisfaction? Well, so much for our invincible might! The gods laugh while we watch on helpless, having fallen prey to the pranks of a mere monkey.

'Catch at once that insolent fire-god. Get at that monkey before he flees,' he ordered. As his men rushed to obey him, the seven heroes, ever ready for war, rose up like the waves of an angry sea and got ready to command their armies.

Seeking that hero, they looked high and low for him and finally spotted him in the sky. Maruti watched them unperturbed as with cries of, 'Catch him! Catch him!', they rushed to kill him with their spears.

He tore up a burning tree and beat them all with it, till they lost their weapons and lives. Their blood ran in rivers and Lanka, until then on fire, suddenly transformed itself into a city in flood: the red blood finally put out the flames that had been feasting on the kingdom.

The vidyadharas, who had witnessed the burning of the city, noticed a curious thing: 'This fire has left untouched the grove where Sita is confined.' Upon hearing these words, sweet as ambrosia, the great hero rejoiced. 'I am saved,' he thought, and in a minute, was at Sita's feet.

Seeing him alive and well, all of Sita's anxieties fled. And Maruti, in a hurry to get back to Rama with the good news, merely said, 'Why waste time on words? Farewell, mother!' and left.

With Hanuman gone, the fire-god thought, 'If the rakshasas see me, they will surely seize me,' and went underground!

THE RETURN TO RAMA

'I must get away soon,' Hanuman thought. Reaching a hill with a steep summit, he stood on it, glowing like the sun and expanding like Vishnu who swallowed all the worlds. He then bowed in the direction where Rama waited anxiously and took the aerial path back home.

Soon he reached, as promised, the hill where his friends awaited his return, alert as hooded cobras. The monkeys who had been chattering in nervous worry at Hanuman's long absence, burgeoned with joy at seeing him.

Like a nest of chicks celebrating their mother's return, a few shed tears of relief; some hurrahed, still others laughed and danced.

They swarmed all over him, as if they intended to feast on him; they clasped him close in warm embrace and carried him on their triumphant shoulders!

'Your glorious face has given away all the news,' they said. 'Partake of the food we gathered for you: honey, roots and rare vegetables, all excellent and specially sought for you.'

Exclaiming time and again at the wounds inflicted on his chest, head, hands and shoulders by swords, spears and arrows, too many to count like the stars in heaven, they were filled with great sadness.

He bowed to Angada first and then fell at the feet of the king of the bears. Thereafter, he greeted the others and conveyed to them the blessings of the mother.

Hearts brimming with joy, they said in unison, 'Mighty one, tell us everything, from start to finish.' Matchless Maruti spoke at length of Sita's chastity and patience and of the jewel she had given him to show to Rama. Modesty personified, he said nothing of his fight with the rakshasas or of the burning of Lanka.

'Your wounds are witness to the battles you have fought,' they said. 'Your escape is witness to your victory. The smoke we saw is evidence of the burning of Lanka. That the lady we seek is still there, proclaims the strength of the enemy. All these we know without your telling us a word. Now tell us what we have to do.'

'There is no time to lose,' he said. 'We must rush back and tell our hero of the discovery of his wife and assuage his sorrow.' Angada replied, 'Since the time prescribed for our return has lapsed, take pity on us and go on ahead to put an end to Rama's pining.' Maruti, never one to disobey a command, readily agreed to do as Vali's son ordered.

Having recounted from beginning to end all we know of the exploits of the messenger, let's now proceed to see what happened to anxious Rama in Kishkinda.

Having ordered the monkey brigade to go and seek Sita, wherever she might be, Sugriva stayed behind to console Rama.

Disappointed that those who went north, west and east had come back with no news of her, Rama hoped fervently that Hanuman would succeed where others had failed. Worried, he told Sugriva, 'Our efforts so far have proved fruitless. The time set for the return of the troops is past.

'All except those who went south have returned empty handed. And those who went that way have not returned. Do you think they are dead? What could have happened to them?

'Did they discover that she was dead? And decide that rather than carry bad news, they themselves would give up their lives? Or are they still searching for her?

'Did they chance upon those rakshasas and get embroiled in a fight? Did they get killed by their witchcraft and ascend to heaven? Or have they all been imprisoned? Not having returned at the appointed time, are they afraid to come back? Tell me, what could have happened to them?'

Even as he was thus lamenting distractedly, Hanuman appeared like a sun that had for once risen in the south and fell at the feet of the great hero. Turning southward, in the direction of Sita, he prostrated himself full length on the ground and thanked her for having cooled the fire.

'She is alive; he has seen her and her chastity is intact,' thought Rama exultantly, even though not a single word had been spoken. His shoulders swelled, his eyes dimmed, his sorrow vanished and love overflowed.

'I have seen that jewel of chastity in southern Lanka, girdled by the sea; lord, be rid now of doubt and sorrow,' said Hanuman, excited.

'She, the great goddess, has proved she is every bit worthy of being your wife, your father's daughter-in-law, and the daughter of Mithila's king. Like gold, unrivalled among metals, she, unique in every way, has brought you fame that can never be surpassed. In so doing, she has made me too a creature without rival.

'She has made you the symbol of your race and consigned to dust the fame of her tormentors. My race too is eternally blessed, thanks to my association with her. What more can one ask for?

'O doughty bowman, I saw in sea-girt Lanka that incomparable woman engaged in penance. Her breeding, patience and chastity shone through it all, proving her high birth.

'You are in her eyes and in her thoughts and forever on her lips, and in the many unhealed wounds in her heart. How can one say she is parted from you when you live forever in her heart?

'In a grove where morn and eve are the same, so thick is the foliage of the *karpaka* trees that skim the skies, in the very same hut your brother fashioned lives that lady, penance personified! She was uprooted and taken away with the earth on which she stood for Ravana dared not touch her.

'That Brahma's cosmos has not burst, Sesha's hood remains intact, seas have not risen to the sky, stars and planets have not plummeted to earth and the vedas still remain, all testify to the fact that she remains untouched. By virtue of her steadfast nature, every person of her gender has now become worthy of worship.

'Siva's wife is no longer just his other half, but deserves instead to be borne on his head; Vishnu's wife should leave his heart and ascend his thousand crowns.

'Having combed every inch of Lanka, including Ravana's home, I saw her at last in the Asoka grove, a Lakshmi afloat on her own tears! Numerous rakshasis who would frighten the very devil, stand guard over her. And she, fearless, because of her love for you, is like misery that has taken the form of a woman, alone and imprisoned.

'As I watched her from a secret hiding place, waiting for the chance to approach her, the king of Lanka came beseeching her to give in to him, going so far as to shamelessly prostrate himself before her. Enraged when she spurned him with contempt, he got ready to kill her. But her chastity, your grace and Dharma combined to save her life. Telling those rakshasis, "Torture her and make her see reason," he walked off in a huff. But I cast a spell on those wicked women and sent them into a deep sleep.

'Finally, when in despair and desperation she bound a creeper to the branch of a tree to hang herself, I, a dog, fell at her feet and recited your name. Though she feared it was yet another rakshasa trick, she told me joyfully, her breasts drowned in tears, "You have invoked my husband's name and saved me from killing myself."

'When I recalled to her memory the episodes you had described, she scanned me thoroughly and satisfied herself that I was trustworthy. But it was that lovely signet ring you gave me that convinced her that I was whom I claimed to be and proved her Sanjivani, the life-saving drug.

'Lord, then I saw with my own eyes the effect of her love for you. When she placed that gem-set ring on her breasts, it melted with the heat of her long separation from you. But in the same instant, her joy at receiving it cooled it and once again made it whole!

'I informed her of everything that had happened after

you had parted from her, adding, "Gracious lady, since no one knew where you were, there was some delay in finding you." I also let her know, my lord, of your own agony in separation, at which she revived somewhat.

'She then told me all that had happened to her after she had been carried away. And, finally, she said, "For one more month I will stay alive. If by then it doesn't please my lord to rescue me, I shall die."

'She then took out this great jewel she had hidden in the folds of her cloth and laid it tenderly on my palm, asking me to give it to you. Feast your lotus eyes on it, O lord,' said the one whose fame will last as long as the sacred vedas.

The love within him sprouted, spread its fragrance, and put an end to the anguish he'd suffered so long. That jewel he now held in his palm, made him feel that Sita's gentle hand had once again been placed in his.

Tears of joy streamed from his eyes as his body quivered with pleasure. He breathed hard with uncontrolled emotion.

Sugriva finally spoke up, 'Lord, since we now know where your wife is, it is time we set about taking steps to bring her back.' Rama replied, half in jest, 'What are you doing here, wasting time?' The son of the Sun, with hill-like shoulders, rose abruptly, commanding, 'Army, arise!' Drums of victory resounded in the forest as hordes of monkeys started advancing southwards, like the waves of a tumultuous sea.

Hanuman turned to Rama, hands clasped in salutation: 'O spotless one, don't despise me as a mere monkey! Get on my shoulders.' Rama agreed graciously. On the way, Hanuman briefed Rama about Lanka, about the dark and cruel rakshasas, and about their might and weapons and much else that would prove valuable in the war to come.

So they marched along that long trail, the righteous princes and the monkey-king. They tramped through the hills and groves for eleven days, and on the twelfth, they saw, spread in front of them, the southern sea!

YUDDHA KANDAM

RAVANA IN COUNCIL

In a hall that had more than a thousand pillars set with rubies and other rare gems, Ravana held court, sitting on an awe-inspiring throne borne by sculpted lions. He was in a towering rage.

'A monkey bringing down my state! What humiliation greater than this! So much for my authority! And here we sit as if nothing has happened.

'We set fire to a monkey and our city of flags was burnt down. Friends and kinsmen lost their lives. The scandal has spread all over the world, while I continue to sit alive and well on this throne!

'Our wells ooze blood and our kingdom is still not rid of the fire. The tresses of our women, ever fragrant with *akhil*, now stink, burned beyond repair. Couldn't we have at least died fighting him? Submerged in the scandal of it all, we sit unmoving; what good our birth? Tell me what must be done now to redeem our tattered reputation.'

(One by one the counsellors spoke. First to have their say were the army chief and his deputies, pot-bellied Mahodara, diamond-fanged Vajradanta, ugly-faced Dunmukha, Maaperupakkan of the thick sides, smoky-eyed Pukainirakkannan, and so on. By turn blustering and obsequious, self-exculpatory one minute and shifting blame the other, they counselled a fight to the finish, advised pursuit of the monkey and taking the war to his master's doorstep.)

At long last, with a sharp word ordering the chattering elders to stop giving contradictory advice, Ravana's brother, Kumbhakarna, spoke his mind fearlessly:

'You, peerless one, who know the vedas by rote, fell in love with fire, impelled by fate. Where will it all end now?

'You are distressed that parts of your pretty city have

been reduced to ashes. But was it right to covet a woman who was not only another's, but of a different class, and put her here in prison? Is there a greater sin than that?

'The day you abducted, against all prescribed codes, another man's chaste wife and imprisoned her cruelly, the very name of rakshasas was dragged through mud. We put a spotless woman in gaol and yet hope to achieve fame without blemish. We talk of honour and pursue lust. As a consequence, we beat a retreat before mere men. Great indeed is our victory!

'You have brought great shame to our race. But now to give up Sita of the honeyed tresses will also shroud us in disgrace. Far better we give them a fight, even if we die in battle at their hands.

'In that forest full of trees, one man, single-handed, laid Khara and his army low with his bow. It is now for us to show our strength. What other option do we have? We should at once cross the sea and kill the lot, monkeys and men,' said Kumbhakarna, clear-headed.

'Well said, my boy!' said Ravana, 'That is just what I feel too. Any other alternative is unthinkable. We will kill our enemies. Let our army start from this day to raise the flag of victory!'

At these words of his father, Indrajit shot up from his seat and said jeeringly: 'Will you in wrath rush to battle those contemptible men? What great heroism would that be!

'What am I here for then? Be they the primal gods themselves who attack you, if I do not ensure victory for you, you will have got me in vain. I would not be your legitimate son were I to stand by and watch!

'Indignant one! I swear I'll not return without destroying all, men and monkeys. The battlefield will turn into a stage, where headless warriors dance wildly. In the course of a single day, I shall make earth, water, air and sky change places. Great potentate, give me leave!'

Then spoke Ravana's youngest brother, Vibhishana, the wise. Biting his lip in anger, he first addressed Indrajit: 'Your immaturity makes you speak in this reckless way.'

Turning then to Ravana, he said, 'You are my father, mother, elder brother, the god I worship, everything. That you should lose your God-like stature is what pains me and makes me speak.

'Is it correct to imagine that your fair city and great repute were burnt down by a monkey and not by Sita's flaming chastity?

'Consider well this one question: why does one ever lose one's station in life, be it high as the sky itself? It is either because of love of a woman or a piece of land.

'O hero, are those words going to come true? Is the king of sea-girt Lanka going to lose all the fruits of his penance because of his love for an earthly maid?

'You obtained all kinds of powers from the all-knowing God. But you never asked for a boon ensuring that you'd not be vanquished by men. What hope now that you'll not be defeated by the best of men?

'You have already tasted defeat at the hands of a mere man. Kartavirya once overcame you, the conqueror of the seven worlds. No doubt he had a thousand shoulders, but for all that, he was only a man! And Rama and Lakshmana are no ordinary men.

'You, whose energy is infinite! Remember the day you lifted Kailasa? Remember four-shouldered Nandi's curse that monkeys will cause your ruin one day?

'Your enemies, lord, are mighty Dasaratha's sons. They are a pair, you must surely know, whom none can equal. Even sages and gods cannot comprehend them. They have come down in the form of men to settle our fate!

'Sage Kausika, that creator of the other cosmos, has endowed them with powerful weapons got from Siva, which can in a moment destroy any creature anywhere.

'Rama is also in possession of Vishnu's bow and the arrow used by Siva to burn down Tripura, both bequeathed to him by the dwarf-sage, Agastya.

'Their arrows are like serpents, whose tongues flick out to lick the world and, darting this way and that, measure its exact length. They can belch poison, and prey solely on the sinful lives of those who take pleasure in tormenting sages.

'That arrow pierced the indomitable chest of Vali, the one who churned the sea. Maramaras, the mighty trees that cloaked the world, fell before it. The hill-like heads of Khara and Virada collapsed likewise. Should a war break out, who can escape those shafts?

'Our army chiefs, who have been spending sleepless nights, are afraid to tell you what they really think. The gods, who till now were begging favours from us, have been rejoicing secretly, at the thought that we'll all soon go to hell!

'Innumerable bad omens have been appearing. The horses and elephants left behind by foes we defeated, walk into our houses, right foot first!

'The tongues and teeth of the rakshasas are drying up, their mouths spitless. Jackals larger than devils are walking the streets. And the hair of our women and men are getting singed. What worse omens can there be?

'When we consider how Khara and Trisiras, Maricha and Vali met their end, we may do well to ask who these men are, if not the one who wields the discus and the other who wields the trident?

'One thing more. In league with these two men are our inveterate foes, the gods themselves. They have taken on the form of monkeys to assist them. It is not wise to antagonize them.

'In order that you may not lose your fame and fortune, prove unworthy of your birth, be hurled from your lofty height and be destroyed with all your kin, give up that lady, steadfast in virtue. There can be no greater victory than that,' concluded that eminently wise brother.

That man of valour heard it all and applauded mockingly. Laughter shaking his sides, he said 'You have found fault with me for never having asked for boons to protect me from mere men!

'If my great might is entirely the result of these boons, tell me, youngster, whose boon was it that made me triumph over Siva and Vishnu? Did I get a special one to help me Vanquish the *diggajas* or lift Kailasa, Siva and all?

'You have spoken vain and thoughtless words. What can

gods, let alone men, do to me on the battlefield? Or even to you, for that matter, O brother still in the womb?

'You talk about Nandi's curse that we'll be destroyed by monkeys. Haven't I been cursed by anyone and everyone? What has been the consequence of those ill wishes?

'Who among the Siddhas and Yakshas haven't wished our death? What has ever come of their prayers and curses?

'I failed against Vali because of Siva's boon, granting him half his enemy's might in any battle. What makes you conclude from that, that any old monkey can overcome me?

'Had Siva and Vishnu themselves faced him in war, half their might too would have gone to him. Hence, even that man avoided confronting him, and shot instead from a place of hiding.

'Who but you will sing the praises of a human being, for breaking a bow already damaged? Or for piercing trees, sapless and dead? For going off to the forest outwitted by a hunchback? For losing his wife because of a plot I hatched? And after all this, still clinging to the burden of his body?

'You are a fool. Get up and leave,' he commanded. But love for his brother made Vibhishana persist: 'That unique God, second to none, is not here by accident. He has come down to earth as man, in keeping with a plan devised by the gods. Do you still wish to defy him?'

Ravana replied in a towering rage, 'If he is indeed the discus-bearer, in how many battles hasn't that weakling and fool been defeated? All my life I have done what I pleased. And yet, your Primal God has been afraid to even breathe in my presence.

'When Indra was imprisoned and the diggajas' tusks broken, and heaven itself cut into pieces, was that God of yours in his infancy? Siva, Brahma, Vishnu and all other gods hold their peace, while I rule the worlds unchallenged, is it because he is not there, or being present, impotent?

'You tender your friendship to total strangers. Your bones melt when you think of them. Driven by your greed for kingship, you have made plans to usurp my throne. With a friend such as you, do I even need a foe?

'When that monkey destroyed our grove and I ordered it to be killed and eaten, you stopped me, saying it wasn't the proper thing to do. No doubt, even then you had already made plans to befriend this man, Rama.

'I have allowed you to live so that I am not accused of causing your death, but you keep on saying whatever you please. Get out at once. If you continue to stand before me, I'll kill you.' He was thoroughly incensed.

Nothing daunted by the rebuff, Vibhishana, insistent, said, 'If you wish to live, listen to me. You've never bothered to look at your life. Nor do you wish to heed unpleasant truths, preferring to listen instead to the soothing lies of obsequious underlings.

'I have told you the stark truth in so many words, but you refuse to understand. Forgive me, lord,' he said, and resigned to the fate of his kinsmen, left the city.

Along with sorrowful Vibhishana departed Anala, Anila, Hara and Sampati, four virtuous and wise heroes of the rakshasa clan.

VIBHISHANA TAKES REFUGE

(Vibhishana and his four companions crossed the sea and came upon the monkey army assembled on the shore.)

More in sorrow than in anger he told his friends, 'Because I refused to stray from the path of virtue, I have been banished. Tell me, my wise friends, what should we do now?'

'There is nothing more noble,' said they, 'than doing one's duty. Let us approach that image of Dharma. He will help those who seek him out.' Vibhishana agreed wholeheartedly, 'Anything else, we'll remain rakshasas forever. Let's touch the feet of Rama, whose virtue is infinite, and gain salvation.'

'I haven't seen him in person, only heard of him. But my bones melt and my heart liquefies whenever I think of him. The boons I have obtained ensure that I will always love the Primordial, remain steadfast in the path of virtue, forge friendships with all things living and enjoy the grace of brahmins. Let us take shelter then at the lotus feet of that Ancient Being.'

Knowing it would be improper to seek them out at night, the four wise rakshasas hid in a dark grove and waited for the sun to rise over Udayagiri.

Meanwhile, having arrived at the shore, Rama gazed at the vast sea and wondered how he would ever cross it and see his beloved Sita. His mind full of her, he saw her everywhere—in the blue lotuses and lilies that flourished in marshes, in the swans that sported with their mates.

He saw her in the fisher-girls, drawing *koodals* on the sand, trying to ascertain whether their husbands, away fishing, would return safe. Even as he watched, their tears washed away the patterns they drew.

Spotting him from a distance, Vibhishana felt hope rise in his heart. He called out, 'Peerless victor, is there any greater than you! I, a fugitive, seek your shelter.' Rama heard these words in some puzzlement. He scanned his friends' faces, querying them about the identity of the refugee.

(Monkeys being monkeys, there was instant cacophony as all chose to hazard a guess at the same time.)

'They are rakshasas come to infiltrate our forces,' said one. 'No, no, it is Lanka's king himself, repentant, come to surrender at the feet of our lord. But what's happened to his twenty hands and ten heads?' wondered another. 'Let's fight him,' said a third, rash and foolish.

Hanuman then sent Mainda and Dwivida to investigate. Seeing no sign of treachery on the saintly visage of Vibhishana, they asked, 'Who are you? Why have you come? Have you come in war or peace? Don't be afraid, tell us the truth.'

(Anala spoke up, narrating the incidents that had led to their presence in these parts in an effort to seek Rama's lotus feet. Much impressed by what they heard, they returned and reported to Rama what they had learnt. He turned to his friends for advice.)

His hands clasped worshipfully, Sugriva, his crown flashing, ever mindful of what he owed the bowman, said,

'Do you, the lord of fate, who knows well the bounds of the four vedas and all the codes from Manu down, have to seek advice from us, mere monkeys?. Even so, since you have asked, I will speak my mind for what it is worth. Foolish or sensible, it is for you to decide.

'Since he is not a victim of cruel war, nor a hapless fugitive escaping death, has he done the right thing in abandoning his elder brother? No doubt he is our enemy's kin. Even so, when his vicious elder flourished in the lap of prosperity, he was kin to his wealth.

'But now, when the threat of war hovers over his head, he severs ties with him. Ocean of grace, whose kinship will he abandon next, this fickle-minded brother of Ravana's?

'Forced by his nephew's evil intent, Maricha gave up his life of penitence and turned a treacherous deer. Should that incident not serve as a warning against what could well be another rakshasa ploy?

'We have embarked on a war unparalleled in history, how will an enemy's brother help us? What aid will he give us? I am convinced he has come to us in deceit and with no good intent.'

(*Rama heard him out and then asked Jambavan, unrivalled in wisdom, what he felt.*)

The bear-king said, 'I am old and know the ways of the world. Even the wise will come to grief if they choose to befriend an enemy. Judging by their past behaviour, one cannot trust the rakshasas easily.

'Deserters such as these may seem at first to add to our strength, but demons are deceitful by nature and lying is a habit with them. They will finally wreak havoc.

'Why talk in the air? Or make wild guesses about what might or might not happen? We have the bitter experience of the past to guide us.

'This one's arrival at this time is like that of the opportune coming of another rakshasa, the one who deceived you and your queen by taking on the form of a golden deer,' he concluded.

It was then the turn of Neela, the army chief, to speak his mind. He said, 'O master of knowledge unlimited! There are ways and ways of befriending a foe.

'Likewise, many are the kinds of fugitives who fall at the feet of those who were once enemies—I will list them out. Please don't laugh and dismiss what I have to say as the prattle of a mere monkey.

'Among those who come seeking shelter at their enemies' feet are some who have killed their kinsmen. Some there may be who resent the treatment meted out to their wives. Others might have lost their property. Some may have been humiliated publicly.

'Some may turn their backs on their own kind out of fear of the enemy, while others might have been impoverished by their agnates.

'What kind of deserters should one accept, what kind to reject—these are difficult matters to decide. Those who have been ruined on orders from a neighbouring kingdom are all right even if they happen to be the enemy's brothers. But those who have not been humbled, and have the strength to defy the one who gives them refuge, won't hesitate to leave when they wish.

'Let us now consider where to put the one who has come to us. Seeing the time of his arrival and his claim that he doesn't care for his brother, can we, who have only the goodness of his reputation to go on, accept him without suspicion? I am not sure,' he concluded.

(Thus it was that these and other faultless counsellors, loyal and loving, advised Rama against accepting Vibhishana. Then Rama, that incomparable being who transcended all knowledge, looked at Hanuman and said, 'All of them are of one mind, learned one, what is your view?')

Hanuman replied, 'Lord, it is so like you to consult your people, however little they may have to offer. What these knowledgeable and pure-minded leaders have said with such confidence, is bound to be good advice. But I do not share their distrust of him. I shall, if I may, state my reasons.

'Great one, one look at a traitor's face will reveal his character. Also, will an enemy of ours, deign to take refuge with us? Will not darkness seek a pit rather than come out into the light? Deceit will stay hidden, not show itself, even if it were without words.

'Learning of your love of truth and justice, aware of your generous nature, he has come to you. Knowing how Vali died and how his brother got the kingdom by the strength of your bow, he has come to join you, hoping for a kingdom that might become his one day.

'Seeing also that Ravana's kingdom based on evil will not last, and having heard of how you gave away the sea-girt earth to your brother, he has come in the hope that he too will get his brother's kingdom.

'I know things about him that the others here do not know. When that rakshasa king ordered that I be killed, it was he who stopped it, saying it was wrong to kill a messenger. It was his wonderful daughter who comforted my queen, when she was in the lowest of spirits, telling her, "Never you fear, bright-browed one! Brahma's curse ensures that death will possess that sinner if he ever dares touch you."

'He has come to you because he knows that the boons his brother has obtained, his rakshasa cunning, and everything else he possesses will be burnt to ashes by your arrows. As for the boons he acquired, what asura has ever thought of asking for infinite wisdom instead of infinite power?

'Why should you fear his intentions? Can a shallow well swallow an ocean? You stand here committed to a task that the gods, even the Trinity, cannot accomplish. So give shelter to one who seeks it,' he concluded.

Overjoyed at such lucid and cogent advice, Rama said, 'Wise one, you spoke well.' Turning to the others, he said, 'Vibhishana's action is both thoughtful and timely. He wants to be king of Lanka, as he well deserves to be. He is without faults and on the side of right, this much we can be certain by his desire to join us.

'Hanuman's thoughtful advice is the best. Even if it is not, whether we win or lose, live or die, it is but proper to give shelter to one who seeks it. "Give me refuge," he pleads, so we must accept him as our friend. Even if he betrays us at some later date, our having granted him the shelter he sought, will be no blot on us.

'Don't we all know the story of the one who ascended the scales, to compensate for the life of a dove? Are you not aware of the trident-wielder who swallowed venom when the sea was being churned to help those who sought his aid in distress?

'Don't you know the story of the dove that sacrificed its own life when it found that a hungry hunter had caught its mate? To save the life of its beloved, it lit a fire, leapt into it, making itself a meal for the hunter?

'Who can forget how God rushed to the aid of the elephant-calf that called out to Him in distress, when it was caught in the jaws of a crocodile? When Sita, ashen-hued, cried, 'Who will help me?' did not Jatayu bravely step forth and die fighting that cruel tyrant? Should that not be an example to me?

'Isn't it honourable to be remembered for giving up life rather than for refusing to help and carry on living? If one won't help a broken man, won't give what he can to one that begs, denies refuge when it is sought, why even talk of virtue or valour?

'To one who seeks refuge, shelter must be given at once. Son of the sun, go and fetch him with all honour.' Thus spoke Rama.

Ordered thus, Sugriva went to Vibhishana, embraced him, and said, 'Gracious Rama has given you sanctuary. Come and worship at his feet.'

Limbs trembling, hair on end and eyes full of tears, Vibhishana saw Rama for the first time and said, heart melting, 'Is this a dark mountain with red eyes, or a rain cloud adorned with lotuses? This must be Vishnu, ever merciful.'

His hands clasped prayerfully and raised above his gem-set crown, he bowed low and fell at Rama's feet. That ocean of compassion looked at him with overflowing love. He stretched out his hands to embrace him and said, 'Rise and be seated.

'As long as the fourteen worlds and my name endure, this Lanka in the sea with all its rakshasas is yours—my gift to you!' Turning to Lakshmana, he said, 'Sleepless one, crown this faultless comrade the king of this land.'

Vibhishana, well aware of actions and consequences, said, 'Lord, if you would erase my sin of being that deceitful rakshasa's brother, please crown me with your sandals, the same that you bestowed on your younger brother.'

'Once we were four brothers and then become five with Guhan. Then, with the Sun's son, became six. With your having joined us, we are now seven! Sending me to the forest, my father has multiplied his progeny!'

'I am speechless, my lord! You have taken me, a cur, as a brother! I am a mere servant, lord, and you have made me great.' All his doubts and fears vanishing, Vibhishana crowned himself with Rama's sandals.

Everyone celebrated the forging of this unique relationship, and the gods above rained flowers and blessings. The seven seas and the clouds acclaimed their joy. Soft and fragrant dust was sprinkled on them. Golden showers drenched the land.

Brahma on the lotus rejoiced. 'My family's name, laid low by the abduction of that jewel of chastity, has today been redeemed'. Dharma exclaimed in happiness, 'Utterly ruined is Ravana's ill-gotten wealth!'

VARUNA HUMBLED

The sea-girt earth came out of the darkness that was dispelled by the rays of the morning sun. It was as if the full moon was emerging from the mouth of Rahu, that striped and spotted snake, who had swallowed it in anger.

'If we could but cross this sea with our loyal army, we could, if we wish, destroy the whole world,' said Rama. 'That should be no problem, lord,' said Vibhishana, 'The sea-god Varuna knows your incomparable greatness and will readily help, if you pray for safe passage.'

Lying on a bed of dharba grass, Rama recited the prayer to Varuna, as inscribed in the vedas. 'O god of the rains and the oceans! Show me the way,' he said, and repeated the holy verses.

Dust settled on his divine body and the fierce sun beat on his face, as he lay for a whole week, each day an aeon. But the sea-god did not appear. 'I asked him humbly to guide me,' Rama said, eyes red with anger, 'and in his silence he hides his refusal.

'One who really needs nothing, goes to a minor God for a favour, out of grace, and gets treated thus with contempt. Perhaps he despises me because Ravana has robbed me of my wife and thinks that my bow has lost its power. His seven seas, which mistook my graciousness for weakness, shall be scorched and reduced to dust.'

His patience exhausted, his face burning fierce like the sun at Dissolution, he strung his bow with his mighty hand. Its resounding twang put an end to the coquetry of sulking Parvati, and made her rush back in terror to Siva's bosom.

The fiery shaft converted the depth of the sea into a sacrificial pit and the fish, snakes and sharks in them became the sacrificial twigs. The foam of its waves became the sacred ghee of sacrifice. The sea that swallows the earth was thus itself swallowed by fire.

Bhatavagni, the fire in the belly of the ocean, fled from this new fire that threatened to swallow it. The clouds thundered. Varuna screamed, dry-mouthed.

Hair singed, body baked and roasting, he appeared before Rama, groping his way through the smoke of the rising flames. He threw up his hands in desperate prayer. 'Forgive me, O god of Dissolution! I was at the far end of the sea and did not know that you wanted me.

'You are the sea, the fire, indeed all the five elements. You are creation and dissolution. Caught in this red fire, I am being tortured. Please save me. When lowly creatures err, the great must forgive. Save me!' he pleaded piteously, and fell at his feet.

His rage abated at the sight of the contrite god, Rama

relented and said, 'Don't be afraid. I have forgiven you and given you the shelter of my love. But tell me why, when I sued you with great devotion, you didn't come, till I got vexed and angry.'

'Merciful lord, I was engaged in settling a dispute among fish in the far off seventh sea and heard nothing, I swear.' Merciful Rama smiled and said, 'Let it be. But this arrow of mine must be appeased with a surrogate target. Show me one.'

'Lord merciful! There is an island by name Marukantaram wherein dwell a hundred crore rakshasas. They are a menace to all mankind. Feed them to your deathless shaft.' The divine shaft departed singing, destroyed those demons, and came back.

Rama then turned to Varuna, 'You sought refuge at my feet and I have forgiven you. An unfinished task awaits me in the island across your sea. Tell me how to get there.'

Varuna replied, 'Lord, the depth and width of this sea defies even me. To dry it will take infinite time. Moreover, if I do so to enable you to walk on its dry bed, countless creatures that live in its waters will die. Instead, I will myself bear the burden. Build a bridge across me that shall be named Setu and just walk over my head.'

BRIDGING THE SEA

(Sugriva then sent for Nala, the royal architect of the monkeys, and ordered that the sea be bridged at once. 'It will be done, my lord,' said that builder. Then, beating a drum, Jambavan announced, 'Except for Rama and his brother, Vibhishana, king of Lanka, and our own king of countless clans, all else should come forward to complete the task of bridging the sea.')

They came forth like waves, like a mighty ocean ready to swallow a smaller sea. Some dug up mountains while others dragged out what had been dug up. Yet others roped their tails around other hills and brought them down with a mighty tug.

With innumerable dark hills balanced on their hands,

shoulders and heads, they marched, singing and dancing, and dumped their load into the sea.

Flung one upon another, the uprooted mountains produced fiery sparks from within the sea, making Varuna wonder whether he was being punished once again by Rama's flaming arrows.

As those hills hit the water, they created huge splashes that startled the bathing apsaras, completely wetting their clothes and, much to their abashment, revealing their middles.

Then, with his own hands, Nala dressed the stones, aligned the hills, spread the sand evenly, and levelled the surface. So adept at the task was he, that even if some of the stones broke and fell, he caught them with his legs, saving them from falling into the sea.

The bridge took three days to build. When it was finished, the joyous shouts of the monkeys echoed back from the mountains of Lanka. The structure itself seemed to say, 'What are you waiting for? Walk on me quick, and relieve the distress of the lord, desperately seeking Sita.'

The goddess of Lanka, devoted to virtue and disapproving of sin, seemed to stretch out her hand to welcome Rama's army out of abundant love.

LANDING IN LANKA

(After the great bridge was completed, the lord of the monkeys saw with his own eyes that marvel of architecture a hundred leagues long. Delightedly, he then went with his entourage to Rama. His heart welling with love, the lord embraced them, and said, 'Let us go and see it.' On doing so, he asked in wonderment, 'If the Creator himself had done this, how long would he have taken?'

Led by Vibhishana and followed by valiant Hanuman and Lakshmana, the great hero strode like a young tusker across that new-built bridge. Answering at last the prayers of the gods, he reached the city where Sita was immured. There they occupied a small hillock.

Nala at once put up an encampment for the monkey army that was on its way. Tents of gold and gems, all alike for kings and commoners, were soon up. In a trice, a goodly city came up at the *spot. Then, with his own hands, Nala levelled the rocky land and put up a house of bamboo and lath, with a roof of fragrant grass for the bowman and his brother.)*

Just then Vibhishana's vigilant eyes settled on two of Ravana's spies, disguised as monkeys. He seized and brought them before Rama. To his, 'These are deceitful thieves,' a perplexed Rama said, 'Have they done anything amiss? Since they ask for mercy, don't torment them. Let them go.'

'But these are not our men of the forest, lord,' said Vibhishana. 'They are spies sent out by wicked Ravana. This is Suka and that is Charana.' The two tried to bluster their way through, insisting they were indeed monkeys at the service of Rama. But Vibhishana uttered a mantra and the true form of the spying rakshasas was revealed.

Looking at those frightened spies, Rama said graciously, 'Don't be afraid. Tell me what brought you here?' Stuttering and stammering, they said, 'Lord, ill-fated Ravana abducted that tapaswini, the mother of the world, little realizing that that act would be his death. We are his spies.'

Addressing them, Rama said, 'Tell him I said this: that the infinite wealth of Lanka has been bestowed on his brother; that the heroic monkeys have crossed the sea on a bridge of stone; that the bowmen, long delayed, have both arrived in Lanka.

'Tell him that even if he were to be aided by Siva on his fierce bull or Vishnu on his lovely bird, he will still be cut to pieces. You have seen everything and gone everywhere. You have no further business here.

'I am offering you a safe passage. So get away quickly without harming anyone. Repeat everything I told you to Ravana. Now be gone,' directed Rama.

(Roused by the noise of Rama's army settling down at the camp, the king of Lanka held a midnight meeting of his council. News of the feats of the monkey army—the way the sea was bridged in three days, the way they had triumphantly marched across— had already reached his ears. When despondent Malliyavan, his mother's father and elder of the council, recounted all he had

*heard and seen of these unprecedented events and counselled caution,
Ravana merely laughed.)*

The obsequious army chief scoffed at the old man's fears
and said, 'You praise a bunch of monkeys that threw a few
hills into the sea. Have you forgotten that our lord here has
uprooted Mount Kailasa itself, Siva and all? Impelled by fate,
a few impudent fools have come here to fight us, that's all.
There is no reason to panic.'

Just then, the arrival of the spies was announced. They
duly entered and were ordered to relate what they had seen.
'My Lord,' said Suka, one of the spies, 'is there any need for us
to describe the strength of the enemy, when we already have
telling evidence of their massive presence here in Lanka?

'However, great lord, we must report that your brother
has been bestowed all the wealth of Lanka, for as long as the
sun rises in this world and Rama's name remains on earth.'

*(They then related the incident of their capture and how Rama
had forgiven them, of his terrible vow to bring to naught all of
Ravana's boons. Dismissing them, Ravana resumed consultations.)*

'The two bowmen with arms swift as a curse have
bridged the sea and come to our island with an army. What
do we do now?' he asked.

The army chief rose. He said, 'If you surrender the lady
now, the gods will jeer and call you a coward. If we decide
to fight and the enemy wishes to sue for peace, your brother
will prevent it. It was because of him that we did not pursue
the monkey when he created havoc here.

'Now that they have come to this island, the die is cast.
We can no longer avoid war. We have on our side a thousand
invincible vellams of the asura army. It will take hundreds of
aeons for the enemy, however powerful, to decimate them.
Your appearance on the scene will make it look like a lion
amidst a group of whining curs.

'Even without your personal intervention, our army is
strong enough to decimate them and plunge them into the
sea. Just say the word,' he said.

Once again, venerable Malliyavan, Ravana's grandfather, demurred. 'Only if you give up Sita, will you escape disaster, not otherwise,' he said.

Inexorably impelled by fate, Ravana said, 'I don't need your wisdom, get out! I'll not give up Sita to avoid a war. You talk with awe of the strength of monkeys and mere men. Let them attack if they dare, with or without the aid of the gods.

'Even if the one who wields the trident should take on a monkey's form and attack me, what can he do except retreat? And even if the one with the flaming discus—and don't forget he once ran away from a fight with me—should pick up the courage once again to confront me, the shaft in my hands will burn a hole in his chest.'

Then broke the dawn. Darkness departed from the hill. Emboldened by Rama's presence on the island, the sun, who all these days had not dared peep over Lanka's ramparts, decided to have a look at that famed city and appeared on the horizon.

THE ARMY ORDERED OUT

(Though war had formally not been declared as yet, there were skirmishes.)

During one of his routine rounds, quite by chance, Ravana came upon Sugriva. To the demon-king's 'What brings you here?', the monkey-king answered by pouncing on him, and to his utter consternation, rained ceaseless blows on his chest. Enraged, eyes darting fire, Ravana made short work of Sugriva, threw him into a lime pit, and trampled on him.

Then dragging him out, the rakshasa pummelled his face with his twenty hands and drank up the blood that issued from his mouth. The unequal combat went on for a while with courageous Sugriva putting up a spirited fight.

Finally, failing to quell the demon, Sugriva wrenched the gems from the diadems on Ravana's heads as trophies of an inconclusive war, and returned to Rama.

Rama, who had begun to get worried at the monkey-king's absence, was relieved to see him and embraced him warmly. Abashed, Sugriva said, 'Shame on me. Braggart that I am, I said I'd fly faster than your shaft and bring back the head of your foe. It has proved an empty boast.

'I am no Jatayu, that dauntless warrior, who died fighting. I have not brought Sita back, but I've not returned empty-handed. I have brought some souvenirs of war. Here they are! The gems from Ravana's crowns!'

'These gems are the foundation of the victory to come,' said Rama generously. When darkness descended, those bright stones illumined the entire camp. Rama retired to his tent, well content with Sugriva's exploit.

The scent of war permeated the air of Lanka. Returning after his inconclusive encounter with Sugriva, Ravana held yet another meeting with his war council. Apart from the lone dissenting voice of Malliyavan, all else present were agog at the prospect of war.

Sardula, the spy, had brought news that the monkey hordes were in full battle gear and had besieged all the city gates. Hanuman was at the western gate with seventeen *vellams* at his command and Angada, with an army of similar strength, was at the southern gate.

Two *vellams* were on commissariat duties and busy gathering fruits, vegetables and other articles of food for the fighting soldiers. 'Your brother, Vibhishana, is to go to each gate by turn and appraise Rama of the latest situation. He himself is staying back at the camp, with his brother and Sugriva.'

Digesting this latest bit of intelligence, Ravana ordered the positioning of his own troops. The commander-in-chief was asked to lead a horde of 200 *vellams* to the eastern gate.

Pot-bellied Mahodara and Maaperupakkan, the general with the thick sides, were directed to go to the southern gate to take on Angada.

Crooked-eyed Virupaksha was asked to guard the ancient city, and son Indrajit was to proceed to the western gate to take on Hanuman. 'I myself will guard the northern gate,' Ravana concluded.

The night lifted and all was dust. The fine dirt raised by the rival armies was enough to silt the sea and make it look like a shallow pond. Spread thick with the men of the rakshasa army, that ancient city of that sinful king looked like a dark sea swallowed by the milky ocean of the monkey army.

ANGADA AS ENVOY

Rama, who had under his command nothing less than seventy *vellams*, proceeded to the northern gate to await the arrival of the thief who'd stolen his wife. He then outlined a plan to Vibhishana.

'We must send a messenger to Ravana with an offer. If he returns Sita without more ado, there'll be no war. Should he refuse, it will be my duty to fight. This is both righteous and lawful.' Both Sugriva and Vibhishana agreed, but Lakshmana demurred.

'To show mercy at this point would be a mistake,' he said. 'This lawless tyrant had troubled the gods, grieved the brahmins, killed and ate up a number of living things. By a wicked trick, he has deprived you, lord, of your dear wife and plunged you into eternal misery.

'He has mowed down and killed Jatayu, the compassionate, who went to her aid. But for this encounter, the one you called your second father might have lived on for ages and aeons.

'If you now let such a creature live, on condition he returns your wife, what happens to the word you gave the brother who sought refuge in you? And what of the vow you made to the gods? What price Rama's words? This city must be destroyed, even if you spare Ravana,' he said angrily.

'I have not forgotten, dear brother,' said Rama patiently, 'but we should never disregard what the wise have prescribed as the kingly way. War is the ultimate weapon. Every possibility of peace must be explored and exhausted before we take up arms, even against Adharma.

'Whom shall we send on this delicate mission? If

Hanuman is sent again, the enemy will think we have none else of calibre. Let's send Angada.'

When Angada was sent for and told of the decision, his shoulders swelled higher than the hills. His heart expanding with pride, he said, 'The lord said, if not Hanuman, it has to be Angada. Who can equal me now!'

That virtuous messenger of Rama wasted no time and arrived at Ravana's palace. He saw before him a fierce lion, with a dazzling crown, stretched wide on a couch. Eyes darting fire, Ravana looked up and asked, 'Who are you? What brings you here? Answer quick before you are killed and eaten up.'

'I am the messenger lord Rama has sent to find out if you'll mend your ways and return Sita,' said Angada. Ravana replied, 'Is this man who sent you the lord of the world?' and burst out laughing. 'Siva or Vishnu dare not come here to talk to me as an equal. Who, then, are you?'

'There was a certain Ravana whom the son of Indra tied up with his tail and dragged across many an elephant-filled hill. I'm the son of that great king and my name is Angada,' said the young cub, all arrogance.

Not angered by his insolence, Ravana said, 'Your father was my friend and I can prove it. Isn't it a shame that you come now as an envoy of the man who killed him?

'Come. For old time's sake and because your father was my friend, I shall make you the head of my monkey brigade. You can then be saved the dishonour of being the errand boy of the one who killed your valiant father. You shall be my son. And when these men die in battle, as they are sure to do, I myself will crown you king of the monkeys.'

Angada burst out laughing and clapped derisively, 'What for? To take the place of your brother who has come to us to be crowned king of Lanka? You grant and I receive! Wouldn't that be like a lion accepting a gift from a cur?'

"For this impudence I'll kill him,' thought Ravana in rage. Then told himself, 'No, No. No weapons against a mere monkey.' Bringing himself under control, he said, 'So you don't want the crown I offered. Tell me quickly what you have come to say.'

'I have already told you,' said Angada impatiently. 'These are Rama's words: "Tell that sinner whose entire race is doomed, who is afraid to face battle and hides in his fortress, that he must either surrender my lady to me right away, or be prepared to give up his life in battle tomorrow."'

Ravana was furious at this ultimatum. Forgetting his earlier resolve not to punish an envoy, he cried, 'Seize him quickly. Dash him to the earth.' When four rakshasas moved towards him menacingly, Angada seized them and sprang high in the air, wrenched their necks with a twist of his arm, and threw them down.

The blood of the rakshasas he had just killed made him look as if he'd been smeared with red sandal paste. He then descended before Rama and said crisply, 'He is a fool, lord. He will yield only his crowned head to you.'

THE FIRST DAY OF WAR

Drums beat on all sides, announcing the coming war. Soldiers in the encampment were told to man the gateways, and exhorted to display their might:

'Heroes! Use your skilful hands with thrice the art you showed in bridging the sea. Fill the ditches in the city with all the hills and trees that you can find. Fell the trees and block enemy movement. Challenge them to come forth and fight, and seize them the minute they do. Now get to the top of the fort, whose ramparts the sun could never cross.'

Thus ordered, that huge leonine monkey army started flinging rocks and trees into those ditches, wide and deep. Under the impact of these missiles, lotuses sank and bobbed up, looking like the beautiful faces of bathing women. Soon the ditches lost their depth, flooded as they were by the solid rain of rocks and trees. Crocodiles scrambled to escape, and water gushed out into the city.

Amused monkeys plucked the lotus plants from the emptying drains, as if they were symbols of Ravana's fame that had once flourished but was now under threat. The bees that'd been gathering nectar from these glorious blooms, scattered in different directions. Swans that'd been taking their ease, flew away in panic, carrying their eggs in their beaks.

The great drums rolled and the sky echoed with the din raised by the monkeys. Conches blew, garlands rustled, halters of horses tinkled and chariot bells chimed, filling the sky with the noise of war. Dust diminished the quarters.

The arrows discharged by rakshasas, dark enough to cause night itself to flee, made the monkeys bleed profusely and writhe on the ground. The stones hurled by the daring monkeys from atop the Meru-like ramparts of Lanka, shattered the lives of those sinners, like thunder falling on a mountain.

Lances with leaf-shaped heads hurled by rakshasas, with eyes bright as the sun, dislodged the monkeys perched on the ramparts. The enraged monkeys bit and cuffed, pummelled and kicked, dug trenches with their nails on the bodies of the enemies. They twisted off the heads of innumerable rakshasas, killing them instantaneously.

The sky looked like a red-hot river of blood where headless corpses swam, stroking their dark-as-night hands through its waves. In their bid to try and escape the ferocious rakshasas, many monkeys too ended up in that gory flood. Many simply collapsed. A few ran away.

Confronted by demonic might, having lost a good part of their own army, the exhausted monkeys retreated to Sugriva who stood watching, eager to jump into the fray. On seeing the plight of his men, his heart hardened. Eyes belching fire, he quickly seized a tree.

In a towering rage, he attacked elephants and horses, charioteers and foot soldiers, bringing to mind Hanuman's exploits in the Asoka grove. The rejuvenated monkey heroes, once again joined the fierce battle, led by their king.

The day wore on and so did the war, neither side winning or losing. Countless were the treacherous demons killed by the stone missiles hurled at them. Innumerable the monkeys killed by cruel shafts that'd found their mark. Devils sang and headless corpses danced. Blood ran like a stream and joined the sea. Chaste women looked for the bodies of their dead husbands on the battlefield.

Told of the rout of the rakshasa army, Ravana went himself to the field of battle, bow in his hand, and prayer in his heart. His broad front covered with a steely armour and with a *thumbai* wreath around his neck, he was a grand sight indeed. As he twanged that bow, the sky resounded with a noise that might have killed Yama himself.

The flywhisks on either side of him gave him the appearance of a dark, foam-filled sea. The white umbrella, decorated with pearls, made him look like a rain-cloud under a full moon. Conches blew and drums thundered, the clamour making the worlds explode and the gods sweat.

Spies reported back to Rama, 'Lord, the demon-king himself is on the battlefield, with an army that resembles a dark sea.' Rama's heroic shoulders swelled. Diamond-sword around his waist, clad in bark, with a lovely anklet on his foot, he tightened the spangled armour that adorned his chest, making it look like a million glittering stars. He then stepped forth to confront his enemy.

With a quiverful of arrows on his shoulder, each one true and sharp-tipped like the words of poets, he tied around his head a brilliant band and joined his brother who stood ready with his great bow. He looked like awesome Rudra at Dissolution, ready to burn the seven worlds. Behind him was the monkey army.

The seven seas of the rakshasa horde and the flood of monkey warriors stood ready to engage in a combat that would make Yama's task look trivial!

Heads were severed; innards scattered; chariots shattered; horses and men were sliced to death. The earth that bore the corpses swelled as blood flowed like a river. The monkey corpses piled up to a silver hill and the rakshasa bodies became a black mountain.

Eyes darting fire, Ravana twanged his bow, terrifying the gods. The monkeys scampered in all directions and serpents fled their hollows to avoid that thunderous boom. Some sobbed in terror and others died in fright. Many rolled on the battlefield, fear rendering them senseless.

Rooted in Dharma, righteous vibhishana, steadfast Lakshmana and fearless Sugriva, the king of that tree-wielding army alone stood their ground, undaunted. All else had fled, and the gods sulked!

The king of the monkeys then let fly a flashing rock that looked like Indra's thunder. It blazed forth with the speed of lightning, shedding sparks of fire. But an arrow from Ravana reduced it to ashes.

Then the monkey-king ripped out a tree from the womb of the earth. This too the demon's arrow shattered to smithereens.

Then the Sun's son hurled a huge hill that set the sky on fire. Breaking that missile too with an arrow, Ravana bent his great bow and aimed at Sugriva a fiery shaft that would pierce the target but leave no mark.

When that hot shaft touched him, Sugriva winced and fell into a swoon. In the twinkling of an eye, Hanuman, who had been keeping vigil at the western gate, rushed to the spot.

'While the son of the Sun recovers, will you, great rakshasa, attempt a few rounds with me? Step forward, if you dare!' he challenged, and casually uprooted a mountain from nearby and hurled it at that monster.

When he saw that missile setting fire to the clouds that floated in the sky, the enemy of the gods sent out ten shafts that broke that mountain into a thousand fragments. Hanuman picked up another hill and tossed it with all his might at Ravana. Travelling with the speed of thunder, it made fine dust out of that rakshasa's shaft and epaulette.

Thus it went on, the ding-dong battle, every hill countered by an arrow, and every arrow blunted by a hill. Finally, one of Hanuman's deadly missiles took off the head of Ravana's charioteer and crushed many a rakshasa who stood behind the chariot.

The king of Lanka had had enough. Like an angry sea, Ravana sent forth a hundred divine shafts. His doughty foe fell at last, blood streaming from his body.

Still unappeased, Ravana shot a thousand crore arrows,

and the monkey army scattered like a sea beset by a tornado. Lakshmana, who had been witnessing the fierce battle, could no longer bear to stand apart and watch Ravana wreak havoc. 'Today he shall be my target. I'll kill him.'

When the wrathful son of that mighty emperor was thus provoked to string his bow, need one conjecture about the chances of survival of that wicked rabble? The world spoke in hushed whispers, 'This is the thunder of the *yugapralaya*, the inundation that ends eras.'

The mighty rakshasa heard the twang of that bow and perceived a change in the morale of his army and exclaimed, 'Can this be a man?'

Lakshmana's arrows came thick and fast and downed countless chariots, elephants, horses and white-fanged rakshasas. Corpses piled up to hills so high that the streams of blood were unable to find their way to the sea. Yama soon grew tired of the feast.

The rakshasas were defeated and Lakshmana's bow was crowned with victory. Lanka's king was outraged, his heart boiling in humiliation. In his chariot drawn by horses fleet-footed as the god of wind, he appeared before Lakshmana and glared at him, eyes shooting fire.

Having been on a killing spree like Yama gone mad, Rama's brother stood undaunted, wrath personified, refusing to budge an inch. 'You reckless trespasser in my kingdom,' fumed Ravana, 'you shall not escape me today.'

He let loose a torrent of arrows, blazing and deadly. In his turn he, young and fearless hero, emptied his quiver on the king of Lanka.

Hanuman who had recovered, saw what was happening, and shouted, 'You conquered the three worlds, your might undiminished; you traversed the quarters and gobbled up Indra's fame. But today your end has come.' He stood before the king of Lanka, growing huge like the one who measured the worlds.

'You are skilled in the use of the bow and similar weapons. You have, in addition, twenty strong arms. You are tough, pugnacious and skilful. Come, fight me.

'You stand before me self-assured and insolent; you rely on your weapons, your boundless energy, your matchless fortitude and strength. But all this along with your fame, I will wipe out with one blow!

'Why waste words? Let us see if you can withstand the lone fist of a monkey. If you can survive even one of my blows, you can go ahead and sock me with all your arms. If I fail to withstand your onslaught, I swear I shall never fight again.'

Darker than a rain-cloud, that rakshasa savoured Hanuman's words. 'Valiant hero, you have spoken well. None but you would have dared challenge me. Your fame will last as long as the worlds.

'You have no weapon save your hands and are all alone. You have killed my kinsmen and now confront me, even as I stand in my tall chariot, bow in hand, surrounded by my army. Who can rival your towering strength! In all three worlds, what god from the Trinity down, unless he had lost possession of his senses, would have dared challenge me as you have done?

'I have twenty hands and great is my fame. You have taken on a form that'll put an elephant to shame. What praise will I earn through such an absurd fight?

'But let's waste no more time in idle chatter. Here I stand, come quick, hit me as hard as you can, for the whole world to witness,' invited that rakshasa, wedded to wickedness.

'What heroism!' said Hanuman admiringly. He leapt onto Ravana's chariot and landed a blow on his chest that powdered his armour and shredded his garlands. That chest of valiant Ravana withstood his assault and scattered sparks all around.

With that punch on his chest that was dark as a cobra's poison, Hanuman dislodged the broken tusks embedded there—a souvenir of his fight with the *diggajas*. With them went Ravana's reputation of invincibility.

Regaining his breath, words failing but eyes darting fire, Ravana said, 'That quality called strength, O hero, you certainly possess in abundance. However, if you now survive my attack, I'll accept that you are second to none. You will then live, today and forever, without a foe!'

'Having survived my blow, you are already the victor,' Hanuman praised. To which hill-shouldered Ravana countered graciously, 'Now take your due,' and landed a punch so deadly, that the four quarters might well have been dislocated, had they been the target.

Hanuman, who wouldn't be rattled even if the earth shook to its foundations, staggered, as if Kailasa had been battered. When he shook, all heaven shook, the foundations of Dharma shook, as did truth and propriety. The vedas and justice shook, so did mercy and penance.

Then the monkey chiefs decided that it was time for them to step in. Looking like the clouds at the time of Dissolution, they lifted more than a thousand crores of snowy mountains and flung them at the rakshasas.

'Dead is the world today!' they roared. Ravana, whose mind was dark as his skin, was stung to the quick. Picking up the bow that had quenched the fame of the gods, he shot as many arrows as it took to smash those mountains to smithereens.

Then Ravana, by now grown impatient, said, 'Enough of playing games, I'll kill this monkey horde this instant and vanquish those two men.' He hefted in his left hands ten huge bows and let fly a ceaseless shower of hot arrows.

The monkey chief, Neela, stood transfixed. Anila fell and Gavaya well-nigh lost his life. Angada hovered between life and death and Jambavan was immobilized. The sea of monkeys dried up. Those who hadn't died had fled. And Lakshmana was furious.

Removing with his own arrows Ravana's innumerable shafts, Rama's brother shot down the ten deadly bows of the enemy. The gods jumped up in glee and bumped their heads on heaven's ceiling. The sages showered flowers on that intrepid hero. Dharma did a jig.

Ravana spoke words of praise: 'You fight like a true warrior, courageous and learned in the arts of warfare! Who can stand against you, save he who quelled Khara in the forest, or my son who vanquished Indra, or I who stand before you!'

Deciding that the young hero must be killed that very day, he seized a shining spear given to him by Brahma and hurled it straight at Lakshmana.

Belching fire, that deadly lance went straight into the heart of Lakshmana and he fell on the ground in a dead faint. The monkey army scampered in confusion, even as the rakshasa hordes raised a roar of victory. The gods were stricken, sages trembled, the earth whirled and the sun grew dim.

'He has only fainted,' thought Ravana, and strode towards him. 'I will remove his body,' he decided. Wading through the blood and gore on the battlefield, he seized with his twenty hands that mountain of gold and attempted to lift him, as he had once hefted the silver mountain that was Siva's abode.

Too weak to move him, much less carry him, Ravana let out a sigh of despair. Hanuman appeared on the scene, as if from nowhere, lifted Lakshmana and carried him away with gentle care, like a mother-monkey might have carried its young one.

He reached the place where Rama stood getting ready for battle. The relieved gods showered flowers on Vayu's son. And Ravana turned his chariot towards his greatest foe.

When Hanuman saw the rakshasa approach on his magnificent chariot while Rama stood on the lowly ground, he quickly went up to his lord and said, 'It is not becoming to watch you fight from the ground when that arrogant rakshasa rides a chariot drawn by a thousand horses. So be pleased to get on my shoulders, however inadequate they may be.'

'Very well,' acceded the hero. Hanuman rejoiced, proud as a cow with her newborn calf. Seeing his lord perched on a new mount, the golden Garuda who'd always thought that the privilege of carrying Vishnu was his and his alone, felt jealous and neglected. Serpent Ananta, that vast bed on which Vishnu always reclined, was bewildered and felt threatened by a new rival.

How can one describe this picture of perfection, except to say that Hanuman was *Prakriti*, of which all things are wrought, and Rama, *Purusha*, the essence of all things sentient and insentient!

Rama twanged his bow, unique and undefeated. The ascetics showered blessings on the two warriors. The sky grew full as all the gods, Siva and Brahma included, took their place to watch what was sure to be a fierce war.

Ravana then shot seven shafts, hot as the coral-coloured fire of Dissolution, powerful enough to drink up the seven seas. Rama, in turn, sent out shafts that could split each of those seven into seven more, and, in addition, a batch of five of his own. Yali-like, that rakshasa neutralized those five with five of his own, and then sent ten more. Rama countered them with an equal number discharged from his bow.

Even as the two great heroes engaged in single combat, the two armies clashed anew. The missiles that the rakshasas discharged shattered the rocks hurled by monkeys. A hundred thousand heads rolled and the two armies were reduced to a mountain of corpses and headless wonders

His army decimated, Ravana stood alone in his chariot. He bent his formidable bow and drew its string right back, and aimed a pair of strong arrows at Rama's emerald shoulders. With a smile on his face, Rama sent forth a spotless arrow that split Ravana's bow right through the middle.

Before he could attempt to string another bow, Rama beheaded with a swifter arrow the horses that drew Ravana's gem-set chariot. Before he had time to react or send a retaliatory shaft, a swift one from Rama's bow brought down the rakshasa king's white parasol and flag and dismantled his armour.

Red-eyed Death danced on that field of blood and Ravana fumed at his inability to destroy his enemy. Rama's relentless shower of arrows did not cease. One of them, quicker than Hanuman, when as a child, he'd leapt to seize the sun, knocked Ravana's crown off his head. It plunged into the sea, looking like the bright sun that Rahu'd swallowed.

Deprived of his crown, Ravana, who'd known only victory and never tasted defeat, seemed like a night without the moon, the day without the sun. He was like great fame laid low by a lampooner's wit.

There stood Ravana, reduced to a paradigm—'thus do sinners fare'. Looks darkened, eyes downcast, faces dim, toes clawing the earth, hands bare and drooping, he was a banyan tree whose roots seek the earth from its branches!

The great lord looked on with compassion at seeing Ravana reduced to this sorry state. Noting that his enemy'd been disarmed, he had no wish to kill him. Speaking without wrath, he said, 'Go away, sinner!

'I pity you, all alone and bereft, and don't wish to kill you. Come later, if you dare, with all your kinsmen and the many weapons you have hoarded. Or else just go and hide somewhere.

'Take this lesson to heart—even the gods can win only by right, not might. If you'll but release the one you've caged, I shall even now refrain from placing your heads on the floor.

'But if you still choose to fight, come again with all your strength and tell me, "Here I am." I'll be ready, but don't expect any mercy then. Next time, I won't spare your life.

'You have seen with your own eyes how all your men scattered like cotton before a breeze. Go now. Come tomorrow,' said the Lord of Kosala.

THE KILLING OF KUMBHAKARNA

The breast that had defied the *diggajas*, the shoulders that had hefted that loftiest of mountains, the tongue that could take on Narada himself, the hand that held Siva's sword, the ten chapleted crowns and, finally, the very valour that had made him an indomitable force in the three worlds— all these Ravana left behind in that battlefield and went home empty-handed!

Dogged by disgrace, his hands a burden, he trudged back home on foot, as the sun sank behind the hills. He paid no heed to what he saw, not to his tattered army or his anxious children. When his wives, their hair adorned with flowers, searched his face anxiously, the only woman his humiliation permitted him to look at was the earth beneath his feet!

Back at his palace, he sat on his throne of gold, lost in thought. Then he summoned all the rakshasas in the seven big islands and repaired to his flower-decked bed like a wounded tusker. They came almost instantaneously, trembling in fear, not knowing what was on his mind.

As he brooded on what had happened on the battlefield, the thought that hurt him most was that heaven and earth would now mock him. His one-time foes, the same ones he had often jeered at himself, would now snigger at him. He withered in shame at the thought that the spear-eyed maid from Mithila, red-lipped and soft-limbed, would now look upon him with utter scorn.

At that moment entered Malliyavan, his grandfather. As he sat next to Ravana, his gaze perceptive, the venerable man whom age had bent like a bow, guessed that Ravana must have lost the day's battle. After a while, he asked softly, 'You look weak and depressed. What happened?'

Heart sundered, eyes shooting sparks, nostrils breathing fire, Ravana burst out: 'The gods themselves had assembled to watch that war between me and those ascetics. And in that gory field surveyed by bloodthirsty vultures, our kinsmen were all killed and shame eternal descended on our clan.

'Venerable one, had three-eyed Siva himself come to the aid of my great army, we would still have been unable to withstand the younger hero's arrows, so accurate was its aim. Who can describe that skill? The moment he thinks "These rakshasas must die," the whole world takes on the form of arrows.

'Rama's shafts are like words on the tongue of a born poet. They weave themselves into feet and metre, appropriate ornaments and all, and take on the eternal quality of music that never dies!

'And what a man! When the aim of delivering the shame of defeat was accomplished, he evinced no more anger than when he shot his mud balls at that hunchback, Kuni.

'There is nothing comparable to Rama's bows. The vedas may fail, but not the shafts from that bow! Can words ever do justice to them? If they can destroy even my pride, what need for any further proof of invincibility?

'For his vehicle, he had a monkey! But don't you sneer. Not even Garuda could have bettered that mount. Was it wind, fire or Death himself on which he rode? My destruction might well be near but, at long last, I have secured a worthy foe.'

Shaking his ancient head in sorrow, Malliyavan said, 'When I counselled returning Sita, you were livid with fury. The same advice from your sagacious brother too you rejected with scorn. Look at what's happened now.

'Everything of importance and worth, including your kinsmen, learning, culture, wealth and all else has been destroyed along with your tired army.'

At this point, Mahodara, the pot-bellied chief, intervened. 'What cowardly counsel are you giving?' he thundered. 'When a stout-hearted man takes on a mission, in the hope that it will bring him a certain result, he sticks to his resolve, whether or not it brings him instant success. If instead, he retreats halfway faint-heartedly, he will surely earn dishonour, not only here on earth but in hell hereafter.

'Haven't the wise said that those who succeed will sometimes taste failure, in the same way that those who seem always to fail will at some point know success? That the ones who stand tall have fallen and those who have been down have risen in stature? You acclaim the valour of these puny ascetics only because your generosity is above all praise.

'Give up the lady, and your fame will vanish forever. If you don't, what do you have to lose but your life? Alas! Why would you now think of humbling yourself when you have never bowed down before? If you quit fighting, Lanka is sure to become an orchard of fruit trees, where monkeys will roam at will and gorge themselves.

'Lord, are you so bereft of valiant aides that you think of surrendering before mere men? All too soon you plumb the depths of despair. How come you have not thought of Kumbhakarna, your matchless brother? The very sight of his mountainous body will drive our enemies into hiding. Those who don't run away at the mere sight of him, he will kill single-handed.'

'That is good advice indeed,' said a greatly cheered Ravana who then ordered his brother to be brought to his presence. Four rakshasas ran swift as Yama's messengers to do his bidding.

On arriving at his palace, they saw that huge mountain of a rakshasa fast asleep. 'Prince,' they beseeched, 'please get up.' They began to pound his head with the iron rods they'd carried, but to no avail.

Exasperated beyond endurance, they said, 'O sleeping Kumbhakarna, at this rate, Yama's bow-wielding messengers will soon send you to your eternal sleep! Then you can sleep, sleep, and sleep forever!

'Your brother knowingly chose the path of evil. His life of endless happiness looks as if it'll end today. And still you continue to sleep.' With wearied hands they shook him insistently. When even then he did not move, they went back to Ravana in despair.

Knowing his brother, he said, 'Send in a thousand horses and *yalis* to trample upon him.' This too was tried out but in vain. Ravana then ordered a thousand wrestlers to be sent to punch Kumbhakarna into wakefulness. But even as they entered the gates of his palace, they found themselves sucked into his nostrils as he inhaled, and thrown out when he exhaled!

Totally baffled, unable to escape his wide nostrils and cavernous mouth, they finally hit upon the idea of blowing conches and trumpets into his ears. Men of immense strength pounded his jaws, chest and head, with clubs and hammers. They poked him with spears, but still no result.

Ravana then ordered a thousand horses to be raced over his prone body. All that happened was that he stirred as if he had been patted by some kindly hands and turned over and went back to sleep!

They returned to Ravana once again. 'Forgive us, lord. We have tried every trick we knew and some that you suggested. Our hands are tired and so are the horses that trampled him. We await your orders.'

'I don't care what you'll do. But you must bring that inseparable brother of mine, who refuses to wake from his sleep even when chariots go over him. If need be, use spears and axes, but bring him somehow.'

A thousand rakshasas went once more to Kumbhakarna, who lay in dreamless sleep. Taking up positions on both sides, they used their cruel strength to pound his cheeks with long and sturdy pestles.

(At last he woke as if from death, rolled over and stood up.

Once awake, he was activity itself. When told, 'Your brother wants you,' he left at once for his palace, his excitement mounting with every passing minute. He fell like a mountain at Ravana's feet who at once gathered him fondly to his broad shoulders. Remarkable that sight, like two mountains embracing each other!

Ravana sat him down and fed him massive quantities of choicest meat and gave him pots of blood and toddy to drink. He then clothed him in silk white as foam and decked him in many a bright jewel. He smeared his body all over with red sandal-paste and fastened around his chest the sturdy coat of mail given to him by Siva.)

Kumbhakarna asked in puzzlement: 'What is all this preparation for?' The left side of his sky-high shoulders had begun to tremble inauspiciously. Ravana replied, 'Mere men have led a monkey army into our fair city and won an unheard of victory. Go forth and make mincemeat of them!'

'Has the cruel war broken out? Has your far-reaching fame, that had touched all corners of heaven and earth, departed from this land? Has our end finally arrived?' Kumbhakarna's anxious queries poured forth in a flood.

'The war is on then?' he repeated. 'And golden Sita is its cause? Have you not, despite being warned of consequences, given up yet that symbol of chastity? Alas, alas! The power of Fate!

'There is one thing I wish to say to you, Chief. If even now you release that lady, bow to that bowman, and patch up with your brother who is above suspicion, it will be the best thing you would ever have done.'

Ravana was furious. 'I did not send for you to have my future read out to me thus. You are not my minister. Just go and kill those men.

'Or is it that you are afraid and your reputed prowess a myth? You have lost the capacity to fight. Eaten too much meat, drunk too much toddy. Close your eyes and sleep away your days and nights,' he said woundingly.

'To bow to two mere men and salute that hunchback monkey is only becoming of you and that brother of yours, whose only wish is to save his skin. I can never contemplate such an action. Get up and go away,' he said witheringly.

'Bring out my chariot,' he commanded, 'and here is the order of the day. Let everyone in heaven and on earth join those little boys in their battle against me. I am ready, waiting to fight.'

Upon hearing Ravana speak so bitterly, Kumbhakarna intervened, 'One moment, if you please.' He picked up a long spear in his hand and took leave of his brother, 'I'll not say I'll return victorious. Those decisions are left to inexorable Fate who pushes us towards our destiny. I am sure to die and if I do, please return that golden lady to her rightful husband for your own good.

'Indrajit too is sure to die by an arrow from the younger brother. Our army will disperse like ashes in the breeze. Before I leave for battle, I repeat once again that, if they defeat me today, they'll surely vanquish you on the morrow. Once again I beseech you, lord of Lanka, return the lady.

'I now take leave, my lord. I don't think I'll see you again,' he said. 'Forgive any mistakes I might have made, knowingly or unknowingly, from when I was born to this day.' On seeing him depart, Ravana's twenty eyes ran with blood and tears.

In a golden chariot that looked as if the earth had slipped off the head of Adisesha, he came towering like Meru, the king of mountains. Rama saw him and wondered who he was. 'The flag on his chariot carries not the vina but a lion. Who is he?

'His form so huge and dark has swallowed up the rays of the rising sun. Frightened at the sight of that humongous body, our army has scattered in all directions. Who is this intrepid hero?

'Has Ravana disguised himself to frighten the monkeys? I am not able to fathom this mystery.' Turning to Vibhishana, he asked, 'Who is this person? Tell me quickly.'

Bowing low, Vibhishana replied, 'Lord, he is the younger brother of the great lord of Lanka, and older than I. This is the heroic Kumbhakarna.

'Cursed by an ambiguous boon, he sleeps most of the time. But once awake, he is the death of Death. Swifter than the wind is he, and defeated once the mighty Indra himself, with naught but his spear.

'He can squeeze fire and air with his hands and drink up their essence. He can kill all the fish in the sea, and wade across it, as if it were a mere puddle. Strong of limbs and stronger of mind, when that garlanded one sleeps, the world breathes a sigh of relief. But when awake, he is a terror to all.

'Time and again did Kumbhakarna advise that thoughtless tyrant that what he'd done was not right and that we'd all be destroyed in the war. Disgusted at his brother's obduracy, nonetheless prepared to die for him, he now stands before you in full battle array.'

Sugriva said thoughtfully, 'We'll gain nothing by killing him now. It'll be better if we can persuade him to join us. Vibhishana too will be glad of it.' Rama immediately dispatched Vibhishana to talk to his elder brother.

On reaching his camp, Vibhishana was warmly received by Kumbhakarna. Eyes raining tears, he embraced his younger brother and inhaled deeply of the scent of his hair and said, 'I was so happy when you went away and saved yourself from the consequences of this battle. Why have you come back now, as if you have had second thoughts and shattered my hopes?

'Having taken refuge with virtue in person, having wiped out the three deadly sins of lust, rage and delusion and obtained eternal release during this lifetime, why have you come back to us, we who run after other people's wives?

'There stands Rama with his bow, and beside that lotus-eyed hero who is God to all, wait Death and Fate ready to exterminate our race. Why have you come to us when it is clear we are on the losing side?

'All the rakshasas here will be killed in a shower of arrows and this place will be destroyed. If you, son, do not survive this war by staying with Rama, who will remain to offer sesame and water to those of us who die?'

Vibhishana said, 'Brother mine, wisdom incarnate! Don't jump to conclusions. I am here on a mission. The hero who bestowed his grace even on someone like me, flawed by birth, will certainly grant you the same, in this life and the next.

'All the wealth and kingship of Lanka that he has promised me, I'll gladly give you and be your servant. No better fate can attend us. End my woe, save our race and live!

'O brother steadfast in virtue and ever just! There is no way we can save our brother or change his sinful ways. You may lose your life and enter hell, the gods will laugh and rejoice—then what?

'If only you listen to me, by the grace of Vishnu, you'll give up your sleep and live a wakeful life. Your days shall be endless and this land will be yours to reign without anyone else staking a claim. This is not a gift undeserved, but your right. The time has come to make this change. Say yes.

'The first of the Trinity has descended on earth in the form of Rama to establish righteousness. If you accept Lanka from his hands, you will indeed be second to none. Who'll dare oppose you?

'Merciful Rama, out of love for me, has sent me to fetch

you. Do not turn your back on Dharma. Come with me and see him,' pleaded Vibhishana earnestly and fell at his feet.

Pulling his brother up, Kumbhakarna embraced him and said with tears in his eyes, 'Son, life is no more permanent than a picture drawn on water. You live your life but once. I'll not abandon the one who nursed me so long and has now sent me here geared for war. If you wish to rid me of my sorrow, return quickly to Rama.

'Thanks to Brahma's boon, you have been endowed with deathless virtue. Your life will never come to an end. You are the lord of the world. The action you chose to take is worthy of you. For me, however, renown will come only in death!

'If a thoughtless king decides to sin, it is correct to try and reason with him, if he is corrigible. If he shuts his ears to the advice of the wise, nothing is served by joining his enemy.

'We owe to the one who fed us to join him in his fight against his enemy and die shielding him. Will it be proper for one who's ruled the three worlds to lie dead on the field without his brothers by his side?

'His shoulders had once shaken the mountain on which sits Siva. And when those shoulders are bound by the noose of that same God he had once defeated, will it be right that he is taken away, all alone and shamefaced, while those who had been shaken and frightened by his victories look on and laugh and make loud music?

'I, who have defeated Death himself, will not raise my hands and bless those who want to kill my elder brother. You'll see me overcome Hanuman, Angada, Sugriva, Nila, Jambavan and all those hordes of fruit-eating monkeys. Except for those two men, the black mountain and that golden hill, whoever else comes to fight me, will not escape with their lives.

'So, dear son, don't waste your time any further. Nothing you'll say will make me change my mind. Go back to Rama. But obtain from him the permission to perform for us all the obsequies prescribed by the vedas and save us from the fearful pain that awaits one in hell.'

So saying, he clasped Vibhishana tight to his bosom and

said with infinite sadness, 'Our connection has now ended.' Turning around abruptly, he left.

Returning empty-handed, Vibhishana reported to Rama, 'My father, I spoke to him with all the skill I could garner. But he remains insistent he will not change sides. He knows that Ravana has sinned grievously, but will not abandon his brother in his hour of need.'

Shaking his head sadly, Rama said, 'I did not want to kill your brother in front of your eyes. That was why I sent you to win him over. But who can alter destiny?'

Even as he was speaking these words, the noisy sea of the rakshasa army began to surround the monkeys, raising enough dust to fill the three worlds. Horses galloped, elephants ran, strong-wheeled chariots rushed in, swift as the wind. The monkeys flung rocks, and blood ran like a river in the battlefield. Headless corpses danced wildly on the ground, even as vultures and eagles danced in the sky above.

For a while, Kumbhakarna watched silently the fight between the two armies, a battle that looked more like a whirlwind set against a torrent. Then he decided to intervene.

He drove his chariot right into the middle of the mêlée, wielding in one hand his bloodstained spear. All at once, a blanket of dust enveloped the field, like the whirlwind at Dissolution.

He flung the monkeys against the hills, dashed them on the ground, caught them by their tails and threw them in different directions, rubbed them against each other and crushed them, kicked them and trampled them beneath his feet.

He seized them by the fistfuls and chewed and spat them out. He twisted their necks and crunched them between his teeth, flung them high up in the air, kneaded them and smeared himself all over with gore.

He drowned them in the sea; rubbed them on the ground; fed them to fire and water; smashed them against chariots; beat them on bushes and trees; whirled them around endlessly and bashed them against the hills.

The gods fled in terror. The birds hovering over the

battlefield were sated. The eight quarters disappeared. The flood of monkeys ebbed, the army whittled. Kumbhakarna's slaughter had put even the god of Death to shame.

'We'll leave no trees or rocks in sight,' vowed the monkey chiefs and hurled everything they could lay their hands on. 'Evil shall end today,' they promised, and flung stones, trees, roots, logs, and even the grass under their feet.

Kumbhakarna took it all on his broad chest, never wincing. When nothing more was left to throw, the monkeys ground their teeth and hurled themselves upon him.

Like a flock of sparrows attacking a hill, they descended on him, pummelling, biting and clawing with all their might. Frustrated when their attack had no effect whatsoever on him, they got down and ran away.

Then Kumbhakarna flung his trident at Angada. In reply, Hanuman invoked Rama's name and hurled a hill at the demon's head. Kumbhakarna caught it with his hands and flung it back at Hanuman. On impacting on that mighty chest, it produced sparks, like a hammer hitting red-hot iron.

The gallant monkey heroes carried away Vali's injured son. And Hanuman seized a huge hill that obscured the very sky and challenged Kumbhakarna, 'I am going to fling this on you. If your strength remains undiminished in spite of it, I'll acknowledge you as a hero who cannot be vanquished and fight you no more.'

Kumbhakarna opened his cavernous mouth and laughed. He said, 'Done. I'll take your hill upon my chest and if I go under, my might will certainly prove itself lesser than yours and I shall so declare to the whole world.'

The son of Vayu tossed that mountain and Kumbhakarna made no attempt to dodge it. He took it on his shoulder and it broke into a hundred bits. Looking at him with admiration, Hanuman said, 'Only Rama's shaft can pierce him,' and moved away, defeated.

'Where have those tapaswis gone?' yelled Kumbhakarna triumphantly, now that he had sole possession of the field. 'Where are they? Are they attacking someone else in Lanka?' Then Sumitra's lion got ready to take him on.

To the great delight of the gods, gloomily watching the

rout of the monkey army, Lakshmana strung his bow and straightaway released a shower of arrows. The distant quarters were deafened by the ensuing noise, as if earth itself was thunderstruck. The devils threw away the meat they were eating, and striking their thighs in delight, began the *thunangai*, the devil's dance.

Their thirst unappeased for too long, Lakshmana's fiery arrows hissed with rage, as they winged their way to rakshasa targets to slake it with blood! Seeing the numbers slain by those shafts and witnessing first-hand Lakshmana's valour, the descendant of Pulastya repeated a thousand times, 'There are only two bowmen worth their name in this universe. One is that God who burnt down Tripura, and the other this one.'

In a tall chariot advanced Kumbhakarna roaring ferociously, quicker than the wind and swifter than the mind. Uneasy at the thought of what he deemed would be an unequal contest, since Lakshmana had no mount, Hanuman went up to him and offered once again his sturdy shoulders: 'Young lord, be pleased to get on,' and the lion cub graciously agreed. Hanuman's shoulders were six times as wide as the rakshasa's chariot drawn by a thousand horses.

Said Kumbhakarna, 'You are Rama's brother, and I, Ravana's. Even the gods have come to witness our combat. Let us speak words worthy of the occasion.

'In your wrath, you cut my sister's nose off. She was innocent, and to us, a lovely tendril, a boon. I'll now cut off the hand that grabbed her tresses and throw it on the ground. Be on guard.'

Ever valiant, Lakshmana said, 'A fitting reply to you should be given with the bow, not the tongue. We are not used to idle words, our valour speaks for us.'

Eyes darting fire, Kumbhakarna shot a batch of eighteen bright arrows. The gods flinched, thinking that the sky, the mountains and the earth would all be riven in two. But Lakshmana shattered those shafts, sent out by that vengeful brother of Ravana, with just four of his own!

Shouting, 'Destroy this, if you can!' the rakshasa let go

an arrow given by Brahma, capable of taking on a thousand forms. Lakshmana countered it with a divine shaft of his own, and lo! all its thousand forms fell.

Angered, gigantic Kumbhakarna dispatched a dozen deadly arrows at Hanuman, two leaping ones at Lakshmana, and another 150 that scattered in every direction and hid the sky and the quarters. Countering each of them with appropriate missile, Lakshmana killed the many creatures that drew Kumbhakarna's chariot.

Elephants, horses, *yalis* and demons all fell dead and the chariot itself was shattered. Kumbhakarna's huge bow melted into nothingness.

Deprived of his chariot and bow, Ravana's favourite brother raged like a stormy sea and vowed, 'I'll drink up his sweet life.' He then seized the fiery trident that symbolized the three worlds he had conquered and sprang to the ground.

The impact of that leap almost sundered the earth. Lakshmana too promptly jumped off Hanuman's back, not being one to be charged with taking unfair advantage in battle.

Meanwhile, the reinforcements sent by Ravana surrounded Lakshmana. The terrified monkeys fled in confusion. Undaunted, Lakshmana carried on fighting and his shafts pursued and broke into bits all the weapons Kumbhakarna sent his way—swords, clubs, axes, spears or *kulisas* shaped like thunderbolts.

When the fierce battle seemed unending, Kumbhakarna turned to look for an alternative foe and sighted Sugriva. The son of the Sun hissed, 'I will break that rakshasa's shoulders,' and hurled at him a huge mountain. Ravana's brother caught it with one hand, powdered it and blew it away!

Baffled, Sugriva stood about indecisively and Kumbhakarna immediately hurled his trident at the monkey king, with an instruction to 'kill him', as if he were a tapaswi flinging a curse on a demon who had dared to interfere with his penance. 'He is gone, he is gone,' wailed the bystanders. But Hanuman caught that deadly missile just in time and broke it in two.

(Then Kumbhakarna and Sugriva began to wrestle, neither yielding to the other. Finally, the rakshasa squeezed Sugriva's chest till he fainted. Flinging his unconscious body over his broad shoulders, Kumbhakarna said, 'With this, the war is over for the day and I am going home.' Terrified at the sight of their king being carried away, the monkeys ran to Rama and fell at his feet crying piteously, 'Our leader is gone. Save us, lord.')

In an instant, his eyes grown redder than the hot arrows in his hand, the cloud-hued bowman strung his bow and reached the battlefield. 'The very thought of it is intolerable—that my friend, dearer to me than life itself, should be immured in Lanka, when there is still fire in my arrows. I must prevent it at once.'

The shafts released from that mighty bow filled the sky and the quarters disappeared. The sun's bright rays lost contact with the earth and darkness spread all over. Kumbhakarna looked up, and all he could see was a rain-cloud in the shape of a man wielding a golden bow.

His mouth belched smoke and curled sneeringly. His lips quivered in rage, his brows shot up and his eyes sparked. His thundering shouts of derision caused the surrounding hills to come down in a heap.

'You have come to save this creature, deluding yourself that I am another Kabandha or Vali, a monkey feeding on nuts. Never mind, I have at last a foeman worthy of my steel! Your army fled, your brother got tired and stepped aside, Hanuman too has lost his strength. This one here, I took easily.

'If you have come to save him, I'll indeed consider it a blessing, I'll fight with all my might and rid my lovesick brother of the disease that consumes him. But if, on the other hand, you manage to release with your bow this bemused monkey in my captivity, I swear, with the gods as my witness that you have as good as released your Sita too.'

'If I do not,' countered a smiling Rama, 'bring down the shoulder that holds my dear friend prisoner, 'I'll indeed be lesser than you and shall never again pick up a bow in my hand.'

Rama selected from his quiver two arrows, broad and sharp as swords, and shot them at the demon's wide forehead. His face covered with blood, Kumbhakarna stood stunned, reddening like the sky before the arrival of Aruna, the charioteer of the sun.

Till then unvanquished, the rakshasa fell in a swoon. The blood issuing from his forehead, like a cascade down a hill, wakened Sugriva from sweet sleep. Guessing that the bright shaft on Kumbhakarna's forehead was Rama's arrow, he turned around and saw the lord in person. In anger, and shamed by his earlier defeat, he bit off the enemy's nose and ear and went back to join his people.

When Rama saw the chief escape from the hold of the fearful rakshasa, he was as relieved as if Sita herself had escaped from her prison in Lanka. The monkeys cheered; apsaras and ascetics celebrated, as did the noisy sea and its many fish. The mountains grew taller and Dharma showered blessings.

Regaining consciousness, Kumbhakarna realized that the monkey-king had slipped away. Nose, ears and chest covered with blood from the wound on his forehead, he saw the gods jeering him and was filled with deep shame.

'Before he sees me thus, I too will reduce him to the same state,' he swore and picked up a golden shield and sword to face the enemy. Before anyone knew what happened, Rama banished that shield with a sharp arrow. Another one was brought at once, carried by 2,000 demons!

'This is your chance,' said the stout Jambavan to Rama. 'Don't miss it.' Rama strode towards Kumbhakarna declaring, 'Today, I'll introduce him to Death.' Thirteen shots with the noise of thunder and the speed of lightning Rama discharged, but that trained warrior cut them to bits with his sword.

The king among men then sent arrows sharp as the rays of the summer sun. These too Kumbhakarna broke without effort. Smiling, Rama shot an arrow that demolished that curved sword, like Garuda pecking to death the serpent.

But that nimble rakshasa plucked out of the air another diamond sword so quickly, no one watching would've believed he had lost the earlier one. Shouting, 'I'll kill you, I'll kill you,' he advanced upon Rama, breathing hard, as if he was trying to rouse the fires of Dissolution. Cutting to pieces that long sword, the prince of Kosala brought down his shield of gold and unleashed many a lightning-swift arrow at the demon's rock-like armour.

The rakshasa army had already melted away like snow at the touch of the sun. Seeing him all alone, Rama said: 'You have lost your weapons and your men and are all alone on this battlefield. I grant you life since you are brother to a good man. Do you wish to leave now and come again later? Or do you choose to fight and die right away? Decide your course of action and let me know!

'I offered you refuge, sending a message through your younger brother, but your past sins prevented you from taking up that offer. You decided to stay in the sinner's camp and death awaits you now. Tell me what you wish to do.'

The valiant Kumbhakarna shrugged, 'Let it be. I wouldn't care to live and show my face like my sister whom you deprived of ears and nose. I spoke out against the abduction of another man's wife, but in vain. Nonetheless, ever loyal to my brother, I came here to cut off your head and shoulders to gift them to him along with the woman he loves.

'Do you now expect me to go whining up to him, hiding my head in my hands to keep blood and tears at bay, and fall at his feet crying like my sister, Surpanakha, so that the gods can laugh at the sight?

'You are unique in all three worlds. Surely you know what is proper? Do you not know what a soldier's duty is? Is it possible to cut off heads in this field and then try to fix them back upon the bodies? What you've suggested is unworthy of you.'

He then transferred his spear to his left hand; with his right, he pulled up a hill that had its entrails embedded in the earth, and chucked it into the sky, shouting, 'Kill him!'

That great king reduced it to the ash that adorns Siva's body and in a second, unleashed a torrent of arrows in reply.

Those shafts flying from Rama's bow, capable though

they were of drying up the seas, extinguishing fire and silencing thunder, couldn't, however, pierce the armour that was Siva's gift to Kumbhakarna. Rama was puzzled at first, but soon realized the reason behind the immunity and let fly Siva's own astra. At once that armour, obdurate thus far, fell down and was shattered into a million pieces.

Driven to frenzy at the loss of his precious armour, the rakshasa picked up a club of iron and, whirling it around, killed every monkey in sight.

'My army and that club in his hand cannot coexist,' thought Rama and shot ten fierce shafts that pulverized that weapon. The dark rakshasa boiled with rage and picked up next a sword and a great big shield.

The frightened monkey chiefs took to their heels. The sky resounded with the cry, 'Death stalks the earth again!' Rama immediately released an arrow with an instruction to 'Go and cut off his mountainous shoulder.' Sin was desolate, virtue cheered.

The rakshasa troops broke into a sweat and ran away. 'His right hand, that dark sea of Dissolution is gone, sword and all,' they cried out in fear. 'Like the moon that has been eclipsed, gone is the guardian of Lanka, gone Ravana's sentry.'

Still refusing to be cowed down, courageous Kumbhakarna picked up that severed hand with the other and used that very limb to clobber the monkeys that ran helter-skelter in a bid to escape those punishing blows. More terrified were they of the hand that had come unstuck than of the one that was wielding it.

Despite knowing that Rama himself stood guard over the monkey army, Death, unafraid, continued to decimate the entire force. The world watched the mayhem, anguished and wan, thinking, 'Today is the last for monkeys on this earth.'

Stepping on the corpses scattered around him, Kumbhakarna ran to attack Rama. The gods begged, 'Please cut his other arm too.' In response, that faultless king shot a fell arrow that severed it and flung it into the sea.

What a sight it was! Weaponless, both hands gone, he went around using his legs to churn the dreadful gore of monkey flesh! Even when disabled, it appeared he was made of the five elements, absolutely indestructible.

The incomparable bowman then felled his right leg. Still he hopped along on the remaining leg, eating everything in sight. Great Rama then sent a burning shaft to take away that limb too, and the earth was relieved of its burden while Dharma danced in joy.

Hands and legs gone, mountainous chest riddled with two lakh arrows, the red blaze in his eyes doubled in intensity. The sound that issued from that cavernous mouth was louder than thunder.

Wrathful and distressed though he was, Kumbhakarna could not help but admire his foe. 'A thousand Ravanas are no match for this hero's bowmanship. I have lost my hands and legs and there is no hope for me for I am dying.

'But he who could have lived forever, has limited his time on earth, because of an unreasoning infatuation,' he said with infinite sadness.

He then looked at the handsome shoulders of the one who stood before him and said, 'You are a descendent of that king who ascended the weighing scales for the sake of a dove which sought his refuge.

'You now have an obligation to fulfil. I beg of you with my last breath, guard with care the one who left our ways and sought shelter with you.

'My brother knows only the path of virtue and justice. He is not given to the sin and pettiness of the race to which he was born. Primordial one! You who have taken an earthly form to rid the world of rakshasas, it is my dying wish that he should always be under your umbrella.

'O steadfast hero, that rakshasa who hopes to defeat you bears him a grudge and will do anything he can to kill him. Please, I beg of you, take good care of him. At no time should he be apart from you, Lakshmana or Hanuman.

'One more thing. In order that the sages and gods may never see me deprived of my nose, I plead with you to cut off my head and plunge it into the sea.'

'He has requested a boon that I cannot refuse,' said Rama. Fixing a long string to a powerful bow, he shot off that head with an arrow. Then with the aid of the Vayuvastra, he plunged it into the depths of the dark sea.

Into the ocean filled with a million creatures, its waters traversing all the directions, the arrow carried that huge face with its two smoking eyes and dropped it into the bottom of the sea's sand-filled depths.

(News of Kumbhakarna's death shook Ravana profoundly. He summoned his war council again and berated his army chiefs. 'Get away from my sight, you cowards and weaklings. You once boasted about taking the war to the enemy's territory. But when it came to that, you made me send my brother to his death. What a bunch of heroes! Go forth and fight, if you have the courage to do so. Or else get out of my sight!'

Stung to the quick, Attikaya complained that he had never been given a chance and was now unfairly being labelled a coward. 'Let me prove my worth and if I fail, disown me as your son.' Mollified, Ravana sent him to the battlefield along with Kumbha, Nikhumba and Akamba, all warriors of proven valour.

They went and fought a fierce battle but all of them perished with their army, as fate had decreed. The remnants of the straggling army returned to report to Ravana: 'Of the vast army you'd sent, only a few of us have survived, Attikaya and all other princes are dead.')

To Ravana, stunned and desolate, came Danyamalini, mother of Attikaya. Boiling with rage and grief, she wailed, beating her breast: 'Tyrant, what endless harm haven't you caused, with your lust unappeased! The progeny of Pulastya have all but been wiped out.

'Akshya is dead. And now my beloved son Attikaya is gone. The great heroes have ceased to be. Only Mandodhari's son is still alive. Do you want him to go too? Hasn't Sita done enough harm?'

'You wouldn't listen to your wise brother. You spurned your uncle's advice. You have had Kumbhakarna killed and made my prince prey to the enemy. Aren't you satisfied yet?' Stunned as he was, Ravana had nothing to say.

(Great Lanka's sorrow on that day equalled Ayodhya's grief when Rama left for the forest.)

THE SERPENT NOOSE

(When Indrajit saw the large group of rakshasis beating their breasts, hair in wild disarray, he was dismayed.)

'Has the conqueror of the world lost yet again or died in battle this time?' he speculated wildly. 'What happened?' he asked whomever he saw. But terrified and struck dumb, none answered his anxious queries.

He went at once to his father's palace and saw to his relief that Ravana was alive and well. But the king was weeping—a sight unseen and unheard of. Somewhat reassured to see him safe, he asked Ravana what'd happened.

'Death has taken your brothers,' he said. 'That brave warrior, Attikaya, accompanied by Kumbha and Nikhumbha, has reached heaven.'

'Who killed them?' he asked in shock and was informed, 'Attikaya was killed by Lakshmana. The rest by Hanuman and others from the monkey army.'

Indignant, Indrajit shot out, 'Who says they killed them? It was *you* who invited the enemy to kill them by sending them. You knew full well the might of those two men. You should have sent me instead.

'But what is the point of lamenting now? I swear I'll neither rest nor return to this great city without slaying at the same spot the one that killed my brother.

'I still have the sword given to me by Siva. If that along with the Nagastra and the Pasupatastra that I've never used thus far, guarding them as one guards a treasure, do not come to my aid today, may I wander this earth forever idle and aimless.

'I'll give to Death on a platter the one who took the ambrosial life of my brother. If I fail in this and yet continue to bear this bow, I'll be a laughing stock for the gods and unworthy of being called Ravana's son!' he swore.

'Go forth and fulfil your vow. Take away my grief,' Ravana blessed his son. 'There is nothing in this world you cannot accomplish if you set your mind to it! I thought of you in my distress, and you came promptly. Now bend your great bow against my foes and give me back the confidence I have lost.'

The hero who had conquered heaven, bowed to him, fastened an impenetrable armour and picked up in his hands that great bow crafted out of a diamond rock by Brahma specially for Indra. This was his souvenir from that famous war that had exiled the king of heaven from his own kingdom.

With a thousand chariots as reserve, he departed eagerly for the battlefield. I cannot measure the might of the army that went with him. But Valmiki himself says it was forty vellams and who can dispute that great man's claim?

Lakshmana spotted Indrajit in battle array from afar and asked Vibhishana who it was. 'Lord, this is the one who fought the mighty Indra. Who can resist his bowmanship? He trussed up even Hanuman, remember? Will the marks left by those cords on Maruti's shoulders ever disappear?

'Spotless one! Today's fight will be no walkover. You must engage him with all your might, with assistance from Hanuman, Jambavan, Sugriva, Angada, and even Nila and other warriors.'

When he saw Indrajit, Hanuman left the western gate and came to Lakshmana with the speed of wind. Angada got there even before him. All the strong monkeys put their might behind him and Sugriva took his place at the front.

Eager for conflict, the two armies confronted each other like two warring seas. The gods in heaven thought, 'Witnessing this clash today, our eyes and minds will at last reap the benefit of their existence.'

Conches blew and drumbeats resounded, making Indra and the other gods shut their ears to block out the din. Hit by rocks, trees, spears and arrows, heroes on either side fell in heaps, creating deep gorges on the surface of the earth.

The angry rakshasas, their heads knocked off by trees hard as clubs of iron, did a devil's jig on the field. Monkeys, their heads chopped off, blood spurting from their necks, looked like a forest of burning trees.

Crushed and ground by Hanuman's adamantine hands, the body parts of the rakshasas could not even be identified. The river of blood that flowed on that battlefield carried away heaps of monkey corpses to the sea.

Finding none to fight against, Indrajit turned to go back. But he had reckoned without Sugriva, who had seen his army brutally decimated. Innumerable monkeys lay around cut to bits by their cruel foes.

His face dark with rage, he shot up from where he had been hiding, and whirled a huge tree at retreating Indrajit. The speed and power with which it hurtled towards them, frightened the rakshasas out of their wits.

With an admiring 'Well done!' for the skill with which Sugriva had scattered the forces around him, Indrajit shot two well-chosen shafts aimed at his forehead, and five that winged their way towards his chest. Deadly as venom, those seven arrows split that tree into several tiny pieces, filling the air with dust.

Hanuman, his wrath lethal as the poison Siva had swallowed, slapped his shoulders and roared like thunder, vowing, 'He shall die this instant.' He flung at that mighty hero a hill that was promptly reduced to powder by more fearsome shafts.

Indrajit sneered, 'I came here specifically looking for you. With no bow in hand, you risk your life as if in sport! You challenge my deadly arrows with rocks and trees. Do you actually hope to win?'

'We have with us, stripling, some who can handle a bow as well as you. Also some who can hurl a rock at you. You'll realize all this for yourself in a day or two.

'Unlike us monkeys, Indra and his gods had powerful weapons and yet they were defeated by you and fled, fearing for their lives.

'We've not come here like them, to kiss the dust and eat the grass. We have our own ways of fighting.

'Will you fight with me or with my chief Lakshmana? Or is it that you wish to face the lord who has come here to pluck off your father's heads? Whatever be your wish, we'll not deny it to you.' Thus spake Hanuman, unperturbed.

'Where is that fool Lakshmana, who, by killing my brother, has now set aside his own life for me to slaughter?' queried Indrajit. 'I came here to kill him and quench my wrath. Be warned. I can single-handedly cut off all your heads without any help from my army.'

Hanuman laughed: 'Do you think it possible for all the elephants in the world to defeat a lion in ferocious rage? If you cannot wait till my lord Rama's brother reaches here, this rock will put out your life before your arrow can hit it. Save yourself, stripling, with your bow.'

The hill that Hanuman chucked with hands well trained in the art of war hit his foe on the chest. It was as if an irresistible force had met an immovable object, two mountains colliding against each other.

Even as Hanuman's missile was reduced to dust, the crafty demon's anger rose and his arrogance peaked. He sent a thousand arrows at the flower-decked chest and shoulders of Hanuman.

(*Blood streaming from his breast, Hanuman remained outwardly calm but was deeply disturbed within. While he was recovering, Nila the monkey chieftain took over charge and then followed a fierce battle between his valiant forces and the rakshasa army. The monkeys suffered a great defeat and Nila himself was wounded and fell down in a dead faint.*)

Lakshmana who'd been witnessing the goings-on, said, 'Vibhishana, it is our strategy that's greatly at fault. Our great chieftains are wading in gore. The numbers we have lost are not small. Shouldn't I be challenging him to a single combat?'

'You are right, my lord,' said a worried Vibhishana. 'Thousands of gods have sought to kill him in the past but could do nothing, except run away in the end. Unless you kill him, all lives on earth are threatened.'

Lakshmana stormed to the fore like a golden cloud bearing a bow. On seeing him at close quarters for the first time, Indrajit sneered, 'So, this then is the great brother of Rama?'

Immediately, a hundred crore rakshasas formed a protective circle around him. Not disturbed in the least by the vast army confronting him, Lakshmana killed them rank and file and crowned himself with triumph.

With no one left to speak for the rakshasas' might, Ravana's son stood like a lone hill in a sea that had dried up. He then approached Lakshmana on a chariot, and swift as thought, Hanuman was there, saying, 'Ascend my shoulder, lord.'

The two heroes slugged it out. Arrow snapped arrow, and those that remained unbroken, clashed and burst into flames in the sky, scorched the air and fell down, reduced to nothingness. The gods grew faint and shrank; the ground shook; the globe tottered like a vessel in a turbulent sea.

The entire world became a forest of arrows. The sea overflowed with shafts that fell in its waters. And as for the bull-like heroes, their anger waxed but their strength never waned.

Aiming a thousand arrows at those shoulders, strong as pillars of iron, Indrajit tore Hanuman's skin, making him look like a red fruit. He took aim at Lakshmana's coat of mail and shot twice 700 shafts, red-hot like *Bhatavagni*, the fire in the belly of the ocean. Lakshmana, in turn, sent hundreds of arrows that tore apart the lions that drew Indrajit's chariot and rent his mail of gold.

Blood flowed from all the spots where the arrows had shredded his flesh. Unaware of the death of the lions yoked to his golden chariot, not knowing when his charioteer fell, Indrajit said in wonder, 'He must be the Primal Man. Who else among the kings alive, can compare with this man who uses his bow to such irresistible effect?'

(The inconclusive ding-dong battle went on all day long. And as the sun was about to set, Vibhishana told Lakshmana: 'Lord, unless you dispose of him within the next few minutes, he will escape. Night is the time propitious to the rakshasas, a fight after sunset is bound to swing in his favour.'

Frustrated, Indrajit decided to end the stalemate by deciding to use the ultimate weapon in his possession, the Nagastra or the arrow of the serpent. Disappearing into the deep darkness of the moonless evening sky, he reverentially picked up the missile that would never return to its sender without binding the body and shoulders of its target, be they Siva or Vishnu themselves.)

Thinking that it was fear that'd made the rakshasa prince flee, the monkey hordes cheered lustily. Not understanding the guile of rakshasas, Lakshmana too relaxed his vigil. He descended from Hanuman's shoulder, handed his bow to Angada, pulled out the shafts that had stuck on his person and rested awhile, unaware of the disaster that awaited him in the not too distant future.

Then it was that the rakshasa's missile hit him and the ten directions filled with darkness. The astra bound the mountainous shoulders of that bull, the younger brother of Rama.

Suddenly, he felt as if a thousand fanged serpents were tightening their coils around his trunk and shoulders. He, who never faltered even when the whole world opposed him, suddenly grew weak, unable to make out what was happening. Puzzled, he looked at that field of headless bodies and then at the sky!

The golden shafts the unseen rakshasa continued to send, fell from the sky like lightning, and scattered fire and smoke. Heads fell like rain in monsoon, when the north wind sets itself against the clouds; most of the monkey leaders fell to the bolts from the sky.

Angada was struck but survived without coming to much harm. Sugriva was pierced through and through, the arrows on his person making him resemble *kazharchi*, that fruit with the prickly skin.

Only Hanuman was unharmed, though a thousand arrows had hit and bounced off his person. Eyes red with indignation, he quivered when he saw Lakshmana immobilized thus.

(Bound by the serpent noose, struck by countless arrows and bleeding profusely, Lakshmana resembled the prostrate sun swallowed by the serpent at the time of eclipse. Seeing him in a

faint, Indrajit mistakenly took him for dead and rejoiced. Delighted, he thought, 'I have accomplished what I had set out to do,' and returned to Ravana's palace to the beat of drums in a triumphal procession. He gave a brief account of the day's proceedings to his father saying, 'Your troubles are over. But I have been wounded. So please permit me to go and rest awhile. I'll tell you the rest of the story tomorrow.'

At the battlefield:)

With Lakshmana prostrate in a dead faint, desolate Vibhishana didn't know what to do. His mind a whirl like curd being churned, he wailed, 'People have been known to give up their lives for dear ones. But here I am, supposedly a friend sworn to eternal loyalty, continuing to breathe while Rama's brother lies fatally stricken by that arrow. What will people think of me?

'Will they say, "He posed as a friend and had him killed?" Or will they say, "He hauled him to his brother's son to have him defeated thus?" Or will they say, "He knowingly prepared the field for the massacre of the monkey army?" Every one who loves Rama will accuse me of some such misdeed and abuse me in whichever way they fancy.'

Startled, he realized that Rama must be informed of his brother's death at once. He ran to the lord, fell at his feet, and told him all that had happened and plunged him in a sea of sorrow. Stunned by the news, Rama at first said nothing, shed no tears, didn't wail or scream.

He hastened to his brother's side and found him in a deep faint. He fell on his body and clasping him tight, said in despair, 'He won't live.' Tears streaming from his eyes and distracted beyond endurance, he kept calling, 'Lakshmana, Lakshmana.'

From time to time he'd place his fingers against Lakshmana's nostrils and mouth and ask in desperation, 'Will you survive?' Then he would place his hand on Lakshmana's heart and upon hearing it tick, his own heart would lift and his spirits rise.

'You didn't call me in time,' he lamented, 'nor did you inform me of the battle between my brother and Ravana's son. Had I known, I would have cut off the head and hands of that sinner that let fly the serpent noose. You have harmed me deeply, Vibhishana,' said the one whom nothing could harm!

Ravana's brother heard him in silence, weeping all the while. 'We did not know of Indrajit's coming. When the battle was on, I was confident that the sinner would be defeated.

'This wizardry is not a human trait. I did warn dear Lakshmana, if Indrajit escaped with his life, he'd make use of witchcraft.

'Even as I was telling him this, the sun sank. The sea-girt earth grew dark, as if to aid him in his dark deed. Flying into the sky, he used his treacherous boon, the serpent noose, from a place of hiding and drove the monkey horde into a trance,' he said, eyes full of turbid tears.

'Who is the god who gave it to him? What is it, and what is the cure? Tell me all that you know of it,' said Rama. Vibhishana then related all that he knew of the astra.

'Gracious lord,' he said, 'this astra was created by Brahma ages ago in a yaga. Siva begged it of him and then gave it to Indrajit as a reward for his penance. It has the strength of the thunder at Dissolution.

'This was the astra that bound the sturdy shoulders of the thousand-eyed Indra. It was also the one that bound Hanuman in Lanka. It will leave only when it pleases or when the victim dies. No one in heaven, including its creator Brahma, can make it release its hold.'

Turning again to study that noose, Rama told himself, 'If this should kill him, I too will give up my life.' It was then that the great Garuda descended from the sky, to put an end to Rama's misery.

Rolling up the carpet of darkness and scattering brightness everywhere, he flew down, his white throat looking like moonbeams gathered in a bunch. The wondrous splendour of his outspread wings made him seem thrice as bright as the sun and tall as Meru.

He came down like a hill in flight, his lovely neck

adorned with crores of gem-set necklaces and garlands of cool flowers, and landed forcefully before Rama.

Addressing Rama, he said, 'O you ancient God! O Creator's creator! What is this play-acting you are engaged in? You who assuage the sorrows of all humanity, now sit and cry in deep distress!

'You whose names the gods, and the gods they worship, chant all the time, how can you feel grief and destroy yourself in this fashion?

'You, the beginning, the middle and the end, the one who can grant any wish in the world, are pretending to seek favours from others! In the guise of a man, you worship other gods, make pleas for help and cry in distress. What mystery lies behind this strange play you are enacting?

'You are the Word and the Thing, you exist beyond the vedas. Bow, arrow and shining conch in hand, you are the killer and the killed.

'And yet you pretend to grieve at possible death. What mystery lies behind this strange play-acting?

'Your ways are contradictory and inexplicable. You seem to forget and yet remember; are without bonds and yet seem attached. You, who grant your devotees the boon of release from the cycle of birth and death, choose yourself to be born, no doubt to establish Dharma on earth. What mystery lies behind this strange play-acting?

'A sharp arrow you hold in your hand and indeed look quite solid. But if one begins to investigate you antecedents, it is like skinning an onion. Who has found its core? What mystery lies behind this strange play you are enacting?'

Unable to see anything but a light bright as the sun, Rama wondered who this glorious creature was. But wonder of wonders! As soon as he landed, all those snakes dispatched by that sinner melted away. With Garuda around, they had no more strength to bind their victim than a thread to bind a lotus stem!

The breeze from those wings, that had not moulted even a single feather for a thousand years, blew away the arrows from those who lay on the field in a dead faint, leaving not a mark behind. It was like wisdom dawning after a temporary lapse.

The entire monkey horde got up from the battlefield, fresh as on the day when Brahma had created new lives after the Dissolution. But the cruel rakshasas, who had never known Dharma, continued to sleep the sleep of the dead.

Clasping joyously to his bosom the brother who had miraculously woken from a dead faint, Rama said, 'The God who created this trouble came himself to put an end to it.'

He then embraced all his friends who'd become his kinsmen by aiding him in this fierce war.

Turning to Garuda whose talons were bright as the crescent moon, Rama asked, 'Who are you, great one, coming here at a time like this to save our lives, as if to reward us for rare penances undertaken in the past?

'You have given us back the lives we had thought lost. Is there anything at all in heaven or on earth that we can offer you as a gesture of our gratitude? Though, if truth be told, nothing we poor people can give you will ever be adequate for what you have done for us.

'Great one! Will you be so good as to let us know who you are? We have never seen you before, nor indeed could you have heard of us. You owe us nothing; you have no needs; you seem like you were made for giving. You helped us when we lay here half dead, though we share no previous history of friendship. What can we do for you? Please, tell us.'

'After you are done with the rakshasas, I shall return and tell you of our old bonds. But now, O foe of illusions, give me leave to go,' said the guardian of the birds and flew away.

Rama mused on what he'd heard, 'He was not obliged to give us life, yet he did. The noble seek no recompense. Does the earth requite the sky for rain?'

(With Lakshmana's revival, there was great rejoicing among the monkeys. Hanuman suggested to Rama, 'Let's have a noisy revel. I say this for two reasons. That dear lady might have been misinformed that Lakshmana was no more. The sound of our *riotous merrymaking will reassure her that nothing of the sort has happened. Secondly, the rakshasas who have gone home in the smug belief that they have won a famous victory will come to know that they are suffering a delusion.'*

Rama approved of the idea and the sky resounded with noisy celebrations. They raised such a clamour that the seas were perturbed and the earth opened up. The world grew faint and the clouds broke and scattered, while the mountains split in two!)

Hearing the deafening din, Ravana was intrigued and became uneasy. Perhaps the happy news Indrajit had given him earlier in the day was not correct?

The noise that assailed his ears seemed to indicate not gloom but riotous joy. 'So much for the message that the enemy has collapsed!' he told himself sardonically. He got off his bed and proceeded to Indrajit's palace to verify the truth of the matter.

That prince was not celebrating his famous victory either. Instead, he lay nursing his wounds from the day's battle. He looked more like a mauled lion than an exultant victor, unable to even rise to welcome his father.

Seeing Ravana's surprise and concern, Indrajit confessed shamefacedly, 'It was a close fight, Father. I was nearly beaten and managed to save myself only through magic. Though I've killed Lakshmana with the Nagastra, my wounds hurt badly and my thoughts even more.

'I tell you Father, this man's strength seems boundless. If such is the power of the younger brother, I fear that Rama's valour might well be beyond us. In the encounter to come, we certainly cannot take success for granted.'

'You haven't killed Lakshmana, my heroic son,' said Ravana, lips curling in a sneer. 'Didn't you hear the twang of his mighty bow splitting the sky, and the din made by the celebrating monkeys, louder than thunder?'

'But Father, he was bound by that fearsome noose,' said Indrajit, thoroughly rattled. 'What could have undone that death-like embrace? Even the thought of it is an insult to its deity.'

(Just then the spies sent out to find out the reasons for revelry in the enemy's camp returned to report. They related how Rama in his grief at seeing Lakshmana immobilized by the serpent-arrow had vowed to reduce the whole world to ashes. They also told them how Garuda descended from heaven in the nick of time to avert disaster. 'As soon as those sharp-fanged serpents that bound Lakshmana and the monkeys in their death grip broke to pieces, all those who had fallen prey to it were healed of their wounds and got up whole, as if from a deep sleep.')

'So, the noose my son'd cast with such effort was undone by the breeze from Garuda's wings! What a shame! What price Ravana, the terror of the gods! I may as well be in my dotage!' said a bitter Ravana.

'I, who had struck unconscious the discus-wielder who once had swallowed the fourteen worlds, live to hear of a mere bird's insolence.

'I remember that the very same Garuda, brother of Aruna, was once hit by one of my shafts aimed at Vishnu. He has now come to help my enemy and taken belated revenge!

'Ah well! Let it be. What's to happen, will happen,' he said resignedly. Indrajit replied, 'Father, let me rest today. Tomorrow, I shall avenge our humiliation by using the missile sacred to Brahma and wipe out my disgrace and your sorrows.'

DECIMATION

(Fighting resumed the next day with renewed vigour. Though demoralized, the rakshasa forces returned to the field, led by numerous army chiefs, and fought and perished with unfailing regularity, as did the monkeys, though they too fought with courage and enthusiasm. Pukainirakkannan engaged Hanuman, Angada took on Maaperupakkan, Nila targeted Mali, and monkey Pasnasa joined issue with the ghostly Pichachan. The son of the Sun fought Surianpakaignan, the sun hater, and Lakshmana took on Velvipakaivan who abhorred sacrifices. Vajradanta engaged Idaba, the fearless monkey leader. And Rama himself intervened from time to time to relieve the monkey chiefs.

Thus continued the war between the rival forces, one side led by fierce white-fanged rakshasa generals and the other by leonine monkey chiefs. They fought with such ferocity that the gods were filled with fright. When the blood of the slain and the wounded flowed into the sea, it was not blood that lost colour. Instead, it was the sea that turned a molten copper. Not one of the rakshasa heads survived that slaughter of the generals.)

While bees bore the glad tidings to smiling Sita immured in the Asoka grove, Ravana heard the dismal news of his army's defeat from Yama's messengers in his palace. With a bitter heart, he agonized over the next move, as he sat in council. Then Khara's only son, Makarakkannan, the carp-eyed one, spoke his mind.

'How is it, lord, you never thought me worthy of taking on those monkeys? Have you forgotten that I have a score to settle with my father's killers?

'Don't you know that my grieving mother has vowed not to part with her marriage thread until she can put it around the skull of her husband's killer? Please let me go and fulfil her dearest wish.'

'Very well, then,' said Ravana, giving his blessings. 'Go forth and feed fat your ancient grudge.'

Confronting Rama, no less, that villain said, 'You killed my father. I abhor the Trinity, but for now, I shall direct all my hatred towards you alone.' The hero nodded, saying, 'You are Khara's son, then? You spoke well, my boy. It is indeed a son's duty to avenge his father.'

Then the fight took its dreary course. Blessed by the boons he had once obtained from Vayu and Varuna, Khara's son rose to the sky at will and sent down thunder, wind and fire, to destroy the hapless hordes who stood below.

(Baffled, Rama asked Vibhishana to explain the source of his power and was told the story of the boons. Vowing to turn things around, within a second, he dispatched two arrows that chased away all the flying missiles and plunged them into the sea. At last the rain and tempest ceased.)

Undeterred, the rakshasa fought on. Gaining invisibility through his knowledge of witchcraft, he showered lesser missiles from the sky and killed many a monkey.

Exasperated, Rama shot an arrow into the sky that followed the trail of blood that streamed from the invisible mouth of that demon. Carp-eyes crashed to the ground, beheaded.

Thereafter, the rest of the rakshasa army was completely decimated by the arrows of those two bowmen and the trees and rocks hurled by the monkey horde. The few that survived ran to report the rout to Ravana.

His eyes blazing, the rakshasa king ordered his son Indrajit to his presence. He came at once and consoled his father saying, 'Don't you grieve.

'Today you shall see, as will Sita and those innumerable gods, a heap of monkey corpses and the dead bodies of those two bowmen.' Going round his father thrice in a *pradakshina*, he then bent and touched his feet to seek his blessings.

Upon entering the battlefield, Indrajit stood transfixed in his chariot, bow in hand, and saw how his men lay about in heaps, with no means of identifying any of the corpses.

'Have all the elephants been killed? Have all the chariots been ruined? Is there no soldier left even to remove the dead?' he stood bewildered by the heap of corpses that touched the sky.

'Just two of them! And sixty *vellams* gone without a trace! What is it they use—bows or curses, witchcraft or some such trickery?' he wondered aloud.

Lakshmana saw him and told Rama, 'Lord, the world will say that I disgraced myself in the earlier fight with this canny foe by getting bound by the serpent noose. They will say I could neither guard my friends nor strike terror in the heart of the enemy.

'They'll jeer that I could neither bind my foe as I myself was bound, nor die an honourable death. If my arrow does not bring down the head of this Indrajit today, I'll be considered not a feast fit for Yama, but offal for a despicable dog when I die.'

Flashing a smile, Rama said, 'Wise one, if you resolve on something, dare even the gods stand in your way?' Greatly encouraged, Lakshmana bowed and, blowing a conch that roared louder than the sea, he unleashed a shower of arrows against the forces that had come with Ravana's son.

The slaughter began afresh. A single shaft from that doughty warrior's bow broke the axles of a thousand chariots. Leaping horses fell along with their riders and the lopped off heads of chieftains rolled on the ground.

Though his army was decimated, Ravana's son, who now stood all alone, did not retreat. Speaking with contempt, he asked, 'Are both of you going to fight me at the same time or will it be just one? You'd perhaps wish to attack me with your entire force? Whatever you decide, I intend to give you a fitting answer.'

'I challenge you to a fight, whether with sword, bow or any other weapon of your choice. We can even wrestle, if you wish. One thing is certain: I'm going to kill you today. This I swear,' said Lakshmana.

'And I,' countered Indrajit, 'promise to send your elder brother to the land of death, after seeing you off to the same destination first. If I cannot do this, what use my having been born?

'I am not Ravana's brother Kumbhakarna. I am Ravana's son, Indrajit, one of a kind, unique. My uncle was easy game, not I. I'll offer the blood of you brothers as libation to those of my kinsmen you have killed.'

'Vibhishana is here to offer libation to the entire race of rakshasas. And the obsequies you'd have performed at your father's death, your sorrowing father will soon be performing at yours,' was Lakshmana's sharp retort.

Boiling with rage, the rakshasa sent a shower of incessant arrows towards Lakshmana, Rama and the monkey heroes. Rama's brother brushed aside all the missiles, answering astra with astra, like truth confronting and repelling a lie, told time and again.

The great one stood behind him but never once interfered, for this was *their* battle. Neither combatant prevailed over the other, their shafts flaming in the sky like faggots.

Those missiles brought down forests, hills and golden houses. Seas were set on fire, as were clouds. The whole world burnt as if at Dissolution.

Lakshmana staunched that flood of venomous arrows with shafts of his own. First, he shot dead the thousand lions that drew Indrajit's chariot. Standing on his shattered vehicle, Indrajit let fly countless arrows at Angada and Lakshmana. Sumitra's lion shot in return ten arrows that deprived the rakshasa prince of his armour of gold.

Both heroes were tiring of the stalemate. Thinking that the situation called for a change of tactics, Indrajit used his magical powers and disappeared into the sky, denying Lakshmana an obvious target.

Exasperated, Lakshmana turned to his brother and said, 'If he survives, our army will be utterly destroyed. Please, lord, permit me to use the Brahmastra.'

Rama was not in favour of this. 'If the Creator's unstoppable missile is let loose, it will ruin the three worlds.' Convinced of the justice of what Rama said, Lakshmana did not insist.

The deceiver read Lakshmana's mind and decided to use that divine weapon himself. But thinking it wise to disappear from the scene for a while to mislead the enemies, he left the battlefield. As he'd expected, the gods who had assembled to witness that epic battle were deceived and began to rejoice prematurely.

When those fierce arrows disappeared like clouds blown high, the monkey chiefs were both angry and happy. They thought, 'He has fled like a coward.' The doughty heroes too became less alert and descended from their perch on Hanuman's and Angada's shoulders.

They then put away their bows, arrows, armours and gloves and rested, even as the gods showered flowers and blessings on them.

Meanwhile, Indrajit went to inform his father about his decision to use the Brahmastra. Ravana was taken aback. 'My son,' he said, 'this is not a weapon to be used lightly. Have you thought about it carefully?'

Indrajit replied, 'Father, wise men have said that one should kill rather than be killed first! It is best to dispatch the Brahmastra from a place of hiding. It is quite lawful to do so.

'If they get to know that I intend to use this missile, they themselves will use it first. And I prefer to do this while remaining hidden. For if those ascetic princes spot me, they will surely kill me first. I'll now proceed with the preliminary rites, required to release that deadly astra that will finish them instantaneously.

'In order to distract them and keep them from wondering about my whereabouts, dispatch against them an army equipped with conventional weapons. I'll do the rest.' Ravana promptly sent off Mahodara, the pot-bellied general, to confront the monkey hordes.

(The rakshasa army was back, but without Indrajit. Though this intrigued the monkeys, led by Lakshmana who was assisted ably by Hanuman and Sugriva, they were ready to face the fresh assault. With the erratic swing in fortune, hope followed despair, as monkey leaders were lost and found again, often far from the spot where they disappeared in hot pursuit of the enemy. The rakshasa generals tried all the tricks of black magic to confound the naïve monkeys. At one stage Mahodara took on the guise of Indra on his mount, Airavatham, surrounded by gods and sages, making the bewildered monkeys scatter helter-skelter.

'This is the time,' thought Ravana's son and repaired quickly to a banyan tree. Rakshasa priests brought together everything needed for a sacrifice. With arrows for fuel, the villainous prince strewed thumbai flowers at the site, poured black sesame, killed a black goat that had all its teeth and both horns intact. He then fed the sacrificial fire with its flesh and blood and lots of ghee.)

The breeze carried the fire-diffusing fragrance from left to right—an auspicious omen. Convinced that victory would be his, the scion of that cruel race rose to the sky and disappeared, ready to deploy the deadly astra against Lakshmana.

And then he shot his bolt. That ancient astra, sacred to Brahma, came down like lightning from nowhere.

Lakshmana's body was instantly pierced by innumerable arrows, that looked like a flock of sparrows pecking at golden Meru. He fell down unconscious, like a great tusker gone to sleep.

Shocked and bewildered, Hanuman, whose mind was still on the fake Indra conjured up by Mahodara, asked, 'Why would Indra do this?' Furious, he vowed, 'I'll throw him out, elephant and all.' But the thousand crores of arrows that stuck to his body rendered him unconscious and he fell flat on the ground.

Bathed in blood like a golden hill covered with *palasa*, the Sun's son too became giddy, as the cruel arrows had pierced his entire body. Angada, his eyes red as molten copper, fell and measured the ground.

The great Jambavan, his chest and shoulders punctured, collapsed in a similar fashion. Nila too found himself face to face with Yama. Idaba reached heaven and Pasnasa fell to a venomous shaft.

'The younger one has died with the monkey crew,' jeered Indrajit and blew his conch triumphantly before leaving to tell his father the good news.

'Is that Rama dead?' asked Ravana, still anxious. 'No, he was not there. Otherwise, would he have just stood by and watched while I killed his brother and his dear friends and scattered his army?'

Having made his triumphant announcement Indrajit then left for his palace, his heart swelling with the pride and fulfilment of one who had just accomplished an important mission.

(*Meanwhile, Rama, who had just finished offering worship to the various missiles, decided to join the battle. With a flaming arrow in his hand, he reached the spot and was horrified at the sight that confronted him. The entire field was littered with corpses as far as the eye could see. Scanning them to identify the chiefs, he first spotted Sugriva, then Hanuman, and became utterly disconsolate.*)

Eyes welling with tears, he wailed, 'Valiant son of Vayu! Was it for this you crossed the sea to enter Lanka and churn the rakshasas by their very entrails? All this to rid me of my troubles? The boons obtained from gods, the prophetic words of the sages, Sita's blessings—nothing has borne fruit, all because of my past sins!

'I killed my real father and limited the days of Jatayu, the father who adopted me. So many heroes, my friends all, dead. And yet I continue to live. Is there no limit to my evil?

'I killed the elder to give to the younger. I seem to have done nothing but destroy. I was born only to be a burden to this earth,' he lamented.

And then he saw Lakshmana lying on a heap of corpses, his body pierced by numerous arrows. His heart swelling with sorrow, he seethed, breathing fire. Overcome with grief, he seemed to shrink in body and mind and Dharma pounded his eyes. He drooped like a tree struck by lightning.

He didn't breathe for a long while, numb and cold, his eyes shut. As he lay unmoving, he seemed all but dead! The gods were frightened and asked one another, 'Has he collapsed?'

There was none to support him, none to clasp his hand, none to console him with words. All his allies and friends had been killed, or so he thought. There was not one human soul on that field of headless torsos and devils, except for some red-eyed women searching for their husbands' bodies. Ravenous jackals prowled, pleased at the prospect of a rare feast.

Elsewhere, the gods wept, while apsaras beat their breasts and rained tears. All living things melted. Smiles were wiped off the faces of Brahma and Siva and their eyes welled up with tears of compassion. Why, even sin and wickedness sobbed in sympathy!

Consciousness returning, Rama opened his eyes a little and searched Lakshmana's face. 'He has gone to heaven and won't return,' he said sorrowfully, his heart wilting like a sore exposed to flame.

Breaking into lamentation, he cried, 'O brother incomparable! I lost my father but did not die. I was ready to accept at the end of my exile the kingdom I had given Bharata, only because I thought I could rule with you by my side. I was never alone when you were about. I still hear your voice, but you no longer exist and yet I carry on living!

'You were my mother, my father, my penance. You are my son, my brother, my fortune; you have left me bereft, alone. You are dead and I live, more hard-hearted than you! I see no life in your shattered body and yet I breathe. Wretched that I am, why isn't *my* body shattered?

'For fourteen years, you sought food for me in the forest, trudging long distances in the hot sun, without a morsel for yourself. Are you now sleeping, the effort having finally tired you out? Will you not wake up?

'I always said we were one, not two, but this has now been disproved. For I continue to live when you are no more, wicked and heartless sinner that I am. When again will my life join with yours?

'You gave up everything for my sake—mother, father, wife, relations, your own duties and pleasures. You followed me, not only by birth, but right through your life. Like a shadow, you never once left my side. But now you have left me. How can I bear this pain and live on?

'A virtuous woman is held captive by a tyrannical rakshasa. And instead of destroying him, Dharma goes over to his side. If despite all that has taken place, the three worlds are still left standing, what does that say about the strength of my bow?

'Has all my might been expended only on dry trees that had rotted at the root, on Vali, on a ditch that was considered a sea, on Virada, on a swift crow, on Khara and others of his ilk? Should I not have stayed here and destroyed Indrajit and other demons?

'Instead, I left you bearing the burden of that responsibility, and now sit about doing nothing. I cannot call myself your brother, nor do I deserve to live.

'Knowing that the serpent noose unleashed by the same enemy had laid you low not too long ago, I walked away this time too, like one who knows no love. Won't the world laugh at my amateur pursuit of victory?

'I promised a kingdom to Vibhishana, but now will die without keeping my word. I've learnt to lie like an expert and brought discredit to my clan. Alas! I have murdered my reputation with my own hands.'

So he lamented and berated his destiny, sobbing his heart out, his senses one with his heart. Clasping tight his brother who he thought was dead, he fell into a swoon.

Gleeful rakshasas carried the news to Ravana. 'Your matchless son's unfailing shafts have felled all the enemy chiefs, including the younger brother. Unable to bear the loss, Rama too has died. All your foes have departed this world!' they chortled.

THE MEDICINE MOUNTAIN

(Vibhishana returned to the field after having arranged food for the army and was aghast at the sight that met his eyes. He saw the hordes that looked as if they had fallen to a curse by the Creator and stood transfixed. Spotting Rama's prostrate body near Lakshmana's prone form, he was shaken. But after carefully looking him over and noticing that there were no wounds on his body, he reassured himself that he still lived.)

'He must have fainted in grief. When he wakes, we'll decide what step is to be taken next. He will not live with his brother gone. Have those rascals won after all?' he wondered.

Even so, he refused to give up hope and told himself, 'Just as that serpent noose was loosened, this astra too will lose its power. There is no danger to our lord; his beloved brother and the army temporarily overwhelmed, will survive too. Can the wicked ever triumph?

'Without wasting any more time, I must find out if there is anyone left who can help me.' Wading through the mire of gore with a torch in hand, he scanned the scattered bodies. Luckily, he spotted Hanuman, lying on a bed of dead elephants.

Upon careful examination, he came to the conclusion that Hanuman was still alive and drew out one by one the shafts that'd been embedded in his body. He then brought down some water from the clouds and sprinkled it over his handsome face.

Hanuman opened his eyes and rolled over, bristling. Immediately, he uttered the blessed name of Rama and a relieved Vibhishana breathed a sigh of relief. Weeping tears of joy, the saintly brother of Ravana drew Hanuman to his bosom in a tight embrace. 'Is our lord well?' queried an anxious Maruti.

'Distressed and grieving for his brother, he has fallen into a deep swoon. When he wakes up, we shall know what to do,' answered Vibhishana. Then Hanuman asked about Jambavan. 'We need advice and he alone is capable of giving sound counsel.'

'I don't know. I haven't seen him and have no idea whether he is alive or dead. I came here but a short while ago.'

Hanuman said with some urgency, 'He cannot die, let's look for him. He alone can tell us how to revive those two lying there in a dead swoon.'

'Let's hurry,' Vibhishana agreed. After a few stumbling steps in the dark, they found Jambavan. Age, the damage caused by the arrows and grief at the loss of his friends, had rendered him breathless and his mind a blank. Nonetheless, that doughty warrior's sharp ears caught the sound of their approaching footsteps.

When those two tearful friends reached his side, he said, 'It is the Brahmastra that has felled us all; there can be no doubt of that. But it is incapable of harming the ever-victorious Rama. Describe to me what exactly it has done to him.' Vibhishana told him that he was in a deep sleep caused by sorrow.

Jambavan shook his head, 'How can it be otherwise? Their bodies are two, but their life is one. But let's not waste any more time in idle grieving. We have things to do.'

Addressing Hanuman, he said, 'O diamond-shouldered son of the wind! Do not tarry. Fetch at once the medicine that we need.

'If only you do what I tell you, the entire seventy *vellams* that perished, Rama and his brother, the three worlds, Dharma and the vedas, all shall recover and live once again. Don't waste a single moment, follow my instructions, and run this very instant!

'Stalwart hero, leave this sea behind and travel a distance 9,000 yojanas away. There you will find the Himalayas, that extend wide to 2,000 yojanas. A further 9,000 yojanas will see you reach the mountain of gold.

'From there, go 9,000 yojanas more to reach Nidata, the red mountain. Another 9,000 to Meru, taller than the rest. Nine thousand later, you will come to the blue mountain. Four thousand yojanas from there is the black mountain of medicines. There lies the end of our sorrows.

'Among the medicines to be found there is one that will revive the dead, another that'll join bodies torn asunder, a third that'll help extricate weapons embedded deep inside the body and, last of all, one that'll restore a person to the way he was before.'

He then told Hanuman how to recognize each of these medicinal plants. 'These four herbs rose from the bottom of the sea when the milky ocean was churned. Knowing how valuable they are, the gods keep them a well-guarded secret.

'When that Primordial God measured the worlds, I was the one who beat the drum for him. Then it was that I saw these plants and asked about them and was told of their miraculous properties by the ancient sages.

'Countless guards keep watch over these precious medicines, each one armed with weapons sharp and well-honed. But truthful one, once they know the reason behind your mission, they won't stop you. Now leave at once. May Rama be with you.'

Hanuman was ready in an instant. 'If this is all that is required of me to make the dead live again, nothing can stand in my way. While I am gone, please take care of our lord.'

Expanding to the stature rarely seen, his head touching the floor of heaven and his golden shoulders widening till they covered the sky, he got ready for his journey to the hill of rare medicinal plants.

His shoulders stretched from end to end, more than a

thousand yojanas in breadth. After he took his first step, there was no space left in Lanka to accommodate his second. His outstretched arms extended beyond the quarters.

Then, his long tail curling, he raised his hands and opened his mouth to take a deep breath to broaden his chest. Digging his feet into the earth, he leapt to the sky with such speed that Lanka was soon nothing more than a ship in the sea.

As he sprang to the sky, clusters of clouds were rent to pieces and the wide ocean grew turbulent. Stars scattered in different directions and aerial chariots crashed to the seas. Tempestuous winds blew over the eastern mountains, causing them to lean north.

The seas fled first and the wind rushed behind, his body seeming to have overtaken his quick mind. He passed the world of the clouds and then the kingdom of the sun and the moon. He even crossed the heaven that sages seek to obtain with rigorous penance. And, finally, he landed on the Himalayas.

Patient sages and righteous men, who lived in the bosom of that sacred mountain, blessed him: 'May you succeed in your noble mission.'

Then he sighted Kailasa, the abode of the Destroyer. Speeding north-east, he came to the place where Siva dwelt and folded his hands in obeisance. The lord, well pleased, pointed him out to Parvati as the wind god's son.

To her query about the reason for his presence in those parts, he explained, 'He is Rama's messenger, come looking for rare medicinal herbs.' Turning to Hanuman, he wished him godspeed.

Crossing a 1,000 yojanas, Hanuman reached the top of Hemakuta, where the gods sport and seek endless pleasures. Then with the speed of Vishnu's discus, he reached Nidata. Then, swifter than the thoughts of wise men, he reached Meru, used by heaven and earth as a measuring rod.

Flying past that famous landmark, he saw in a great island surrounded by the sea, the renowned *jambu* tree worshipped by the three worlds. He also saw on the summit of the mountain, the Creator himself, seated on a shining golden seat, and meditating. Folding his palms in reverence, he moved on.

(*Crossing that big mountain, he was dazzled by a light that dispelled the darkness around. Thinking it was already dawn, he lamented, 'Alas, my task has been aborted. The medicine should have been applied before daylight and I have still to find it and am far away from Lanka.' But he soon realized his error. He had forgotten what the puranas say: to those in the north of Meru, the sun will appear in the opposite direction. Therefore, in Lanka, the sun was still in the west, and dawn had not yet broken. Greatly relieved, he moved on.*)

Crossing that mountain that threw night itself into the shade, he sighted at last the place described by Jambavan. He landed on it with a leap, whose impact made that huge hill tilt. The guardian deities were furious and rushed up to him, sternly questioning, 'Who are you? What do you want?'

When he explained the reason for his visit, they blessed him, 'Take what you want, but when you are through, show us that you've done no damage to the place.' Vishnu's discus, which had appeared to defend Vayu's son, in case he was hampered in his errand, also disappeared.

Fearing he would lose precious time if he started looking for particular herbs, Maruti decided to uproot the hill. In a flash he sprang to the sky, with that mountain a 1,000 yojanas wide and deep, balanced on one palm.

(*With Hanuman thus engaged in a vital mission, let us return to Lanka and see what was happening on the field of battle. After Hanuman left, Vibhishana and Jambavan hastened to where Rama and Lakshmana lay unconscious. They vigorously massaged Rama's feet. To their great relief and joy, he soon opened his eyes and saw their distressed faces. Relieved that at least they were alive, he began once more to lament without waiting to hear what they had to say.*)

In despair, he said, 'We are ruined, friends. There is nothing at all we can do. Those who are dead will not return.

What a fool and knave am I to have caused so much misery to so many people who trusted in my so-called valour and came to my aid.

'My whole life is a catalogue of errors. Because I doted on Sita, I let her coax me into a foolish act. I didn't heed my brother's warning and went after that phantom stag. The result, friends, is the undeserved death of all those on this field!

'I confronted Ravana face to face and waged a fearful battle. But the sins of my past made me refrain from killing him, for what seem in retrospect foolish reasons. Because of that act of thoughtlessness, I have now lost all my friends.

'When my brother asked me leave to use the Brahmastra, I denied him permission, impelled doubtless by the grim fate bent on destroying my life.

'Instead of continuing to stay by his side, I went away to offer worship to the weapons. And what happened? Our friends were killed and my brother died without fulfilling his vow to defeat that rakshasa. Fate it was that's once again prevailed.

'Now that I have lost my brother and friends, what purpose will be served by my killing Ravana and destroying root and branch the entire rakshasa race?

'With my brother dead, for whom should I carry on living? For eternal fame? For virtue's sake? For the sake of proving my manliness? For my kith and kin? For the kingdom Bharata promised me? For the sake of friendship? For the future? For the vedas, perhaps? Or to uphold truth?

'With my brother gone, if with a heart hardened in pain and anger, I vanquish the rakshasas and establish my manliness, what will that prove, except that I'm a heartless creature, and that I am a cheat as well? I would much rather die.

'All men of honour will say, "He lost his father, Jatayu, his dear friends, and a spotless brother, who guarded him through thick and thin, all because this man of straw could not think beyond his wife."

'How wonderful it would sound, if I now said, "I've returned to Ayodhya, after destroying that race called rakshasas, to rule this land!" No, I'd much rather kill myself at once,' he said, grief having driven him to distraction and blunted his powers of reasoning.

Jambavan fell at his feet and said, 'Before you do anything, lord, please listen to what I've to say. You who are beyond all knowledge, seem not to know yourself. But *I* have known you a long while. To reveal the secret of your existence now will be a sin, for it would be against the plan of the gods.

'Great chief, I guessed that the missile that pierced your brother's body must be the Brahmastra. O lord who transcends everything, though it is a deadly weapon, capable of sucking up the lives of gods and demons alike, it cannot touch you. That is how you have survived its venomous attack.

'As for the others, including Lakshmana, they are not dead and are only in a death-like faint. At my request, the great Hanuman has rushed north to bring the sovereign remedy required to revive them. That peerless hero will soon be back and all our woes will end.

'Only the Trinity, my father and I know of the nature of these herbs. One of these, ancient and powerful, will remove the missile; another mend the broken bones; a third will bring back the life lost; and the fourth will restore the wounded to their original form.

'Hanuman will soon be here, guided by Dharma himself. Let us wait,' he said. Rama was greatly relieved: 'I don't doubt for a moment what you've said about the efficacy of the drugs or about Hanuman's ability to bring them.'

Even as he was speaking, there was a huge noise in the sky. The sea surged and waves pounded the shores. Cloud-bearing hills cracked and a typhoon blew in from the north.

The stars lost their slots and got scattered, the sun embraced the moon and the deer were terror-struck at the sight of the stag on the moon!

Before you could say, 'Here he is,' Hanuman stood once again on Lanka's soil. But the divine mountain hovered in the air, loath to alight on that land of sinners!

Then Vayu came and took forth the scent of the medicinal plants to the bodies scattered below. Lakshmana, Sugriva and the rest got up miraculously, as if from a slumber and raised a joyous shout!

The breeze from that mountain revived all those who'd till then been guests waiting in Death's parlour to meet Yama. However, those who regained life were all from the monkey army; the bodies of the rakshasas were thrown into the sea and perished.

The shafts fell off, the wounds were healed, and life returned. Innumerable pairs of eyes that had been staring sightlessly, began to move again. Lakshmana hastened to Rama's side.

Shoulders swelling joyously, eyes filling with tears of happiness, Rama embraced his brother. Then, eyes grown dim with tears of love, he embraced Hanuman and said, 'You have banished the very name of sorrow.

'We were born first as the sons of one who never deviated from the code laid down. He died because of the sorrow I caused. We too had given ourselves up to death, but thanks to you, who never depart from the path of righteousness, we have been born for the second time!

'Can a life saved thus last long enough for it to thank its saviour adequately? It is not merely our *lives* you have saved, but our fame and our lineage and, indeed, Dharma itself.'

Jambavan then told Hanuman, 'O you of infinite energy! Lest this mountain revive our wicked foes too, go and replace it at the spot you took it from and return quickly.' Hanuman promised to be back in minutes, and hefting once again that divine hill, took to the sky.

(*Meanwhile, there was much rejoicing in Ravana's palace. Thinking Rama and Lakshmana both dead, a riotous carousal was under way and wine flowed freely at Ravana's command. Kinnaras played divine music and apsaras danced with abandon, the wine having gone to their heads. Naga girls whose breasts had just begun to ripen jostled for space with the more mature vidyadhara women; yakshinis and siddha maidens of all ages danced wildly to* the delectation of Ravana and his courtiers. When their garments slid down their thighs, their luxuriously long tresses came to the rescue of their shame. Getting more and more drunk with every passing minute, they sang and played their strings with no regard for pitch or measure.

Even as this bacchanalia reached a crescendo, there came the sounds of raucous celebration from the monkey camp. Puzzlement turned to consternation among the revellers. Spies came and whispered in Ravana's ears the news of the miraculous resurrection of Lakshmana and others. Startled and shaken, he left abruptly for his private chambers, where he called yet again for the meeting of his council.

Once again he was assailed by contradictory advice. Venerable Malliyavan reiterated his view that Sita be returned to her husband. Predictably, this was rejected at once by an indignant Ravana, who swore that he himself would go to the battlefield to take on his human challengers. At this point, Indrajit intervened, saying that the Brahmastra had failed, 'because I had thoughtlessly targeted Rama too. It refused to touch him, because like Vibhishana had rightly said, he is not a mere man or even an ancient god, but God, the Supreme Being.

'But let the past be. I shall, if you'll permit me, repair to Nikumbhila to perform a yaga to acquire new powers to attain invincibility and put an end to our troubles.' Ravana approved of this idea, whereupon Indrajit said, 'Your brother, Vibhishana, will warn them and they will try to disrupt my sacrifice,' and came up with an ingenious idea to counter any attempt on their part to discover the truth.

'I'll conjure up a likeness of Sita and kill that false image in front of Hanuman who alone knows her face well. I'll also boast that I am on my way to attack Ayodhya. This is sure to rattle them. With Sita "dead", they will all rush to defend Kosala. Even if this fails and they suspect a trick and send Hanuman to investigate, we would still have gained time to complete the yaga.'

He then left for the western gate where he encountered Hanuman. Catching the fake Sita by the hair, he sneered, 'So you've come to fight for the sake of this maiden. My father is no longer interested in her and I've been told to kill her!'

Shocked and baffled at this turn of events, Hanuman tried to argue him out of his decision to murder. He recalled to the wily prince his descent from Brahma and his sterling qualities as a peerless warrior. 'This is not chivalrous behaviour. It is unbecoming of you to kill a woman.' But Indrajit refused to relent and slew the phantom Sita before Hanuman's eyes.

Devastated, Hanuman ran to Rama and told him the tragic news. The entire company was stunned and confused. Only Vibhishana who knew well the devious ways of the rakshasas kept his head. He turned to Rama and spoke, 'Lord, I too was initially stunned by the news that Hanuman brought. But upon reflection, I suspect the whole thing to be a fraud, mere rakshasa trickery. Allow me to find out what has happened.'

He then assumed the form of a bee and flew off, quicker than Rama's mind. Soon, he reached the Asoka grove where Sita was immured and saw with his own eyes the emaciated maid. She certainly seemed sad and shattered, but was very much alive!

Vibhishana also saw that preparations were under way for Indrajit's Nikumbhila yaga, and understood then the reasons for the elaborate hoax that had been enacted. Rid of the confusion about Sita's death, he returned to Rama, his heart uplifted and mind clear of all doubts. Rama was filled with immeasurable joy when he heard the glad tidings and the monkeys leapt and danced with joy. The din prompted the gods to ask one another whether the seven seas and the seven isles had come together to create the din. Some thought yes and some no.)

THE NIKUMBHILA YAGA

(The hero's doubts had been resolved. He clasped Vibhishana close to his heart and said, 'With you, Hanuman and Dharma by my side, and the almighty God looking down upon us so favourably, why should we fear rakshasa wiles?')

Vibhishana, however, was a little worried, 'But lord, if that yaga is completed, we cannot defeat the rakshasas. Give me leave to go with Lakshmana and stop Indrajit from completing the yaga.'

Rama embraced his brother with the advice, 'Son, bear

well in mind that your mandate is only to prevent the use of the Brahmastra, not use it yourself. That weapon, if let loose, will destroy heaven and earth, which you must avoid at all cost.

'He might discharge Siva's missile, and probably Vishnu's too. Counter both with a like missile. As for his life, put an end to it. O clever prince, fix your arrow before he fixes his.

'Anticipate his every move. The shafts he'll send with speed immeasurable, faster than wind itself, you must foresee and deflect even as they are dispatched.'

When that brother who'd never parted from him left in such hot haste, he felt as if his own life had gone, leaving behind the shell of his body. It was exactly as Dasaratha had felt when, all those years ago, he himself had left with that great sage Viswamitra, to guard the site where the yaga was to be performed.

Hands holding aloft torches, the monkey horde left with Lakshmana for Nikumbhila. There they saw the rakshasa army had formed a protective circle around a banyan tree and were guarding the sacrificial fire that resembled *Bhatavagni*, the fire in the ocean's belly.

With stones, trees and bare hands for weapons, the monkeys scattered the bows, axes and clubs of the enemies, and killed hundreds of the rakshasa troops.

In return, the rakshasas threw countless clubs, axes, ploughshares, spears, and shafts and deprived the monkeys of their tails, heads, trunk and limbs.

Vibhishana turned to Lakshmana with some urgency: 'Why waste time? Unless you destroy the yaga, how are we going to foil the enemy's plans?'

Stung to the quick by this admonition, Lakshmana shot off a rain of sharp arrows that sent numerous rakshasas to Death's abode in the south.

The fight that ensued was a sight for the gods. Heads and bodies, severed by Lakshmana's accurate arrows, fell in the yard where the sacred fires had been lit.

Chapleted crowns came flying through the air and broke the *purna kumbha* consecrated with vedic mantras.

The Trinity themselves had come to witness that battle and had taken their place in the sky. Not one god was left in heaven.

Rivers of blood streamed in and doused the yaga fire. Buffaloes and sheep meant for oblations were killed before their time. Headless rakshasa torsos danced wildly, upsetting vessels full of ghee, toddy and puffed rice kept for use at the appropriate time.

Like the wind, like venom, like a weaver's thread, like a disease, Lakshmana's arrows found their way into every nook and cranny and ruined and wreaked every sacred object meant for the sacrifice.

The yaga fire extinguished, everything else scattered and invocatory texts forgotten, Indrajit rose to his feet, a smoking flame!

The killing of his thousand *padma*-strong army in the course of a single moment, filled him with grief, anger and resentment.

His pride destroyed, the silence prescribed for the yaga shattered and the sound of mantras desecrated, he acknowledged to himself, 'This great sacrifice is ruined. It will be childish to proceed with it.

'The fierce fire of the sacrifice has died down, portending that success will not be mine today. Should I stick around, distressed that the yaga along with the mantras has gone up in smoke, I'll merely invite the derision of the gods. They'll sneer, "All his might he reserves for us and can't face mere men."

'No more lamenting,' he admonished himself. 'The sacrifice has certainly been ruined. The powers I wanted to obtain through this sacrifice, are now nothing but tattered hopes.

'But so what? Don't I still have in my possession my famed might? Am I not the conqueror of Indra's godly hosts?'

(*At that moment Hanuman approached him with taunts that made him rage even more.*)

'O you mean sorcerer and trickster! What happened to the phantom Sita you killed? Deceived at first, I begged you to hand her over to me and leave in peace. You refused.

'What happened to that famous invasion of Ayodhya? Why, didn't Rama's kith and kin at home hear the twang of your bow?

'And by the way, what news of that great sacrifice? Was it well conducted and safely concluded?

'Your bag of tricks has been exhausted. When Lakshmana's arrows, hot as fire and strong as diamond, pierce you today, when blood flows from your ears, mouth and eyes, you will rue the day you dreamed them up. Serpent noose or Brahma's astra, Siva's missile or Vishnu's discus, none will avail you now.

'Your head will roll and bite the dust today, along with your boons, your black magic, your heavenly weapons and your native strength.

'Even if Siva, Brahma and Vishnu were to come to your aid, you will still perish. See! Death in person is now stalking you. Your left eye and shoulders have begun to tremble.'

Breathing fire and flashing his teeth in scorn, Indrajit roared: 'How dare you insult me to my face? Have you forgotten that you have been bested in every fight with me until now, only to be revived by means that are against all the rules of warfare?

'And after fighting in an unmanly fashion, you dare challenge me! Is it because you have tucked away somewhere the medicinal herbs to revive you if you die again, as you surely will?

'Rama, Lakshmana, or anyone else, let them all come! The monkey horde will be destroyed, *vellam* by *vellam*. And the brothers themselves will meet their end today.'

He then blew his conch. Heavenly maidens placed their palms over their eyes in mortal terror. The gods were shaken, and Siva and Brahma predicted the onset of a great battle.

(Fighting resumed with renewed vigour and there were the usual ups and downs. Hearing the twang of Indrajit's bow, many monkeys forgot heroism and ran away. Unable to withstand

Hanuman's assault, rakshasas fell like leaves in autumn. Then Indrajit challenged Hanuman, standing ready to hurl a huge mountain, to single combat.)

He taunted, 'Aha! All that boasting and now only a hill in your hand! Are you hoping to kill me for all the gods to see? Not for nothing are you a monkey! But you are a good fighter. Come then, come!'

Hanuman flung that adamantine hill and sparks flew in every direction. All the worlds shrank in fear, saying, 'A thousand thunders have been unleashed!' The rakshasa horde ran helter-skelter.

His earrings flashing, the enraged prince reduced to powder that mountainous weapon. So quick was this riposte, that the gods who hadn't even blinked for fear of missing any of the action, saw the result, not the cause!

The fiery arrows released by Indrajit stuck in Hanuman's body looking like the rays of the sun soaked in blood. As Angada and others rushed to Hanuman's aid, Indrajit sneered, 'Stay, stay! You! Does a lion fight an elephant?

'Go away and send someone worthy of my steel. Where is the one who twice lost his life and came back from the dead?'

(Urged by Vibhishana to finish Indrajit without delay, Lakshmana appeared on the scene.)

Sighting that golden mountain, Hanuman found his strength returning and his mind clearing. He came forward, saying, 'Get on quickly, father.' Happy and relieved, the gods cheered and Hanuman sallied forth with Lakshmana on his shoulders.

Dark as a thousand thunderclouds, Indrajit stood before Lakshmana in a chariot drawn by a 1,000 horses. Like that God with a thousand names, Hanuman expanded till he filled up all space.

Like fire, thunder and wandering demons, like hunger, disease, and the unfailing punishment for evil deeds, the arrows that vigilant Lakshmana shot were deadly and accurate.

The rakshasa countered each shot with its like. So many arrows he dispatched, that one wondered whether there could be any more left in the world. The sky, the quarters, the seas and all available space was filled with the arrows that fell from the sky, like the lashing rains of Dissolution.

It was a battle unparalleled, power and cunning matched equally. The twangs of their bowstrings pulverized the four directions. The fiery arrows rose high and blackened the stars in the sky.

The seas dried up, mountains split and forests were reduced to powder. New islands rose in the sea and the earth lost its way.

The arrows shot by Rama's brother went left, right and centre, smoking, blazing, frying and scorching everything in sight. Those from his rival's bow were water, fire, mountains, clouds, thunder; bright and hot as the sun's chariot and deadly as Siva's smile.

Caught between the torrent of arrows, the firmament shed its stars, the sun its rays, the moon its fawn and the sky its clouds.

Sharp as the eyes of lovely maids, the arrows sent by the two of them penetrated each other's armours and pierced their chests. They struck their shoulders, faces, thighs and legs. Nothing daunted, they fought on.

Finally, the rakshasa prince discharged twenty-five arrows that pierced Lakshmana's chest. He, in turn, let go some fiery shafts that removed Indrajit's armour.

Training his arrows on Hanuman, Indrajit hit him on his broad shoulders. Hanuman bled all over, looking red as the rising sun. Enraged at this attack, Lakshmana rained a tempest of sharp shafts and broke and immobilized Indrajit's chariot.

Indrajit leapt onto another chariot and shot off ten arrows that hit Lakshmana on his head, making him writhe in agony. Recovering, he directed some crescent-shaped shafts in the other's direction.

And before Indrajit could remove them, he shot another, an extraordinary one this time, with the force with which Siva had once kicked the vitals of the god of Death.

That arrow went through his chest and Indrajit became unconscious. The gods cheered lustily. With another arrow that shone like the midday sun, Lakshmana brought down his flag, and with another, pierced his shoulders. His blood streamed out like fire, and Indrajit tottered, shaken.

Recovering, he let go 900 shafts and flew into a rage when they did not even pierce Lakshmana's armour. He dispatched a 1,000 more, aiming to hit Lakshmana's vitals.

But Rama's brother broke them all to bits with a single arrow. He then sent shafts of his own that snapped the string on Indrajit's bow.

Frustrated beyond endurance, the rakshasa berated himself, 'This bow here, is it Siva's or Vishnu's? Whose is it? Here I stand totally disabled by Lakshmana, unable to counter him with any degree of efficiency.'

For the first time, his heart sank and he thought that perhaps he'd never be able to win this battle.

Pulling himself out of his momentary gloom, he twanged his bow for the seven worlds to hear and said, 'Counter this one,' and let fly the wind missile. Lakshmana effectively met it with its twin. Indrajit then sent the fire missile and that too was repelled by its like. Then came the water shaft, which also met with the same fate.

His heart black with malice, he sent the sun missile and Lakshmana countered it with the same ease with which he had done the rest.

'Resist this!' challenged a defiant Indrajit, dispatching the reed arrow. 'Like will meet like,' said Lakshmana, and met it with a reed arrow of his own.

Comprehensively checkmated, Indrajit decided that the time had come to bring out that ultimate missile indestructible—the Brahamastra. He said with great satisfaction, 'Now indeed you are dead!'

Lakshmana, brother of the Primal Lord, who wields the divine discus, saw that missile's blazing approach. 'He must think that I am powerless against it just because I was helpless against it the first time.

'He doesn't know that it was Rama's injunction that

prevented me from using it then. But now that I have his permission to use it if the situation warranted, the sinner is bound to die this time.

'Let all be well with the world,' he prayed reverently, and addressing the astra, he said, 'Please do not hurt anyone, not even the one who dispatched that other. Confine yourself to the single task of countering it.' He then sent off his riposte to Indrajit's Brahmastra.

Indrajit's missile disappeared without a trace, even as Lakshmana's stood, like a huge flame ready to burn the seven worlds.

Abundantly cautious, the scion of the solar race, shot another shaft to prevent the missile, thwarted of its target, from spreading to the sky.

The darting fire of that second shaft brought down the powerful astra like venom countered by venom.

The gods were delighted. 'Is there anything at all that these two find impossible to achieve?' they said in unalloyed joy. Siva smiled, 'You ask that question in ignorance.

'The truth is, the two of them are no ordinary mortals but Nara and Narayana, the Root and the Primal Cause for our existence.

'They were the ones on the milky ocean, to whom you've always taken all your troubles. They have come to destroy these hateful sinners and their kin, and establish Dharma on earth.'

Meanwhile, that fierce rakshasa had decided on the astra of Vishnu and sent it forthwith saying, 'If you can resist this, none will be able to vanquish you. But I know you will surely die!' The gods flinched and raised their arms to protect themselves from what was to come.

But Lakshmana calmly went forward to meet it, recalling that he himself was Vishnu, the presiding deity of the astra, now speeding towards him.

Wonder of wonders! Instead of coming at his body, that missile went around him worshipfully, circling him from left to right, and shot up to the air, where it lost its fire and smoke.

As he witnessed this astonishing sight, Indrajit wondered aloud, 'Is he the deity of that missile?' Then undaunted, 'Whoever he is, let him be! I'll finish him off with Siva's arrow, the one that can end in a single moment all of creation.

'This was given me by the lord of Kailasa himself as a reward for my long penance. He assured me that it was one of a kind and that nobody possessed its counter. He is sure to die by this one.'

He offered prayers and worshipped the astra with flowers, holy water, incense, sandal paste and food. He then sent that irresistible shaft on its course, ordering, 'Kill him and come back.'

At once the field was filled with every possible form of death: tridents, axes, hot shafts, fire, venom, poisonous snakes, thunder of fire and thunder of water; in addition, black demons, devils and other ghouls were generated by the astra.

Fire came from one direction and fierce whirlwinds from another. The terrible darkness that lies beyond the seven seas filled the world. The seas themselves seemed to come together as one to wage war on land.

Great gods fled and sages wilted, fearing that the astra would surely claim its victim. To all those who cried, 'Save us! Save us!' Lakshmana raised his hand to calm them down, 'Don't be afraid. Your safety is assured,' he smiled. He then unleashed the missile of the five-faced Siva.

Prayerfully, he said to the astra, 'Destroy only that missile and nothing else.' Wonder of wonders! Travelling faster than his thought, the missile confronted Siva's astra and swallowed it and all the hell unleashed by its powers.

Heaven and earth cheered lustily. The gods beat their drums incessantly and the seas and the clouds were delirious. Even the confounded arithmetic of the astrologers celebrated the defeat of that missile! The vedas cheered and Dharma danced for joy.

Indrajit could not believe his eyes! Valorous Lakshmana had actually nullified the weapon of Siva, the great God of Dissolution!

But not being one to accept defeat, he told himself, 'Even if that most irresistible of astras has failed, to draw back now would be shameful. My skill remains and will not fail.' He again let fly a few arrows at Lakshmana.

On seeing his uncle standing beside that matchless warrior, he vented his spleen on him: 'What kind of choice have you made, siding with the enemies of your race?

'There is a saying, "A fish lives only as long as there is water." Our lives depend upon our root, Ravana. If something happens to him, we will all perish.

'No doubt there'll still be a Lanka, and you, with a crown on your head, will be its sole inhabitant, thanks to the alms given to you by mere men.

'A scion of a line of brahmins created by Brahma, you were in a position to command the gods. But now you want to enjoy the huge wealth of Ravana. That too, as a slave to a mere man. Where is your sense of shame?

'Is not poverty better than a life of betrayal? Better than joining those who jeered at your sister and cut off her nose? And now, with Death for an ally, you are prepared to kill your brother and us, to bring victory to one who was till now our foe.

'Will those mere men kill the king of Lanka—they who once lost their lives and owe their rebirth to herbs brought from afar? By such vile alliance with our foes, you hope to succeed your brother, my father, as king of Lanka?

'I'll never allow it to happen. My arrow will sooner send you to heaven, even if the whole world spits at me for killing my own kin.'

Vibhishana smiled, unperturbed: 'Never have I abandoned truth. Nor have I had truck with falsehood. I ceased to be Ravana's brother the day he chose to commit sin.

'I repeatedly pleaded with your father, "She is the wife of the one worshipped by the three worlds. It will be sinful to molest that great symbol of chastity."

'Furious with such sane advice, your father it was who ordered me out and I did as he bid. Knowing that sin can never overcome virtue, I sought shelter with the God of gods. What is fated will happen. How does it matter whether I win or lose renown? Will I go to hell? If yes, so be it.'

Said Indrajit, fiercer than thunder, 'The renown you seek as a righteous one will depend on the crescent-headed arrow I'm about to release. What fame can you possibly get other than death?'

He sent off an arrow that headed straight for Vibhishana's golden neck. It sped like thunder, like fire, like poison, like Siva's trident, making the gods exclaim, 'Now indeed he is dead! He is dead!' But Lakshmana broke it into bits with a shaft of his own.

When that priceless arrow was broken, Indrajit, the death of Death, hurled a spear at his uncle. Once again Lakshmana shattered it into bits.

Enraged, Vibhishana, now sped like the wind, with a rod of gold in his hand. Smitten by that rod, Indrajit's whip-wielding charioteer was laid low, along with his milk-white horses.

(Standing alone on his ruined chariot, Indrajit came to the conclusion that this was not his day and that no real combat was possible with nothing at hand except a broken chariot. And before the bystanders could say, 'He has disappeared,' he took to the sky and reached Ravana's side.)

INDRAJIT KILLED

Startled to find his son dripping blood from his wounds, Ravana said with infinite sadness, 'These arrow marks on your shoulder proclaim your yaga unfinished. You look beaten and tired, like a serpent whose hood shrinks at the sight of Garuda. Tell me what happened.'

'Your brother put an end to all the schemes I'd devised. The yaga was broken up. I resumed fighting and discharged three invincible weapons but to no avail. They were all repulsed and rendered impotent.

'The great astra of Vishnu, the author of both earth and heaven, just went round the foe and left. You've made a dreadful enemy, Father. An enraged Lakshmana alone is capable of destroying the three worlds.

'The last time I used the Brahmastra, he did not counter it with one of his own to avoid destroying the world. That was how I won then. But even when we thought him defeated, he was able to survive. And now he is dead set on finishing me off.

'But don't for a moment think that I'm afraid of them. However, Father, there's one thing I wish to tell you. If you'll only give up Sita, they will forsake their anger and go back home peaceably. I say this out of my love for you.'

At this, the king of Lanka laughed till his shoulders shook. He sneered, 'The fight has gone out of you, then? You are bewitched? Afraid of men?

'Why should I surrender Sita? Better lose this bubble of a body in battle and gain fame in immortal song!

'Though I should lose, as long as the vedas remain, my name will last as long as Rama's own. That which is here today will go tomorrow. Bodies die, but fame endures!

'Why waste time? Go back to your palace and pluck out the darts from your shoulders. Take rest and spend the night in ease.' So saying, he rose like an angry tiger and roared, 'Bring forth my chariot!'

Falling at his feet, his son, destined to die, pleaded with him, 'Father, remit your wrath and forgive those thoughtless words of advice. After I am dead and gone, you'll see the wisdom of my words.' He departed once again for the battlefield.

Once again, the war was on. Once again, Indrajit and Lakshmana traded arrows. Those sent by the fierce rakshasa were snapped by Lakshmana's shafts in mid-air. But those sent by Rama's brother made holes in Indrajit's body.

Then Lakshmana sent one that destroyed Indrajit's armour. His eyes darting fire, he answered with well-chosen shafts, but they failed to find their target.

Finding that his arrows were losing out to Lakshmana's, Indrajit now threw a spear, more fiery than the one given to him by Brahma's son. But his rival saw it coming well in advance and severed it with an arrow more powerful than the curse of the seven sages.

'So long as his chariot remains, he can't be rendered powerless,' thought Lakshmana. His next shaft lopped off the charioteer's head and it fell on the ground and rolled away.

Left without a driver, that huge and bright chariot of gold was like a young ascetic without a guru to rule his senses, a prostitute who sells her love for money.

Next was the turn of Indrajit's hand. 'All my arrows he plucks out mid-air and throws back at me. His hand is steady and his mind unperturbed. Even crores of arrows don't tire him. True valour will surely die with him,' said Lakshmana in admiration.

Vibhishana was worried: 'Hurry up, young lord, you know very well that this wretch can only be killed in daylight. He might once again take recourse to witchcraft and drive his chariot into the sky and plan some mischief from behind the curtain of clouds.'

Lakshmana reassured him, 'Why should he not die today? My shaft will go, wherever he goes. He is exhausted and you'll see that victory will soon be ours.'

But far-sighted Vibhishana said, 'Immortal Lakshmana, so long as Indrajit is in the chariot gifted him by Siva and still has his bow in hand, he cannot be killed.'

Lakshmana then skilfully separated the wheel, the axle, and the pins of the chariot. When the bejewelled chariot was thus dismantled, all the horses ran away, as birds fly away from a tree, when its trunk is hewed and felled by a sharp axe.

From the floor of the ruined chariot, Indrajit shot off all the weapons he had with him. When Lakshmana brought them all down, he flew up in a trice, making a din that rent the worlds. But none could see him!

Safe for the moment in his hiding place, Indrajit felt his strength ebbing fast. He was like gory vapour in a crowd of dark clouds. Lakshmana saw his chance then.

'His bow cannot be broken but his hill-like shoulder can.'

With a crescent-tipped arrow, he sliced off his bejewelled hand and it fell to the ground, still clasping the bow.

With his chariot and the hand that held his bow gone, Indrajit, a dark cloud of monsoon, told himself, 'I'll now use the trident given me by Siva.' Addressing Lakshmana, he said, 'You don't seem to know of my ancestry. I swear you'll leave this world before I do!'

With Indrajit manifest before his eyes as trident-wielding Death, Rama's brother decided that the time had come to kill him. Sending up a silent prayer, he told his bow, 'If Rama is indeed the god of righteousness, kill this moon-fanged prince.'

Selecting a crescent-shaped arrow, he drew the string right up to his ears and let go—the straight one setting the world straight.

That fire-mouthed arrow threw into the shade Vishnu's discus, Indra's thunderbolt, Siva's trident and Brahma's missile and neatly cut off Indrajit's head.

His earrings flashing like two moons, red hair blazing hot as the sun, his head came crashing down, as if the sun itself had fallen to the earth.

Just as the five senses scatter and disappear when life leaves a body, the rakshasa army fled to fortressed Lanka, leaving their weapons behind.

Exultant at the prospect that Ravana's reign of terror was about to end, the gods showered flowers and cheered lustily.

Frenzied with joy, they threw away their clothes and stood naked, like the gods of religious sects that refuse to slaughter any living thing.

Happy with his great achievement, with Angada leading the way, Lakshmana marched with Hanuman as his mount, carrying as a trophy that famous head.

Rama had been waiting for Lakshmana to come back, just as Bharata, his other brother, was waiting for *his* return. Never for a moment had he doubted that his valiant brother would defeat that crafty foe.

Eyes filled with joyous tears and pride swelling his shoulders, Lakshmana placed at Rama's feet the severed head of Indrajit. The blood oozing from Lakshmana's wounds left an imprint on his own shoulders and chest, making him look like a dark cloud flecked with red, a black hill flooded by the rays of the sun.

'My heart is warm with the thought that Sita will soon be joining us. You have proved right that ancient saw: he who has a younger brother, need not fear any foe!'

Lovingly, he detached Lakshmana's quivers, undid the armour around his chest, and hugged him again and again. With his touch, the wounds inflicted by Indrajit's sharp shafts disappeared without a trace.

RAVANA'S GRIEF

Crossing a sea of blood, messengers ran to Ravana with news of Indrajit's death. Seized with fear, teeth chattering, mouths, mind and feet trembling, they blurted out, 'Your son is no more.'

In a single action, he drew out his sword and swept off their heads. Shocked and overwhelmed, his grief inconsolable, he staggered and fell as if the earth balanced on Sesha's head and the world on his own shoulders were changing places.

Disconsolate Ravana was beside himself with grief. 'My boy!' he screamed. 'Great son!' he shouted. 'My father! My life! I, older than you, am still alive and Indra's victor is now no more! Are the gods, now relieved, rejoicing? Are Siva and the sulking Vishnu rid forever of their enemy?'

He rose; sat down; got up again; paced about, wailed and fell on the ground; glared one moment and closed his eyes the next; ploughed the earth with his body and rolled around! Lamenting loud and pining for his beloved son, he left for the battlefield, seeking his body.

Crores and crores of horses, elephants and chariots he turned over, looking for his son's body from among the pile of rakshasa corpses littered there. Spotting finally that dark mountain, he fell on it.

Tears streaming from his eyes, he saw that huge hand clutching a strong bow and an epauletted shoulder with its quiver and arrows intact. The cascade of his tears flowed over and covered the corpses on that field.

That chest covered with a rain of arrows, he clutched to his own breast again and again. Plucked the shafts off the chest, and broke them and fainted. Reviving, he again smelt and tightly embraced the inert trunk and cried out, 'I will burn the sun and the seven worlds!'

Finding the trunk but not the head, he wondered, 'Has that man walked away with it?' His wounds opened afresh, and he sobbed and wailed and railed at the gods. The noise he made was enough to sunder the sky.

'Were the *diggajas* and Siva's hill the only things I could conquer? These two men who took away my son's life and carried away his head are still alive. And wretch that I am, I still hold on to my life.

'I once saw Indra's city, Alakapuri, go up in flames and made all the worlds mine. Today, I live to see jackals eat the chapleted head of my son. What kind of a dog's life is this!

'Who in the world is more wretched than I? Because of a pretty woman, I'm now obliged to do for you what you should have lived to do for me.' Lamenting thus, he lovingly carried the headless body of his son to his city.

The length of her dark hair reaching her heels, Mandodhari, daughter of Maya and Indrajit's mother, came rushing in. One hand held to her head, tottering as if she was treading on burning coals, she fell on her son's body and began to wail.

'In the days when you grew like the crescent moon, I prayed to the gods that your bow should vanquish Indra. What's the sin I have committed to see you thus without your head? Why, alas, do I cling like a fool to this wretched life of mine?

'My darling, my beauty, my rare ambrosia! Mighty in battle, the very picture of Death to your foes, you triumphed over Vishnu and Siva! How can I live without seeing your lovely face?

'In the days when you crawled, anklets jingling, you brought two lion cubs and set them fighting in the yard and watched the fun. When will I see such a sight again?

'O my child! I recall how as a child you invited the moon

to come down to earth and picked him up in your hands, saying, "Don't be afraid," and tried to rub off the mark on his face, mistaking it for a rabbit. Won't you rise and enact that scene again for me?

'Are you lost in this deep sleep as if on a bed of flowers, because of the spell cast on you by the poor women in love with you? Or is it because you are tired of war?

'My son! Did you win all those battles against Siva and the other gods, and carry away the three worlds as the spoils of war, only to be killed today by a mere man! Isn't it laughable? Like the towering Meru being brought down by a breeze set up by a palm-leaf fan?'

'The sea of the rakshasa army has completely dried up. The anger of mere men has reduced it to ashes, as if it were a fluff of cotton consumed by a flame. I am afraid the same fate awaits Lanka's king tomorrow, all because of Sita, that venom in the form of ambrosia!'

Moved and hurt by what she said, the king of rakshasas said, 'All this grief has befallen us because of Sita. With my sword I will at once slay that treacherous and stone-hearted woman.'

Mahodara, the pot-bellied general, was shocked and frightened to hear Ravana talking thus. He ran after him and fell at his feet, pleading, 'O king! This act will bring you infinite disgrace and tarnish your name forever and ever.

'If overcome by anger you rashly kill this royal tapaswini, Siva, Vishnu and Brahma will clap their hands and mock you, calling you a low-born wretch, unworthy of your race.

'Besides, if you kill her now and slay Rama in tomorrow's battle, will you not agonize over Sita's death? Or is it that you have begun to doubt your ability to finish off those two men and hope that if she dies, they will go away?'

Seeing sense in his general's advice, Ravana, his anger doused, flung away the sword. He then swore, 'I will come back not only with my son's head which they took away as a trophy, but also with their own.' He then ordered that Indrajit's trunk be preserved in oil.

RAVANA'S CAMP

(Preparations for the big battle got under way and finding that his regular army had been decimated long ago, Ravana ordered his reserve forces to get ready. He surveyed them from the top of an ornate tower and took salute. He was astonished to see the strength of that vast sea of soldiery he did not even know he possessed.

He explained to them at some length why they had been called up. They were astounded. 'Are you telling us, O great king, that two insignificant men have laid low with their arrows Kumbhakarna, Indrajit and the rest of the rakshasa army? And you have summoned us now not to shift the world o ff Sesha's head but to wage war against monkeys who live on fruits and leaves?'

At this Malliyavan admonished them sternly: 'Arrogant fools, don't you know that these two men have sent to heaven or hell, as the case may be, Virada, Maricha, Khara and Dushana along with their mammoth armies, not to forget Vali, the one who conquered Ravana? In which world do you live? Haven't you heard that one of the monkeys you so deride came and set fire to Lanka? Or of the bridge they built across the sea and the road they laid for their armies to march into Lanka? If only Sita had been returned as I advised time and again, we wouldn't be in this predicament.')

Somewhat subdued after this rebuke, they nevertheless said, 'Whatever the wisdom of your advice, it was not followed earlier, and it is too late to act on it now. We can only do our duty and fight.'

And what a war it was! The rakshasas who'd swallowed Dharma, drunk up mercy, wore wickedness as jewels on their sleeves and considered themselves bridegrooms to sin, with hearts black as their skin, went forth to spread destruction.

The gods ran to Siva and said, 'Lord! We are sunk. Were a thousand Ramas to come to our rescue, they still won't be able to quell these cannibals.'

Sapphire-necked Siva calmed them down and assured them that the great hero would indeed kill every single demon on that field. Indeed, they have all been conveniently brought together by fate precisely for this reason.

On the battlefield, a different kind of drama was being enacted. Like rats running for their lives on sighting snakes, the monkey army took to their heels. Only Sugriva, Hanuman and Angada stood firm.

Those who were running away like frightened rabbits told themselves, 'What does it matter who rules the world—Rama or Ravana? All we want are fruits and vegetables to eat and caves to hide ourselves. Of these, there should be no dearth under either regime.'

Puzzled at that uproar and clamour, Rama asked Vibhishana what the commotion was all about. Being told that Ravana had unleashed his reserve army upon the monkey hordes and they'd panicked at the sight of the foe, Rama told an angry Lakshmana, 'Don't fret, my son.

'It is the nature of monkeys to panic when they see no one to protect them and to flee to their own shelters. The moment I pick up my bow, rakshasa, asura or whoever else it may be, will become cotton in front of fire.'

He then asked everyone, including a reluctant Lakshmana, to go and calm the frightened monkeys and leave him to tackle the new rakshasa menace. He convinced his brother: 'If out of your infinite affection and concern for me you stay put by my side, we'll lose the war.'

Then Rama prayerfully bowed to his famed weapon, picked it up, and strung it. Soon enough, the rakshasa hordes surrounded him, like a herd of elephants around a lion. Rama welcomed them with a twang that sent shivers down the spines of those watching the scene.

The rakshasas found their mouths drying up. Horses became reluctant, lions that drew the chariots went mad, and elephants turned on their riders. Utter confusion prevailed on the field. Aided by the strong wind, Rama's shafts fell like the rain in summer and killed all the creatures in sight.

Thus it went on. Death and his deputies, who could take several lives at one go, got tired and left without collecting the thousands of souls parted from their bodies. It was as though Rama's arrows were the fire of Dissolution and the rakshasa horde a forest of tinder.

'Come fellows, come!' shouted Rama. 'Come and yield your lives and your boons.' They came and were promptly slaughtered. All the wily chiefs were killed along with their men. Those who survived ran away. The world was deafened, clouds dropped to the ground, and mountains disappeared from the face of the earth.

Impelled by fate, the reassembled remnants of the retreating forces assailed Rama with axes and clubs, rods and ploughs, swords and posts, javelins, pikes, spears, lances, tridents and every other kind of weapon.

None of them had any effect on him except mildly vexing him. At long last, deciding to end the farce, he sent the divine missile known as *Andhra*.

It went raging like the king of serpents or the monarch of birds. Ten crores of rakshasas, stalwart heroes all, were destroyed in an instant. The reserve forces of Ravana were now extinct.

Pausing after that killing spree, Rama stood, red-eyed and triumphant, amidst the mountain of corpses, looking like the blue-necked God on the cremation ground, surrounded by devils, jackals and ghouls.

His forces decimated, Ravana decided that it was time to end this proxy war and take on his enemy himself. He then invoked three-eyed Siva to ensure victory and set off.

Around his hill-like chest, he girded an armour of gold and his twenty hands were fitted with leather gloves. Buckling on his quiver of arrows, he mounted his chariot drawn by a 1,000 horses that could cover in an instant the earth, the sky, and even the kingdom of Brahman.

'At the end of this day,' he swore, 'either Sita or Maya's daughter will be kneading their stomachs in sorrow.' Exulting at the prospect of the grim fight ahead, he twanged his bow, shattering several mountains in an instant.

Frightened by the noise, the wives of the gods instinctively felt around their necks for their mangala sutras and began to pray. Seeing him approach from afar, Vibhishana hastened to tell Rama, 'Ravana is here, the advance guard of the rakshasa army has arrived.'

RAMA'S CAMP

(Preparations were afoot in Rama's camp too. He himself had girded on all his weapons and was all set for battle. In the heavens above, there was much excitement and joyous anticipation. Siva told Indra, 'Rama is sure to win today. But send him a well-decked chariot drawn by helpful horses.' Indra at once ordered Matali, his charioteer, to equip his own golden chariot with everything that Rama might need and take it to him post-haste.

It was a massive vehicle. Its front was strong as the seven hills, its wheels and axles subdued the earth and its ropes were the eight serpents. Its floor was made up of the years, seasons, months and days of past and future. Its walls were the quarters and its waving flags the clouds. Medicinal plants were used as festoons. It shone with the strength of the five elements.

The shining chariot had for its horses the four vedas and many sacrifices; the seven seas, the seven hills, the seven worlds, the five elements, the four quarters, the three fires; the five senses, the five organs, the three gunas, the ten different winds, the great days and the long nights.)

Matali descended from heaven and stood respectfully in front of Rama. 'Who sent this vehicle and why?' wondered Rama. Matali explained: 'This chariot, lord, was created by Brahma and Siva and gifted to Indra. It is at his command that I am here at your service.'

Rama eyed it with suspicion, fearing that it might be another rakshasa trick. But the vedas flew from the mouths of the horses and Rama's doubts were somewhat allayed. Nevertheless, he asked Lakshmana and Hanuman for their opinion. They reassured him that both the chariot and the charioteer were indeed genuine.

Evil, crestfallen, rolled on the ground. Virtue leapt with joy. Gods and sages, depressed so long, smiled again, finding heir hands strengthened. Rama ascended the chariot.

RAVANA KILLED

The gods saw how the wheels of that chariot sank into the earth when Rama got on. They said, 'Rise, chariot! Rise! Take all our strength! Let the warring rakshasa die today! Victory to the king of kings! May the wives of the rakshasa warriors wail today!'

Ravana saw that wondrous vehicle and said, 'So the gods have given him this,' and ground his teeth. Then, shrugging off the insult with a curt, 'Let it be,' he ordered his own great chariot to be driven towards Rama, holding aloft a shining bow.

The sound of the drums, the battle cry of the warriors and the roar of the two chariots—all mingled to produce such a thunderous noise, that all those witnessing the war were deafened and fell to the ground in a daze.

The emperor's son darted Matali a meaningful look and said, 'No need to act in haste. Exulting in his might, let the enemy make the first move. Then I'll tell you what to do.'

'Lord,' said Matali, 'if I don't anticipate your every move, the horses' thoughts, the enemy's plans, the pluses and the minuses, my skill as a charioteer will be suspect, unless, of course, I aim to betray.' Admiringly, spotless Rama willingly conceded the point.

'Rama is here in the chariot sent by Indra!' Mahodara told Ravana. 'A great fight is on the cards and I can't simply stand and do nothing. Permit me to aid you in some way.'

'I'll kill Rama like a lion slaughtering an elephant. If you take ort his brother, you will be advancing our victory,' replied Ravana.

Before he could even reach Lakshmana, Rama's divine chariot apprehended Mahodara's vehicle. Blazing with anger, the latter ordered his charioteer to get ready for attack.

All deference, the subordinate said, tentatively, 'Lord, even a thousand Ravanas cannot face Rama today and hope to come out alive from that encounter. You'll do well, lord, to leave him alone.'

Livid with anger at this unwarranted advice, Mahodara said, 'I am not eating you up alive, you cowardly cur, for what you said, only because people will talk.' Even as he was berating the poor man, Rama's chariot crashed into his and a great fight ensued.

Rama's shafts, fiery as the *Bhatavagni*, dried up all the golden chariots, horses, elephants and sword-girt warriors around the general. Now left to fend for himself, he trained his arrows at Rama who merely smiled.

With just one shaft, Mahodara's armour broke into pieces. Two more felled his hands, and a third claimed his shoulder and neck. Before he could even register what had happened, that braggart Mahodara was dead.

Seeing his general cut to pieces before his eyes, Ravana furiously urged his charioteer to head straight for the enemy. Rama had, meanwhile, decided that unless the huge rakshasa army, spread all over the battlefield like a fog, was destroyed, Ravana would not yield. Bending his bow, he destroyed them all, before Ravana could even guess what was happening.

His left shoulder throbbed and his epaulettes fell. It rained blood, and vultures and crows swarmed around his flag. These bad omens delighted the gods, but made no impression on him whatsoever. 'Can a mere man ever conquer me?' was the thought that recurred in his arrogant mind.

Like thoughtless action set against wisdom, illusion against true knowledge, sin against steadfast virtue, the two confronted each other. Like Sesha and Garuda they were locked in a timeless and deadly combat.

Ravana blew his conch, making Siva and Brahma blanch. Jealously, Vishnu's conch sounded too, of its own accord! Matali then blew Indra's conch, making the sky, the sea, the earth and the four quarters tremble.

The twang of the red-eyed Ravana's bow sounded like the roar of the seven seas. The twang of Rama's bow was like the thunder at Dissolution. They were like two rainbows against the sky, their strings made of lightning.

Fury throbbed in his head and his eyes sparked fire, as the cruel tyrant bent his bow and discharged arrows that flew as if broadcast by the wind. Rama's shafts intercepted and destroyed them.

A rain of golden arrows covered the sky, blanketed the quarters, and shrouded the mountains. It enveloped the sea and the earth, eclipsed fire and darkness, and obscured the digits of learned men. The gods and sages shut their eyes in fright.

Thus the inconclusive contest went on and on. Against that bowman's rain of arrows, that stalwart fighter would hurl a club, a hatchet, a *tamaram*, a stick, an iron pestle, a discus or a trident. Then he would switch to bows and arrows.

Stung to the quick by Rama's sharp shafts, as if he were an elephant prodded by a goad, Ravana picked up ten bows and rained shafts from all of them, like ceaseless showers from a throng of clouds!

Then, like Mount Mandara brought by Garuda to churn the milky ocean, like the medicinal mountain hefted by Maruti to revive Lakshmana, like the three floating towns destroyed by Siva, like the phantom world of the Gandharvas, the rakshasa's chariot rose in the air.

The rain of arrows sent down by the king of Lanka killed all the monkeys in sight. Furious, Rama said, 'Enough is enough. It is time all those ten heads fell off his shoulders.' Turning to Matali, he directed, 'Lift the chariot to the sky, my friend.'

Instantly, the wise Matali did as commanded. The two chariots circled each other and scattered the clouds, which fled, seeking safety in a place beyond the quarters. The stars shattered into bits and fell to the ground like diamonds.

First to the right, then to the left, they dodged and chased each other. In the sky for a while, then down to the earth, then up once again, they flew fighting relentlessly. In the whirlwind thus created, the sea and the hills, and even the globe, seemed to spin like a potter's wheel!

Even the gods who knew the chariots well, couldn't tell one from the other. No star remained undisplaced; no mountain remained unpulverized, no quarter remained unscorched. Even the gods couldn't make out where the two clashing champions were from one moment to the next.

'Now they are in Indra's abode,' they guessed, 'now in the moon's sphere. Perhaps, they are in Brahma's world,' they conjectured, confused.

A boastful know-all among them said, 'No, they are in the milky ocean'; another equally self-assured, said, 'No, they are beyond the great seas—now in the east and now in the west.' Thus they babbled, each guess more extravagant than the last.

In the seven seas and the seven isles, the seven mountains and the seven worlds and at the borders of the spherical world, the two combatants moved around unceasingly, like the wind at Dissolution.

The weapons that Ravana flung went round the world, leaving destruction in their wake. Rama kept those deadly shafts under check, but never once attacked himself.

Finally, they returned to Lanka, where fighting once again resumed on land. Fiery-eyed Ravana brought down with a crescent-shaped arrow the flag on Indra's chariot, emblazoned with the thunderbolt. Rama, in turn, shot down Ravana's flag that had on its head a vina and a bud that could bring down rain by merely brushing against a cloud.

In full cry now, Ravana targeted and maimed the noble steeds that drew Rama's chariot and dealt a deadly blow to the generous heart of Matali. This caused greater pain to Rama than when Lakshmana was pierced by Indrajit's lance.

Ravana then sent a shower of arrows that completely hid Rama from sight. Thinking that he had been defeated, the gods were thrown into panic.

The wind stood still and earth was frightened. Sugriva and Lakshmana, perplexed and unhappy, stood about like elephants that'd lost their leader.

In an instant, Rama sent out a batch of arrows that dismantled that blanket of shafts, much to the relief of the anxious gods. He then shot at the mountainous bows in each of Ravana's pillar-like hands. All were split in the middle and fell to the ground.

Next followed more arrows that pierced Ravana's compact armour and drank up his blood. For some unfathomed reason, Ravana's shafts seemed impotent against Rama. Exasperated and at the end of his tether, he decided to send the evil missile called *tamaram*, or darkness.

Astounding was the destructive power of this missile. Made up of many arrows; some fire-faced, some blood-soaked, some like gods, some like devils, and some like striped serpents, it stretched from quarter to quarter, baring its teeth.

Darkness on one side, blazing sun in the other, whirlwind here and rain there, wheel on one side and thunder on the other, here was an arrow that could do just what its master wished.

Under its influence, the worlds were caught in the depths of a dense darkness. Nothing daunted, Rama invoked the deadly missile of Siva and put an end to the other, like bad dreams banished by wakefulness.

His hopes belied when that deadly missile failed, Ravana released the Asurastra that in its time had destroyed the fame of gods, filled Yama's stomach with many sweet lives, and frightened divine Indra himself.

Rama dispatched the fire missile to extinguish that astra. Said Ravana to himself, 'I've the club created by Brahma, first used by Hiranya to subdue this world, and then by Madhu with deadly effect. The demon Taraka himself has hammered the gods with it. On one occasion, it'd even drunk up the green sea. I'll use it now to drink up his life,' decided the ten-headed rakshasa.

Alas for Ravana! The emperor's son shattered it to pieces with a missile shaped like a lotus bud.

(Greatly vexed at his repeated failures, Ravana unleashed at last the mighty Mayastra whose versatility was amazing, as we shall presently see. Offering worship as always to Siva, he invoked the appropriate sage and metre and discharged that deadly weapon.)

Miracle of miracles! When that wonder-weapon thundered forth, all those lying dead on that battlefield, seemed to have regained their lives!

Indrajit and his younger brothers, the great army chiefs, ministers and countless others seemed to hide the sky and raise a deafening din of joy. Kumbhakarna and others, the millions of soldiers, all rose as from a deep sleep.

Like snakes from the netherworld, big demons rose to the earth, wearing crocodiles for earrings. Shouting hoarsely, 'You thought you had killed us? We'll show you. Come on, come on!' these resurrected demons ran amuck among the monkey hordes.

Amazed, Rama asked Matali, 'What is all this? Is it magic or the result of the rakshasa's boons?' Matali replied: 'O cloud-hued hero! This Ravana is a fool who'll sell needles to an ironsmith. All this is worthless trickery, a piece of black magic. A single arrow from you will dispel these miasmic illusions.'

Reassured thus by the canny Matali, Rama discharged the *gnana* missile, saying, 'Whether they be the result of boons, magic or sheer strength, whether they be true or false, make them flee!'

Pursued by that great arrow of knowledge, all the magic disappeared, exactly as the delusion brought on by the endless cycle of birth and death disappears when true knowledge dawns.

Scheming now to end the very world, Ravana hurled the divine trident. Rama countered it with every single divine missile he had, but they were powerless against it. He stood helpless, not knowing what to do!

The gods concluded that the fight had gone out of Rama. Even Dharma began to shake. Born a man, he seemed not to have any knowledge of his own powers.

The trident sped irresistibly and hit Rama on the chest. His anger roused, he let out a snort that shattered it to hundreds of pieces. Ravana, who was sure that the trident he had flung wouldn't return without killing Rama, felt utterly defeated at this latest rebuttal.

Once again he wondered: 'Who is this one who frustrates all my boons? Siva? No. Brahma? No. Vishnu? No. A great one who has accumulated penance? No, he is too young for that!

'Is he then that Primal Being of the vedas? Whoever he is, I'll not give up, will stand and fight and win. Retreat now is out of the question. I will kill or get killed.'

Resuming the fight, he invoked Nirruti, the goddess of the south-west quarter, and prayed for her missile. It came and he took it at once, fixed it in his deadly bow, and sent it towards Rama.

It unleashed crores of hooded serpents with flashing fangs. Poison oozing like a sea from every open mouth, fire shooting from every eye, they frightened gods and mortals alike. They shook their heads and said, 'This astra is bound to end Rama's life and swallow the world.'

Seeing all the mountains caught in the mouths of those serpents, Rama shot the unfailing Garuda missile. Taking on a thousand forms of itself, wind-swift Garuda chased the snakes wherever they went and whatever form they took:

A thousand eagles seized and tore the heads of the fleeing snakes with their talons and gobbled up the gems embedded in their mouths. As nonchalantly as if feeding on lotus stalks and blossoms, they chewed up in no time at all the serpents let loose by the Nirruti missile.

The two heroes fought as equals and fortunes fluctuated as the day wore on. But as the war of attrition continued unabated, it began to look as if the skill and strength of the one who had lifted Kailasa was ebbing, while Rama's might was intact. In fact, it seemed to grow with every passing moment.

Then at last the God of the vedas decided that this phony war must end and the king of sinners die. He sent off a crescent-shaped arrow that felled one of the ten heads of Ravana. The huge head that dropped into the sea resembled one of the peaks of Meru that'd fallen into the ocean in a similar fashion, when that mountain had warred with Vayu.

But wonder of wonders! Like instantaneous rebirth that follows death, another head appeared in its place. Could such a miracle have e'er happened but for Ravana's unique penance?

Every time Rama sliced off a head, another appeared in its place, making one wonder whether it'd been cut off at all! Rama soon realized that there was a boon behind this magical replacement. The same happened with his hands.

Every time Rama took off a hand, another sprang in its place and caught the falling bow!

Those many heads and hands fell thunderously into the sea and on the land, on mountains and in every quarter. With a resounding boom, mighty Ravana flung at Rama all the weapons he carried on his shoulders.

Sword, spear, pestle, thunderbolt, club and hatchet flew ceaselessly. The valorous hero was wounded and made up his mind that, 'This ridiculous shadow-fighting should now end.'

Chest and shoulders heaving, he shot thousands of shafts, making that tyrant's body a cage for his arrows to roost in! Such was the speed with which they flew, that contrary to his intentions, those arrows aimed at Ravana's mouth, eyes and chest, went through that tyrant's body and emerged bloodless at the other end of the world!

At long last, one flawless shaft stopped Ravana's breath. All passion and hatred spent, he collapsed like a mountain. He who, erect of form, used to take salutes in parades of gods, now lay unconscious in his chariot.

The stream of blood from his wounds was enough to choke all the sharks in the sea! Seeing his master disabled thus, his charioteer decided to retire from the field.

The gods shouted joyously and jumped about and danced. But Rama, come expressly to rescue the gods from Ravana's oppression, refrained from making the most of the opportunity.

Matali was puzzled at Rama's sudden inaction and said with some urgency, 'Lord, if he recovers, it'll be impossible to defeat him. Kill him now when time serves us yet.'

The great hero was not convinced: 'It is against all codes of war to take the life of one who is unarmed, unconscious, and in pain. I will not fight him now.' Was there even one among the rakshasas fleeing in fear, who did not bow to Rama when he said that? Then, to the terror of innumerable gods, Ravana recovered!

As if waking from a sleep, the cruel-eyed deceiver didn't see Rama before him. Eyes shooting fire, he admonished his

charioteer, 'You turned around the chariot for the gods to
see and for that bowman to laugh at me! You have erred
terribly!

'Despicable traitor! You owe everything to me and have
lived under my protection. Now you have made me look a
coward! You don't deserve to live!'

Intending to kill him, Ravana raised his sword in wrath,
whereupon the driver fell at his feet and begged, 'Great king!
Contain for a moment your all consuming rage. Hear me out
on what prompted me to do what I did.

'You'd stopped your heroic fight. Had I stayed on, you
would have been killed that very instant. I am your true
servant and acted in good faith to save your life.' Ravana
relented and instructed him to take the great vehicle back.

Facing Rama once again, he shot crores and crores of fierce
arrows. He now seemed a different Ravana, thrice as strong
as the one before, determined to wage an incandescent war.

Rama became thoughtful when he witnessed this new
ferocity. 'As long as there is smoke, there is fire,' he mused.
'As long as he has a bow in hand, he will not be easy to
conquer.'

He then sent the Narayanastra and broke into two that
terrible bow made by Brahma. At once the gods leapt up in
delight and exclaimed, 'We have gained at last the fruit of
our penance.'

Ravana replaced the broken bow with innumerable
others. One by one they were all struck down by Rama.
Finally, the great bowman decided that the time had come
for him to unleash the astra of Brahma, who had risen from
Narayana's navel.

He offered worship to the missile of that Primal Creator
and fixed it to his bow. Then, drawing the string right back to
his shoulder, he let it fly.

That four-headed shaft sped with a force and speed
that neither fire nor wind could match. Blazing a trail that
made the sun at Dissolution seem a mere glow-worm in
comparison, it went beyond the Chakravala mountain and
the outermost seas!

(That sacred shaft of Rama's entered the heart of that sinner and put an end to three crore years of strenuous penance. Brahma's boon that no god could vanquish him had indeed come true. It drank up the might that had conquered all the worlds and the quarters.

While the gods, the brahmins, and the rishis showered blessings and flowers on the victorious prince, the astra went to the milky ocean and cleansed itself in its purifying waters. Then, flying across the sea of blood let loose by the killing of Ravana, it joined its fell companions in the quiver of Rama.)

That tower of rakshasa might that'd stood steadfast in battle, fell face down from his chariot. Gems and jewels loosened by that great fall, spilled from his broad chest and shoulders, like thunder rolling from a dark cloud.

His anger stilled, his mind stilled, his schemes stilled, his hands forever raised against his enemies stilled, his love and energy stilled, his lifeless faces shone three times as bright as in the days he had subdued the sages and the gods.

(Disembarking from his own chariot, Rama saw Ravana lying in a stream of blood. 'Take the chariot back to heaven,' he quietly instructed Matali. With his brother and the army chiefs of the monkey army he moved forward to inspect the prone body of one who had never turned his back on a fight.

Countless monkeys clambered upon his dead body and began to dance. What greater proof of the evanescence of wealth and worldly glory, inconstant as a courtesan?)

His task fulfilled and the promise made to the gods redeemed, Rama turned to Vibhishana and said, 'The mean deeds of the rakshasa should now be forgotten. You must perform the obsequies that are his due.'

Impelled by his love for him, Vibhishana fell on Ravana's body, one mountain collapsing on another, 'O brother mine! Of might immeasurable, a typhoon to the demons and death to the gods! Remember what I told you when I left?

"Thoughtless love for a chaste woman, the very life of another man, will breed endless shame," I said, and you got angry with me. Are you wiser now? Has your lust been assuaged, now that it has laid low our race?

'O mighty one, whose single frown could displace the elephants that guard the quarters! I warned you that this was no ordinary woman but the mother of the world, Vedavati herself. But you did not listen.

'Even though your valiant kin were killed in the war, you refused to make peace. Now they are all dead. And you too are dead. Have you realized at least now the truth of Rama?

'The boons conferred by Brahma and Siva have turned to dust, blown away like your ten heads. Having reached his abode, have you, at least now, seen that Rama is the Primal God himself?

'Brother mine! Where are you now? On the hall of the heroes or your grandfather Brahma's land? Or are you with the crescent-crested Siva? O intrepid brother mine! Who has taken you to his abode?

'Your sister swore revenge for causing her husband's death, even though you did it in ignorance. Now the earth bleeds to soothe her ire!

'Everyone hates us, the good and the bad, heaven and hell. They all are our foes. Whom can you face, having fallen so low?

'You embraced the goddesses of war, learning and fame, with no visible harm to you. But when your arms reached out to embrace the goddess of chastity, your luck ran out. Those other goddesses, jealous, have made you embrace the goddess of dust!'

When Jambavan heard him lamenting thus, his grief inconsolable, he attempted to pacify him, 'Hill-shouldered friend, are you also one of those, who in their ignorance question the ways of Fate? Calm yourself, my friend.' Vibhishana brought his emotions under control and stood aside.

(Just then, having heard the news of Ravana's death, Maya's daughter, Ravana's queen, Mandodhari, came rushing to the battlefield and fell upon his powerful chest. The lament that issued from her wailing mouth melted even trees and rocks.)

'Alas! Alas! Are these his crowns and heads that lie here? Is this his body that lies prone? Is this the end of the king, the wages of his sin? What a dreadful fate that I should survive my lord, my firm resolve to die a *sumangali*, a blessed wife, dashed to pieces?

'How could a single shaft suck the life that was hidden in a corner of a chest, wide as a cavernous ditch? Did it go in search of the place where he had hid his love for Sita?

'How many things conspired to crown and reward Indra's penance! The beauty of that gem among women; her chastity; my husband's consuming lust; Surpanakha's severed nose; and most of all, Dasaratha's promise to his queen that drove those princes to the forest!

'I was deluding myself when I thought that one stronger than the gods and the *diggajas*, one mightier than Brahma, Vishnu and Siva, could never die.

'I didn't think that it'd be a man who would one day destroy the fortress of safety your boons had secured for you.

'Taken in by the might of your penance, I never thought that there could ever be a diminution of your prescribed life of three and a half crore years.'

Thus she wailed in deep anguish, embracing his well-adorned chest with her tendril-like hands. She then gathered herself and stood aside, called out his name, sighed deeply and died.

Apsaras, vidyadharis and others from the netherworld, wives of rishis and all the chaste women of earth, wept in anguish and blessed and praised her chastity.

(*Then, with a heavy heart, Vibhishana commenced the rites prescribed and the royal funeral began. To the sound of conches that drowned out every other noise, the emperor's umbrella was held aloft and as flags fluttered in the breeze, he carried his brother's great and beautiful body and laid it on a pyre made of logs of akhil and sandalwood. He then placed the queen's body by his side and completed all the rites and consigned them both to the flames.*)

Rama consoled his friend, 'Wise one, give up your sorrow. Such is the way of life. It is an endless burden.'

RELEASE AND RETURN

(It was now time to think of tasks that remained to be completed. Said Rama to Hanuman, 'Go and inform my coral-lipped wife of all that has happened.' Hanuman faithfully went to the Asoka grove, told the lovely lady the news of Rama's victory which was to her ears, water to a withering sprig.)

'I bring great news!' he cried as soon as he spotted her. 'Your sad days are over and happy times are here again. The Aryan elephant has crushed under his foot that sea-monster that was a terror to all.'

His palms folded over his head, his shoulders towering like hills, he sang and danced and leapt from side to side, to the astonished delight of that jewel of chastity.

Hearing those ambrosial words, she waxed radiant all at once, like the spotless moon that in one night grows from new to full, stag and all.

She was transformed into a new being. Her mouth, a full-blown lily, her bright face brimming with joy, a snow-white moon freed from the serpent that'd swallowed it, she was a sight for the gods.

Her breasts, always a burden to her slender waist, swelled. Drunk with joy, she thought one thing but babbled another.

Joy surged in her heart and her shoulders suddenly felt her jewels too tight. Her breasts grew damp with dewy drops of sweat and her garment loosened and slid low. That stainless model of what a wedded wife should be, gazed at Hanuman, long and dumb, not knowing what to say.

'Is it that boundless joy has left you speechless?' he prompted, 'Or is it that you doubt my words?' Abashed, she spoke up at last, 'Whelmed by that great flood of joy that knows no higher watermark, I search and search in vain for words. Does sudden fortune make one mad?

'O rare messenger, priceless gem so finely chiselled, "I

will free you," you told me when I last saw you. You have done that now and brought me boundless joy. How shall I reward you? Lost in such thoughts, words fail me.

'At first I thought the three worlds should serve as recompense enough. But they are nothing and, moreover, transient.

'I must lay my head at your feet and worship you, since I cannot find anything that will at all match the gift you've given me.

'That was the reason for my silence. Forgive my speechlessness that must have seemed so churlish and ungrateful.'

'My lady, O rare peacock from heaven! What greater thing can you give me than the joy I'll feel when I restore you to your husband?' he said, and added, 'Dear mother, with the exception of Trijata, a pure gem with a flower-like face, I should like to torture all these rakshasis.

'They spoke unbecoming words, fell on you, and threatened to eat you up. I will tear their mountainous bodies with my sharp nails, and yield them up to Yama. I will pluck out their entrails, drink their blood, wring their bodies and eat them up.'

When those fat rakshasis heard these words, they cried out piteously and said, 'Mother, save us. We are your slaves and beg your mercy!' 'Don't be afraid,' Sita reassured them. To the angry Hanuman she said, 'O pure son, what wrong have they committed? They only followed the dictates of their master.

'O you who love me more dearly than a mother, my sufferings were the result of my own past. They were no crueller than Kuni. Do not make much of what is over and done with! Grant me this favour. Do not hurt these ignorant women who have sheltered evil.' And Hanuman bowed, respecting her wishes.

(Back at the monkey camp, Rama told Vibhishana, 'Let my lady be brought here well adorned.' Obeying, Vibhishana left with all dispatch to Asoka Vana, taking along apsaras to adorn Sita and bring her to Rama's presence, as ordered. An astonished and

*troubled Sita told Vibhishana, that the proper thing would be for
her to appear as she now was before her lord, the gods and the
sages. But Vibhishana, polite but firm, said, 'It is Rama's order,
mother.'*

*Menaka, Rambha, Urvasi and other heavenly maidens then
massaged her body with all kinds of unguents and scented oils.
Rambha combed out her matted hair and removed all the tangles,
the way the vedas that had got all knotted up over time had been
smoothed out by almighty God. Other heavenly nymphs brushed
her teeth and applied scented oil on her hair and combed it out.
They cleansed her body of dirt as a whetstone cleans a gem.
They then gave her a bath, all the while joyously chanting vedic
benedictions.*

*They stroked white sandal paste on her body like milk foam
on a coral creeper, and smeared saffron paste on her breasts. They
gave a dark garment to wrap around herself and fastened on her a
waistlet that fondled her winsome middle.*

*Then they adorned her with necklaces of pearls and gold, painted
her lips with red juice from betel nuts. They performed the arti to
avert evil eyes. And, finally, they put a dot of lovely red kumkum on
her forehead.*

*With apsaras, monkeys and rakshasis surrounding her,
Vibhishana took her in an aerial chariot to Rama. Waiting eagerly
to greet Sita were gods and goddesses, sages and their wives, coral-
lipped vidhyadharis and their consorts.)*

That maiden, chaste as Arundhati, saw from above, her
lord still in battle gear standing in the field that had provided
such a feast for eagles, vultures and devils.

Her heart leaping exultantly, she said, 'May my chastity
ensure eternal life to the monkey who helped herald my
virtue. May it keep alive my husband's valour, proclaim my
high descent and preserve the stability of the worlds.'

Surrounded by apsaras, she descended from the chariot.
Her body aching for reunion with one she'd been parted from
for so long, she stood face to face with Rama. 'I've seen him at
last and that is enough. It doesn't matter any longer whether
I live or die.'

He too looked long at the queen of chastity, the guardian

of womanhood. Tears from her long eyes wet her breasts. Alas, far from being moved by this piteous sight, he eyed her like an angry serpent!

'You stayed content in that sinner's city, enjoying your food and drink. Your good name was gone but you refused to die. How dared you think I'd be glad to have you back?

'I didn't come to Lanka, bridge the sea, and uproot the rakshasa race and destroy all my enemies in order to rescue you. It was but to save myself from being known forever as one who spared my wife's abductor.

'You ate the flesh dear to animals, that is theirs by right. You drank toddy and enjoyed yourself. Do you propose to feed us too in the same way? All the good in you that should have shone forth like gems has gone.

'Solely because of the birth of one like you, womanhood, dignity, high birth, chastity, virtuous conduct, propriety and truth have all been destroyed, like the fame of a king without generosity.

'Separated from their husbands, women from good families are wont to control their five senses; make virtue their axle-pin, and live like ascetics, lest there be even a whisper about their conduct.

'Your behaviour has destroyed my peace of mind. Die. If you won't, go where you wish,' said he.

When he spoke these harsh and cruel words, the entire assembly of sages and gods, monkeys and rakshasas was shocked beyond words and broke into a loud lament.

Sita stood stunned and agonized beyond endurance, as if a new wound had been probed with a sharp needle. She shed blood and tears and nearly died.

Like a fawn dying of thirst, who in a wilderness of vultures sees a tank but is unable to reach it, she felt anguished and bewildered, not knowing what to do.

Tears streaming down her eyes, she looked around at the stunned audience and said to herself, 'This, I suppose, is what I have earned through my past good deeds.'

Turning to Rama, she said, 'Hanuman told me you would be coming to redeem me. Did he not, the best of messengers, tell you how I lived? Or was he not your messenger at all?

'All my penance, good deeds and chastity have proved meaningless, never having impressed your mind!

'Here I stand, a model wife! A woman whose mind even Brahma cannot change for all the world. But if you, the eyes of the world, cannot see this, what god can help me now?

'To whom shall I declare my spotless chastity? There is nothing better for me than to die. That is what you have ordered too.'

She called to Lakshmana and bade him light a fire. Distressed Lakshmana looked at Rama, who conveyed his assent with his eyes.

Half-dead, eyes streaming with tears, Lakshmana prepared the stage for an ordeal by fire. Sita of the lotus feet walked to it and started to go around in a *pradakshina*.

Watching her do the rounds, the three worlds wept. Brahma and the other gods trembled. Adisesha withdrew his hood and earth grew hot, as if he had spat out his venom on it. Planets changed places and the seas went dry.

Then she, whose breasts and hands had been adorned with gold only a short while ago, called out to the god of fire, 'If in word or thought I have erred, burn me in your righteous wrath!'

Then bowing to Rama, she leapt into the fire as if she was plunging into a lotus swimming pool in the palace.

The flames went white as cotton, burning in the fierce blaze of her chastity. Agni rose out of that conflagration, two hands clasped over his head in reverence. In his other two, he held aloft Sita. His body sorely scorched, he cried to Rama for help!

The film of sweat her husband's ire had brought out still lay on her; the bees on her chaplet still hummed. The flowers she had worn were fresh as they had been when woven into her hair, moist and cool, their lustre seeming greater!

The whirling worlds steadied again; melting creation lost its fear. The sages' wives, led by Arundhati herself, threw shame aside and danced wildly.

'Never have I erred,' Agni wailed, 'and none has ever complained about my conduct. And yet for reasons beyond my comprehension, you've chosen to punish me with the divine fire of her chastity!'

'Who are you?' said an angry Rama 'that speak rudely to me and save that troll instead of burning her. On whose authority do you act thus?'

The god of fire said, 'Here I am seeking refuge in you, fleeing the fiercer fire of her chastity, and you wish to know who I am! O eternal witness, having seen what you just did, are you still in doubt?

'Troths are plighted in my presence. Women suspected by their husbands swear by me. The purity of all things, I test. O mighty one, the vedas vouch for me.

'You set at naught the words of true Hanuman who vouched for her. Now, will you listen to me, who *am* the test, the ordeal to end all doubts, the one who makes everything plain as the gooseberry on the palm?

'Didn't you hear the gods and sages, all things moving and unmoving, and the three worlds clobbering their eyes and crying? Abandoning virtue this way, where did you manage to pick up sin?

'Will the clouds rain, will virtue walk its wonted way, and the earth stay whole, if the goddess of purity were to get angry? Her curse will kill even Brahma, who sits on the lotus!'

When scorched Agni spoke thus, Rama said, 'You are the upright witness to the world. You have, in words of the highest praise, declared her faultless. That absolves her in the eyes of the whole world. She shall not be discarded by me.'

Four-faced Brahma then gave in to the gods' pleas to enlighten Rama about his true identity, since he seemed to be getting embroiled in the illusive world of common men.

'Listen Rama! You don't seem to know who you are. Though born in an ancient and royal family, you are not just a man. You are Vedanta's ultimate Truth. There is none greater than you.

'*Prakriti*, the oldest of things, and *vikriti* its offspring, and *jivaatma*, that is above all else and rare to realize—you are all these. This enormous world, this great illusion, is what *you* have created.

'The vedas without beginning or end are crowned by the upanishads. And what the upanishads proclaim as the Supreme One, the goal and aim, is none else but you.

'O Primal One, you are the sun who causes day, noon and night, in a manner perceptible to all. In the same way, you create the world through me as your agent. You then preserve it as Vishnu and, finally, as Siva, you destroy it.

'Our wealth and power had inflated our pride and the rakshasas brought us down, making us flee in cruel wars. It was then that in desperation we sought your help. You entered a human womb, only for our sake.

'This then, is the truth about you. Do not display your wrath against the mother, who created the three worlds and is a paragon of a wife,' he concluded.

Then it was Siva's turn: 'Doughty one, you do not seem to know who you really are. You are the Primordial God and Sita, whom you have eternally carried on your chest, is the mother of the three worlds.

'If you spurn her now, it will be a grievous error and many will die. Give up this baseless suspicion,' said that most generous of gods.

Then turning to Dasaratha in Vaikuntham he said, 'Stalwart, go and clear the confusion in you son's mind and relieve our sorrow.' Then the emperor came down to earth, all eager to see his beloved son, and set his mind at rest.

On seeing his father, the lord of the vedas fell at his feet. Dasaratha caught him in a tight embrace and bathed him in tears, pouring his heart out in remembrance of things past.

'Those boons I granted Kaikeyi that fateful day, were like a spear that has remained stuck in my heart to this day. It has finally been drawn out by the magnet of the chest I have now embraced.

'O high-shouldered hero! Though painful at that time, your just action enabled me to redeem those boons. As a result, I've found a place in heaven as a man who kept his word.

'See how the gods and the rishis I worshipped when I was alive, now salute me with folded hands. You have raised me to Brahma's own sphere.'

He then went to Sita and embraced her fondly, even as she fell at his feet. 'My dear child! Do not be angry with Kosala's king. He asked you to enter the fire only to prove your chastity to the world.

'It is appropriate to test in fire the purity of gold. That alone must be the reason for his putting you through this ordeal.

'You are the jewel of womanhood, dating back to chaste Arundhati. You are the daughter of Earth, but descended from heaven. Nothing, but nothing, can stain your sterling character.' He was gladdened to see that the lovely maiden didn't harbour any anger in her heart.

Then, eyes streaming and full of love, he embraced Lakshmana. The tears from his eyes wet his son's hair, till it seemed he had just stepped out of a bath, water dripping off his body. 'My son, by following your brother to the forest, you removed the wound in my heart and brought down the number of births you will have to take.

'The gods have been singing your praise endlessly and the sound of those sweet words is still ringing in my ears. By overcoming Indrajit, you've put an end to the woes of this world and established Dharma on earth.'

Then he turned again to Rama, 'Ask of me a boon,' he said. Rama shook his head, 'I'd hoped to see you in heaven and end my sorrow. Now that I have seen you here, what more can I want?'

When Dasaratha insisted, Rama said, 'O great king, grant that my goddess, the one you discarded as a sinner, should be once again my mother. And Bharata her son, should be my brother.' Everyone rose and cheered his generous heart.

'Hear, generous son,' said Dasaratha, 'may faultless Bharata benefit through this boon. But I cannot forget my anger at that sinner who deprived you of your crown and made you an ascetic.' Getting agitated at the very thought of what had happened, Dasaratha's hands on Rama grew slack.

'Father, was it not I who made the first mistake by agreeing to rule a great kingdom? Wasn't it she, my dear mother, who saved me from making that grievous error?' said Rama gently.

Mollified, Dasaratha granted Rama the boons he'd asked for and left once again for heaven. Pleased that Sita's spotless chastity had won the day, the gods said to the bowman prince, 'Ask of us whatever you desire.'

Rama said at once, 'I wish that all the monkeys who died in the battle with the rakshasas live again. And please ensure that wherever monkeys go, be they forests, hills or someplace else, there is never any dearth of vegetables, fruits, roots, honey and water.'

'May the monkeys flourish through your grace!' the gods said. Instantly, all the monkeys that had died in battle, rose and fell at Rama's feet, eyes bright and delighted to be reborn.

'O prince with lotus hands, you obeyed your mother's orders and went off to the forest and have now rid the world of all deceitful creatures. The fourteen years are now over and today is the fifth lunar night since the last new moon day.

'If you do not join Bharata at once, he'll throw himself into the fire. Therefore, O victorious hero, depart at once for Ayodhya,' the gods urged.

Rama began to get a little worried. 'The fourteen years end today, and if I don't get there in time, Bharata will die and so will all my kinsmen. Is there some means by which I can get there soon?' he asked.

At once Vibhishana suggested, 'Lord, there is the aerial chariot, Pushpaka, that can take you there in a day. Ravana had seized it from Kubera and it is large enough to accommodate all of us.'

As it readied itself for descent, its bells jingling, it shone in the sky like a thousand suns. Rama said joyously, 'Our task has now been made easy,' and ascended the chariot. The gods rained flowers and blessings from their abode in the sky.

Trijata of the slender waist bowed to Sita. Tears of joy fought tears of grief. Her own eyes brimming with love and compassion, Sita said, 'O priceless companion in my days of distress, ever ready with the consoling word, live here as the goddess of Lanka.' Then she too joined her husband in the chariot. And Lakshmana, their inseparable companion of fourteen years, followed next.

Seated in that vimana that resembled the vast stomach of the one who had once swallowed the world, Rama invited Sugriva, Hanuman, Vibhishana and other faithful followers to join him on the journey.

With Lakshmana and Sita on either side of him, surrounded by Sugriva and his seventy *vellams* and guileless Vibhishana and his army, all gazing at him in breathless adoration, Rama, the victorious wielder of the *Kothanda*, shone like the God he was.

(*The journey to Ayodhya began. Rama suggested that all the monkeys take on a human form to avoid vulgar curiosity when they landed. As the Pushpaka raced ahead, Rama lovingly showed Sita the major landmarks of the war just concluded: 'This is where Prahasta met his end at Nila's hand and this the place where Suparsa was killed. This is where Lakshmana killed Indrajit.' Finally, he showed her the northern gate where Ravana lost his ten crowns. Sita heard and saw everything in wide-eyed wonder.*

Then he told her all that'd happened after she had been carried away. He showed her Kishkinda and other places she had not known. As the chariot raced over that hill, Sita said coaxingly, 'My lord, I am the only woman in a chariot full of men. Shouldn't we have some women with us when we land in Ayodhya?'

Rama passed on her request to Sugriva who at once ordered Hanuman to attend to the task. In an instant, he had everything arranged. A veritable procession of women came, bowed to their king, touched Rama's feet and then Sita's. After this short break at Kishkinda, the chariot took to the skies again, flying faster than thought. Finally, they reached Chitrakuta, where Sage Bharadwaja lived.

With an umbrella and ewer in one hand, and a stick in the other, Sage Bharadwaja, the epitome of wisdom and embodiment of asceticism, was walking with measured steps. On sighting him from above, Rama ordered the Pushpaka brought down. He then got down and fell at the feet of the venerable sage.)

The great one embraced and blessed him, inhaling deeply of the scent of his hair as one would a child's and washed away the dust on his hair with his tears of love. When Sita and Lakshmana approached him, their hands clasped in reverence, he blessed them too with tenderness.

Eyes brimming with tears, Bharadwaja said: 'You have with your matchless valour vanquished Virada, Khara and Maricha, the doughty Kabhanda, the seven maramaras, Vali, the sea, Ravana and Kumbhakarna and given back to the gods and sages the peace of mind they'd lost.

'I cannot forget how, fourteen years ago, you left Chitrakuta for the south, with the firm resolve of destroying evil. Now that you have returned, task accomplished, stay here for awhile as my guest.

'And I must tell you how your noble brother Bharata has been living all these years as your proxy ruler. Berating his fate, perplexed at the unwanted honour thrust on him, he barely lives, more an ascetic than a king.

'Knowing no quarter except the south, a stranger to all pleasures, abjuring meat and sleeping on grass, he never entered the city of Ayodhya after you left. He lives in Nandigram, reciting your name day and night, the very picture of suffering.'

Deeply distressed at what he heard, Rama told Hanuman, 'Before I reach Ayodhya, it would be good if you went ahead and informed Bharata of my well-being and imminent arrival.

'Put out the fire he may have got ready to leap into, thinking I've failed to keep my promise. Find out how he is and come back and report to me.'

Hanuman left at once, carrying with him a ring given by Rama. Quicker than his own father, faster than Rama's arrow and swifter than his own thoughts, he first stopped by to tell Guhan of the arrival of the virtuous prince. He then raced across the sky to that other prince.

(Taking leave of Rama at this point, let's speak of what happened in the invincible city of Ayodhya during the fourteen years of his exile.)

That formless and abstract thing called love had taken concrete shape in the form of Bharata! Eyes streaming whenever he thought of his elder brother in the forest, his bones melted by sorrow, he lived like an ascetic, a king only in name. Though food was available in plenty, he only ate what a forest would yield.

Even as he was placing a fresh garland on his brother's sandals, he wondered about the day Rama was due to return. He then sent for the royal astrologer who declared, 'Today is the day assigned for that auspicious event.'

His breath failing, Bharata fell down in a heap. His mind swung between hope and despair. Tears flooded his lotus eyes. 'What is the reason for his failure to arrive on the appointed day? Surely, he wouldn't have forgotten his promise to me?' he thought, perplexed.

'Perhaps he thinks that I might want to continue to rule? Or has something untoward happened to him?' He was most distracted.

Grimly he made up his mind: 'If he's decided to stay on in the forest and do something else, I certainly will not continue a moment more in this agony. I'll give up my life this very moment and erase the stain on my character.'

Having made up his mind, he then called for his brother. And soon enough Satrughna made his appearance. Tears streaming from his eyes, Bharata clasped him to his bosom and said, 'I have a boon to beg that you must not refuse.

'Rama hasn't come as promised. I'm going to throw myself into the fire and you must obey me and take over as king.' A shocked Satrughna clapped his hands over his ears and stood transfixed, trembling. As if he had been poisoned, he fell to the ground. 'What harm have I done that you should ask this of me?'

His anger blazing like a fire, he said, 'One brother gives up the kingdom to rule the forest and to guard him goes another. Because he does not come back in time, the third kills himself. And I, the last, must stay back to rule the land! How wonderful!

'Since the day he left, you never entered the city. You commenced a great penance, even as you continued to rule from afar. And now, if I should do as you say and take over the mantle of kingship, obeying once again your orders, won't they say that I dispossessed you in greed?'

Bharata was despondent, 'He delays his return only because I am here. Should I die, he'll hurry back so that Ayodhya is not left without a ruler. Prepare the fire,' he directed.

When news of Bharata's decision reached Ayodhya, Rama's incomparably virtuous mother beat her stomach in distress and bewilderment. Haggard, the very picture of woe, she rushed to Bharata. Her heart melting, she cried, 'Son, should you die, the world will die with you!

'Even a crore Ramas cannot equal your grace! What on earth can survive, if you, virtue in person, give up your life? If he is not here today, he will come tomorrow. How can you ever think he'll go back on a promise plighted?

'Something must have happened to keep him away. But even if we assume the worst, just because one man has ceased to be, will you deprive all the world of precious lives, the seeds that are still in the wombs?

'Without you, Dharma too ceases to exist. How could you even contemplate such a thing!

'My son, birth, death and rebirth—that is the way of life on this earth. To give up attachment, to renounce bonds, that is what makes for strength,' said the pure-hearted Kausalya.

'Please, Mother, don't think your son defies you. If my brother's word and the deeds of my race are proved to be undependable, I don't wish to live. I at least must keep my word.

'I too am the son of the same king who, for the sake of truth, gave up his life. Is Rama the only man wedded to truth? Don't rules apply to others too?

'Is it only Rama who can be detached, self-sufficient and stainless? Well, I'll die and prove how spotless I am,' he said.

Surrounded by the screams and shouts of people begging their king to desist from taking such an extreme step, he went forward to worship the fire before offering himself to the flames.

Suddenly, from nowhere leapt into that gathering the hill-like Hanuman, shouting above the din, 'The chief has come! The great one has arrived! If you, the embodiment of truth die now, will he then wish to live?' Rushing with his bare hands, he seized the brands and put them out.

He then fell at Bharata's feet. Fingers covering his mouth in reverence, he said, 'Noble brother of my lord and master, thirteen *naazhikais* remain yet for the prescribed time to elapse. If this isn't the truth, I, a cur, will fall into this fire before you.

'Upon my word, how could you be so rash? Tarry till the sun rises behind the eastern hill. If Rama does not come by then, both you, a stranger to falsehood, and the rest of the world are free to die. My lord has been delayed by Sage Bharadwaja's request that he be his guest for awhile.

'Should you disbelieve me, here is the signet ring the king of the world has graciously sent through me. Look at it, O spotless one.' To Bharata, the sight of it was like nectar to one poisoned and about to die.

Sorrow had been his only food since Rama left. He was so thin that a mere breath could have blown him off. But now, he looked a different man, his shoulders rising and falling in excitement.

He took that ring and looked at it reverentially, bowing again and again to the messenger. He swelled visibly, as if to shame those who doubted whether his spare form could bear the weight of Rama's love.

'Dance, dance,' he said deliriously to all those gathered there. 'Sing, sing, sing his fame!' he cried. 'Run, run, run to our lord. Crown, crown your heads with the feet of this great messenger.' Isn't true love kin to drunkenness?

Turning to Hanuman, he asked, 'Harbinger of good news! Please tell me who you are. You've come in the garb of a brahmin but I am not sure you are what you seem.

Though you appear different from them, are you one of the Trinity?'

Hanuman answered with great humility, 'Prince, I have appeared in a guise that is not my own. I am a monkey, son of the wind god. I have the honour of being slave to your brother.

'Cast your eyes on me, a cur, and you will see me in my real form,' he said, drawing himself up to his full height, his head touching heaven.

The two fierce bowmen and Vasishta were taken aback at that wondrous sight. Bharata's army, while not exactly struck down to prostration, was nevertheless frightened by the form Hanuman had assumed.

'What we say will not reach your ears so far from the ground. So be pleased to reduce yourself to a size we can cope with,' beseeched Bharata.

(All sorrow a thing of the past, the proxy-king ordered a fitting welcome for the return of the unconquerable hero. Drummers spread the good news and all Ayodhya went delirious with joy. The citizens felt bewildered, like a poor man who suddenly finds gold and is unwilling to believe what he has seen with his own eyes. An army of 60,000 akshauhini, vassal kings, and citizens went to welcome Rama. The three mothers got into a palanquin, and Bharata who carried on his head Rama's sandals under the shade of the white umbrella of sovereignty went next, Hanuman by his side. Kinsmen and courtiers followed at a distance.

Seeing the great bowman traversing the distance by foot, the sun went down, fearing that the hot ground might scorch his tender soles.

Bharata thought that the journey would be less tedious if Hanuman related all that had happened after Rama parted company with him fourteen years ago. Acceding to his wishes, Rama's most faithful devotee gave a vivid description of the stirring events that we already know. When Bharata heard the thrilling story, he said with tears in his eyes, 'That fortunate brother of mine went, with the unconquerable hero to hunt and decimate the rakshasas in Lanka. And I, who stayed behind, can only hear about it and wilt!'

Meanwhile, Guhan, the hunter-king of Chitrakuta, had arrived at Sage Bharadwaja's ashrama, all agog on hearing the news of Rama's return. His heart and eyes full, he fell at Rama's feet. Rama embraced him as he would a brother, which honour he had in fact conferred on him fourteen years ago. He fondly inquired about Guhan's family and subjects. Deeply moved, Guhan said, 'Lord, I, a cur, lack nothing and yet have nothing, not having been able to accompany you like a younger brother should have, and done for you what that other brother of ours did so ably. How could life have been sweet for me?'

Deeply touched, Rama rebuked him gently. 'How can you talk like this? Are you not like Bharata who stayed behind to please me? And now, I am back. Be happy.' When the sun rose, Rama performed the morning rites, and went with his brother to the sage and took leave of him, got into the Pushpaka, and left with Sita and his friends.)

As the Pushpaka leapt into the sky, there appeared on the horizon the virgin fortress of Ayodhya, beautiful as a living picture, putting Indra's city to shame.

Rama's heart swelled with pride as he told his companions, 'Look at Ayodhya, beautiful beyond words.' All of them rose and saluted that famed city, hands clasped in adoration.

From below, Bharata and his entourage saw the golden Pushpaka in the sky, looking like a thousand suns put together. And there, in all his majesty, was Rama, the king of kings. The joyous shouts that rose from the city could be heard even beyond Ravana's Lanka.

And then the younger brother saw his very life, the lotus-eyed prince who had left for the forest fourteen years ago. He let go the hand of Hanuman that'd been in his clasp till then and rushed forward. He then resembled a man who suddenly sights a precious thing he has deemed lost and rushes to pick it up.

Hanuman too rose and reached the Pushpaka and stood before the discus-bearer. His chest covered with tears, he said, 'I was just in time, my lord and master, to rescue this hero from the fire he was about to enter. I announced your return and drew him back from his rash immolation.'

Rama, grateful, thanked his saviour, 'Valiant Maruti, because of bad deeds we seem to have committed in the past, relentless death has pursued us endlessly.

'But you, son of Vayu, a priceless boon to my family, have saved us time and again, showering us with love that is deeper than a mother's. How can mere words do justice to you, my father, my brother, my mother?'

Then he turned to Bharata, crowned with the sandals he had begged of Rama all those years ago, hands folded worshipfully. He was so emaciated that there hardly seemed to be any life left in him.

Bowing to him, Hanuman said to Rama, 'Behold the brother who's ruled this great kingdom in your absence and all the time hating his mother for this unwanted honour!'

When Rama saw Bharata, he felt overwhelmed. His feelings akin to what he'd experienced when he saw his father descended from heaven on Lanka's battlefield.

He saw also his beloved mothers, the citizens of Ayodhya, the army of 60,000 *akshauhini*, and eagerly ordered the Pushpaka to touch down.

To his mothers, his arrival was not unlike the return of the calf to the mother cow. To the wise who had no illusions, his coming back had revealed at last the Supreme Being, with whom ended their search eternal. To his famished younger brothers, it was like having life come back when on the brink of death.

In an exultant mood, his three mothers, brothers and guru ascended the Pushpaka. The hero fell first at the great sage's feet, who blessed him, and embraced him again and again. Lakshmana too fell at Vasishta's feet and was showered with blessings and held close in an affectionate hug.

Turning to his mothers next, Rama touched first Kaikeyi's feet before turning to the other two. They bathed him with tears from their eyes. Sita too was welcomed in the same fashion. Then the matchless younger brother too touched his mothers' feet and sought their blessings at which, fervently they said, 'Long may you live!'

When Bharata returned the sandals to Rama's feet, the

elder could only hug him, not having words to express the flood of emotions flowing through him. It was as if body and soul were united at last, but exhausted in the effort, could only sob and cry.

Tears from his eyes fell on Bharata's matted hair and washed clean the dirt of fourteen years of separation. Rama fondly nuzzled his head, as would a mother a child, a cow its calf. Tears from his eyes flowing in all directions, Bharata reached out his long arms to embrace Lakshmana.

Then it was the turn of patient Satrughna to fall at the feet of Rama and Lakshmana. After they'd released him from their embrace, he touched the feet of the incomparable Sita.

Rama then introduced his two inseparable younger brothers to his friends. One by one Bharata bowed and greeted Sugriva, Angada, Kumuda, Jambavan, Nila and others from the monkey army, not to forget the new rakshasa king, for whom he reserved special respect.

Then came Sumantra, royal charioteer and sage counsellor. Sorrow and joy warred within him and all smiles and tears, he said, 'Mother Earth sorrows no more.' Rama and Lakshmana clasped him close, memories of that last ride flooding their minds.

They all mounted the Pushpaka and reached Nandigram. The noise of the drums and conches drowned out the music of the vedic chants. Rising like the thunder of the clouds and the roar of the seas, it spread in all quarters and rose to heaven, only to be drowned out in turn by the noisy celebrations of the gods.

THE CORONATION

(Back in Nandigram Bharata and Rama cut off their matted locks, shed their beards and decked themselves in clothes befitting their status. Looking like the king he was, Rama then proceeded to Ayodhya in a golden chariot drawn by four white horses. Lakshmana, tall as a tusker seven cubits high, held the royal umbrella. Satrughna whisked a fan white as milk. Whip in. hand, Bharata drove the

chariot, the tears of joy that fell from his eyes settling the dust
raised by the chariot.

Vibhishana and Sugriva accompanied Rama on tuskers that
had taken up positions on either side of the chariot. Red-eyed
Angada rode in front and heroic Hanuman brought up the rear.
Sixty-seven crore monkey chiefs in human form, their chests
daubed with sandal paste, rode on elephants and accompanied the
royal procession.)

Kings of the earth's eighteen divisions and of the seven
islands, went around them on bedecked elephants and golden
chariots to show their devotion to their lord.

Looking for all the world like apsaras, female monkeys in
human guise accompanied Sita's chariot on elephants, horses
and other mounts, looking like stars to her moon.

Gods and sages strewed sweet-smelling blooms from
every quarter, making the earth look like a veritable carpet of
flowers. It seemed at that moment singularly appropriate to
call the earth *bhu*, a word that also means flowers.

The horses in the royal stable, dumb for fourteen years,
now neighed like thunder, like a mute who had suddenly
been granted the gift of speech. Trees flowered out of turn.
Maidens with brows like bows, came out in spots because of
excitement.

Men and women who held on so carefully to their
clothes, now swelled with joy and leapt about near naked,
as if drunk! Kings were dressed like courtesans and priests
had donned women's garments! Even those who avoided by
habit sandal-paste and exotic scents, smelt twice as fragrant
as those who regularly used them!

Lovely women who'd kept to themselves for fourteen
years because Rama had gone away, now covered themselves
with jewellery to entice their men! Citizens of heaven and
earth mingled freely and the gods acquired the smell of
humans, and the humans that of the gods, making their wives
sulk in suspicion.

Beckoning Bharata, Rama said, 'Show Vibhishana, Sugriva
and our other honoured guests, our glorious family temple.'
Bharata obediently took them across many mansions to the

family fane, glorious as the one on mount Meru where Lakshmi resides.

Dazzled by the blaze of gems, diamonds, rubies, sapphires, and emeralds, those heroes from abroad, stolid and phlegmatic and not easily given to excitement, were struck with wonder and stood wide-eyed, their hearts in their mouths!

They saw a jewel that glittered like the gem on Vishnu's chest and asked Bharata about it. He told them, 'That was given by Brahma a long time ago as a loving gift for his penance, to Ikshvaku, a doughty king of the solar race.'

They rested there awhile and Sugriva ventured, 'How is it that we don't yet know the day for Rama's coronation?' Bharata explained, 'It takes time for the waters to come from the seven seas and the great rivers.' Whereupon Sugriva glanced at Hanuman and he at once leapt across the world to fulfil his king's unspoken command.

(Then came Vasishta, the royal preceptor. After consultations with other great astrologers, he decided upon the next day for Rama's sacred coronation. Eager messengers took the news to the three worlds and their denizens came to Ayodhya to witness the event. Even Brahma couldn't reckon exactly how many turned up for that occasion. Rama was duly informed and all was set for the great event.)

Ordered by Brahma, the stag-faced Maya, architect beyond compare, put up with reverence that very day a faultless hall that could accommodate the entire world! Hanuman had by then brought the waters from the four seas and seven oceans.

Riding hundreds of elephants, kings under white umbrellas brought in gem-set pots the water of the river Sarayu. They set up in that crystal hall a beautiful throne of rubies with legs of diamond and armrests of gold. The shining hero sat on it, shoulders well decked. Comely Sita, coy and bashful, sat by his side.

Benisons were sung, vedas recited, conches blown, cymbals struck, drums beaten, melodies floated, flowers rained.

One by one the gods came and took part in the ceremony. Great sages, vedic scholars, old councillors and other men mature in wisdom were the first to pour the waters. Thereafter, Sugriva, Hanuman and the king of Lanka did likewise.

And what a glorious sight it was! Hanuman bore the throne, Angada the sword, Bharata the white umbrella, and the other two twirled the fans. Then with Lakshmi-Sita beside Rama, sage Vasishta placed the crown on his head! Those who saw that event were rid forever of the pangs of birth and death and the cycle of reincarnation!

Though the vedic sages had placed that shining crown only on his head, the denizens of the three worlds felt as if it had been placed on each of their heads.

Her long distress over, that patient maiden, the goodly Earth, who after rigorous penance had acquired a husband worthy of herself, only to lose him soon thereafter, finally regained him. Reaching out her tendril hands she clasped him to her tender heart that rejoiced at being given back the happiness it had lost.

As advised by the royal preceptor, Rama, ever generous, took the occasion to crown Bharata and gave him the sceptre to rule as his deputy.

FAREWELL

In that hall of gem-set pillars, the king of Ayodhya reclined on his throne with the lotus maid beside him, looking like a raincloud streaked with lightning. Spear-eyed maidens with tender breasts brushed his shoulders with feathered fans.

The moon in the sky waned, depressed because the beams from Rama's forehead lighted the fourteen worlds much better than it did.

In constant attendance were Sugriva, Vibhishana and the others. Guhan was there too, with a leopard's tail for a belt. To all of them said gracious Rama, 'Faultless heroes, stay in Ayodhya for as long as you like.'

Two months passed. The time had arrived for the

departure of the kings of Kishkinda and of Lanka. Reluctantly, Rama gave them leave and loaded them with gifts and mementos.

To his vassal kings he gave lands, palanquins, garlands, gem-set crowns, excellent horses and strong chariots. To Sugriva he gave the bracelet that Indra'd given his father, when he had defeated Sambaran around the time he himself had been born.

To Angada he gave the jewel named Angada that was given to Ikshvaku by Brahma, as if to perpetuate that name on earth. Said he, 'You are your own equal. Live and thrive with the Sun's son.'

Looking at Hanuman with moist eyes, he said, 'Doughty one, there is nothing I can give you. Come and embrace me tight.' Whelmed by shyness at such extravagant praise, tongue-tied Hanuman retreated to a corner. Rama drew him back and presented him a necklace of gold and diamonds and much else.

Her heart filled with the bitter-sweet memories of her encounter with him in the Asoka grove, the daughter of Mithila presented him a string of pearls, given to her by none other than Saraswati herself.

The king of bears was the next to be honoured by Rama. And all the monkey generals led by Nila were also given suitable presents. So were Nala and others who had fought so valiantly on the battlefield in Lanka.

To Vibhishana, he said, 'You have no equal,' and gave him a blazing bracelet gifted to him by the gods. Finally, it was the turn of Guhan to bid goodbye. To the chief of Sringabhera, he said, 'What shall I say to my spotless friend?' and gave him dark elephants, horses, gold, clothes and jewels.

To all of them he bade fond farewell. To Hanuman, Vali's son, Jambavan and Sugriva, he said, 'It is hard to even think of saying goodbye. But the safety of your land is my prime concern. It must be guarded vigilantly—that is why I'm sending you all back.'

To the king of Lanka, he repeated the same words. Like

the monkey heroes, Vibhishana too saw the wisdom of what Rama said. They all reluctantly took leave of Rama and went back to their distant lands.

Crowned king of Ayodhya at long last, Rama ruled the earth, according to the eternal laws of good governance. Neither the goddess of fortune nor Earth herself had any cause for complaint.

The Primal God who had come down to earthly Ayodhya from his serpent bed in the milky ocean, ruled his vast kingdom with his brothers, zealously guarding Dharma on earth. Everyone in heaven and on earth, all the seven worlds hailed him as 'our lord' and gladly did his bidding.

Whoever tells the story of Rama, who appeared on earth to kill Ravana and save the world, will conquer death and live for ever and ever in bliss.

GLOSSARY

Note: The following is an attempt to aid readers through the innumerable references to ideas, mythological characters, flora and fauna in *Kamba Ramayana*. It is not exhaustive in the sense that only those words and references that are not contextually clear have been explained.

Arati: An act of worship or benediction with a lamp or a plate of saffron coloured water.

Ashrama: 1. Hermitage. 2. One of the four stages of life: Brahmacharya or celibate youth; Grihastya or the status of a married householder; Vanaprastha, literally going to the forest for a semi-retired life; and Sanyasa or total renunciation of the world.

Adisesha: Known also simply as Sesha, it is the primordial serpent with a thousand hoods on whom Vishnu takes his ease on the ocean of milk. Also known as one who holds up the earth on his head.

Ayilyam (*Ashlesha* in Sanskrit): The ninth of the twenty-seven asterisms of Hindu astrology in which Lakshmana was born.

Abhinaya: A technical term in dance (*natya*). It is the art of representation of emotion by stylized gestures (mudras).

Aditi: Wife of sage Kasyapa.

Agastya (Agastiyan in Tamil): A great sage, dwarfish in stature, honoured among the Tamil as the founder of their language. He is traditionally believed to have been sent by Siva to south India and to have codified Tamil grammar and written a treatise on medicine. Among his innumerable exploits is his having restored balance to the tilted world, the result of all the other sages having gone to one end, by himself going to the other.

Agni: The god of fire.

Airavatam: White elephant, the mount of Indra. It was one of the bonuses of the competitive churning of the milky ocean by the devas and asuras.

Alakapuri: The city of Kubera, god of wealth.

Akhil: A kind of resinous wood ('eagle-wood') from whose bark is produced an aromatic juice used in cosmetics and worship. Its fragrant smoke is used by women to dry and perfume their hair after a bath.

Akshauhini: An army formation consisting of 21,870 elephants, 21,870 chariots, 65,610 horses and 1,00,350 men, forming a total of 2,18,700.

Amaravati: The capital city of Indra, the lord of heaven. Seven cities are traditionally listed as capable of giving *moksha* (salvation) to one. These are Ayodhya, Madura, Maya, Kasi, Kanchi, Avanti and Dwarka (the seat of Krishna). Indra's capital is not one such.

Amritam (*Amrita* in Sanskrit): Ambrosia or divine nectar, the intake of which ensures immortality.

Anasuya: Wife of sage Atri, a paragon of chastity and wifely devotion.

Anichcham: A flower that is supposed to be so delicate that it will droop even if smelt.

Anjana: Mother of Hanuman, who for this reason is also known as Anjaneya.

Anril: According to the Tamil lexicon, 'a bird, whether male or female, very familiar in Indian poetry, a model of constancy and inseparable love.' The Sanskrit equivalent of this bird is *krouncha*. In a celebrated passage in the first canto of *Valmiki Ramayana*, the inspiration for the epic is an incident in which the deadly arrow of a hunter kills one of the two *krouncha* birds in the act of making love. The floodgates of compassion that this sight opened up in Valmiki's heart took the form of the epic.

Apsara: Divine nymph. Like Rambha or Tilottama.

Aruna: The Sun's charioteer. Every morning, he appears ahead of his master and hence the dawn is often referred to as *Arunodhaya* or the appearance of Aruna.

Arundhati: Wife of sage Vasishta, a paragon of chastity.

Astra: Literally, an arrow or a weapon, often qualified as *Nagastra* (serpent-arrow) or *Brahmastra* (Brahma's arrow). These are dedicated and consecrated by special prayers to the appropriate deity and are gifts from them. They are released with the relevant incantations and are deadly in their effect.

Asunam: A bird highly sensitive to music.

Asuras: Traditional enemies of the devas or gods. Also referred to as '*danavas*' as opposed to '*adityas*', or gods.

Atala: One of the seven worlds below the earth. The others are: *Vitala, Sutala, Taratala, Rasatala, Mahatala,* and *Patala*.

Atri: One of the seven famous sages. The others are: Bhrigu, Kutsa, Vasishta, Gautama, Kasyapa and Angirasa.

Bhatavagni: A fiery mare in the northern sea, also referred to as a volcano, capable of drinking up the waters so that the depth of the sea is kept constant in spite of the river waters constantly flowing into it.

Bhagiratha: An ancestor of Rama who brought the Ganga to the earth from heaven by his penance and took it further down to the netherworld to purify the ashes of his ancestors, Sagaras. Ganga is therefore also known as *Bhagirathi*.

Bhu: One of the seven heavens. The others are: *Bhuvar, Suvar, Jana, Maha, Tapa,* and *Satya*. There are also seven seas, made of salt, sugarcane juice, honey, ghee, curd, milk and water.

Brahaspati: The official guru of the devas or gods, the opposite number of *Sukra*, the official preceptor of the asuras, the sworn enemies of the gods.

Brahmacharya: Celibacy. See also *Ashrama*.

Brahmi: One of the seven sacred maidens. The others are: *Maheswari, Kaumari, Narayani, Varahi, Indrani* and *Chamundi*.

Chakravahas: Twin birds, male and female, always together, their shape resembling a woman's breasts.

Chakravala: A mountain outside the world that guards it like a rampart.

Caveri (sometimes spelt *Kaveri*): The most important river of the Tamil country, repeatedly celebrated lovingly in Tamil literature as the equal of Ganga in the north.

Chandrachooda: Literally, 'moon-crested', one of the names of Siva. Another name is *Gangadhara*, one who holds captive the river Ganga in his matted hair, a reference to the legend associated with the descent of the river. Its destructive fury had to be checked by Siva before being allowed to flow out of his hair for the benefit of mankind.

Chintamani: The gem of plenty.

Chiranjeevis: The seven immortal ones: Aswattama, Bali, Vyasa, Markandeya, Kripa, Vibhishana and Parasurama.

Diggajas: The elephants of the eight quarters, visualized as bearing the earth on their shoulders.

Durga: Another name for Parvati, wife of Siva.

Gayatri: The name of one of the most sacred mantras (incantations) invoking the *Pranava* or the primordial 'om'. Gayatri is also one of the seven horses drawing the sun's chariot. The others are *Ushnik, Anushtup, Brihati, Pankthi, Trishup* and *Jagadi*. These are also the names of seven metrical types of Sanskrit poetry.

Ganga: The most famous sacred river of India, anglicized as the Ganges.

Gajendra: The king of the elephants, whom Lord Narayana once saved from certain death. Gone for a drink of water in a stream, Gajendra was seized by the foot and dragged to a watery grave by a crocodile. In desperation, Gajendra called out 'Oh! Narayana' and He came running and spliced the crocodile with his *chakrayuda* or 'wheel weapon'.

Garuda (Garudan in Tamil): The golden eagle that is the mount of Vishnu in his peregrinations.

Halahala (*Aalahala* in Tamil): The deadly poison that arose when the milky ocean was churned for ambrosia. Siva had to be petitioned to swallow it to render it ineffective. In the process, his throat became blue, giving him the honorific of *Neelakantha*, or the god with the blue throat.

Havis: The ritual oblation by pouring ghee into the sacrificial fire.

Ilangi: Also known as Mazhiampoo, a headily fragrant flower, round in shape.

Indra (Indiran in Tamil): The lord of the devas or gods who rules over swarga or heaven.

Indrajit: Son of Ravana, thus named for his famous victory over Indra.

Janaki: Another name for Sita, as the daughter of Janaka, king of Videha. Hence, another name for Sita was Vaidehi.

Kalanemi: An asura, son of Hiranyakasipu (killed by Vishnu in his incarnation as lion-man). See also *Narasimha*.

Kali: The dark-skinned goddess, wife of Siva, in her fierce aspect, when she killed Mahishasura, the buffalo-demon, and so also called Mahishasura-mardhani.

Kama (Kaman in Tamil): The god of love in Indian mythology whose arrow from a bow made of sugarcane smites one with undying love for someone. Also known as *Madana, Manmatha* and innumerable other names. *Kama* is also a noun for lust, one of the five deadly sins. The others are *Krodha* (anger), *Moha* (delusion), *Mada* (arrogance), *Matsarya* (jealousy).

Kamadhenu: The divine cow, capable of fulfilling any wish.

Kartavirya: A king with a thousand hands who had the distinction of being the only man who vanquished Ravana even before Rama did. He was also the man who killed Jamadagni, a brahmin, and the father of Parasurama. An enraged Parasurama took a vow to destroy without a trace all kshatriyas (or the kingly caste) and killed twenty-one generations (including Kartavirya) of kings. He then made his ritual oblations for his departed ancestors with the blood of the slain kings. However, he was eventually humbled by Rama, a kshatriya. See also *Parasurama*.

Kamandalu: A small container carried by rishis that has water for sacerdotal use.

Kailasa: The mountain-abode of Siva. It is one of the seven mountains of the world. The others are: Himalaya, Mandara, Vindhya, Ninadha, Hemakoota, Gandamadana and Nilagiri.

Kandal: A reddish flower.

Karpaka: The heavenly tree that will fulfil every wish.

Kasturi: A type of deer, supposed to exude a pleasing fragrance.

Kavari Maan: A species of deer that is reputedly so fond of its hair that the loss of even a single strand will make it commit suicide.

Kayal: A kind of fish to whom eyes of beautiful women are often compared.

Kazharchi: A fruit with a prickly skin.

Kinnaras: A class of supernatural beings, whose music is irresistible.

Koel: A singing bird that is to Indian literature what the nightingale is to English literature.

Koodal: Literally, 'joining'. A half-serious game young women play by doodling on sand, seeking to find out when their absent lovers or husbands will return.

Kuni: Literally, a hunchback, the derisive name for Mantara, the royal maid and evil genius behind Kaikeyi.

Kovvai: A Tamil fruit, celebrated for its red colour, used in the stock simile to describe a woman's red lips.

Krodha: Anger. One of the five deadly sins. See also *Kama*.

Kshatriya: The second of the four varnas or caste divisions, enjoined with the duty of ruling the world.

Kubera: The lord of wealth.

Kumkum (Kunkumam in Tamil): A red powder, considered auspicious and worn as a dot on the forehead by women, specially when married. The absence of the kumkum mark on the forehead is a sign of widowhood.

Kurinji: A flower of the mountains that blossoms once in twelve years. It is also the defining flower of the mountainous region, one of the five *tinais* or conventional locales in Tamil, specially Sangam, poetry. See also *Tinai*.

Kusa: A kind of grass used in rites.

Kuvalai: A blue flower that opens only at night.

Lakshmi: Consort of Vishnu, always residing on his chest and incarnating herself as his wife when he himself comes down to this world from time to time to uphold Dharma or righteousness.

Matsarya: Jealousy, one of the five deadly sins. See also *Kama*.

Maddalam: A drum used as an accompaniment in some kinds of instrumental music, particularly the kind produced by wind instruments.

Mada: Pride or arrogance. See also *Kama*.

Madan: Another name for *Kama*, the god of love.

Madhavi: A creeper, dear to Indian poets as a metaphor for lovely women.

Mahabali: Also known as Bali, an asura sovereign, whose austerities the devas feared as leading him to be a rival seat of power. They therefore entreated Vishnu to destroy him. Vishnu took the form of a dwarf (*vamana*) in his fourth incarnation and in the guise of seeking three favours, measured out the earth and the heaven with the first two boons, and exacted the asura's life as his third boon.

Madhu and Kaitabha: Two rakshasas who stole the vedas from Brahma but whom he could not punish because of a boon they had obtained. The task had to be finally accomplished by Vishnu.

Makam (*Maham* in Sanskrit): The tenth of the twenty-seven asterisms in Hindu astrology in which Satrughna was born.

Mandara: One of the *ashtakulaparvatas* (eight generic mountains) one of which is Meru. See *Meru*.

Mantharai (*Mantara* in Sanskrit): The real name of Kuni, the hunchback evil counsellor of Kaikeyi. See also *Kuni*.

Marudam: One of the five *tinais* or locales of ancient Tamil poetry, each with its unique symbolic flower, landscape, kind of people, way of life and mode of love. *Marudam* is agricultural tract; people lead a settled and sedate life. The other locales are *Mullai, Palai, Neytal* and *Kurinchi*.

Maya (*Mayan* in Tamil): The great architect of the asuras. The counterpart of Viswakarma, the architect of the gods.

Mayavi: Literally, a magician. Also the name of the asura brother of Ravana's wife who was chased by Vali for his impertinence. He hid himself in a cave where Vali pursued and eventually killed him.

Meghanadha: Literally, the 'sound of the clouds' (meaning thunder) and the elder son of Ravana. Also known as Indrajit, or the victor of Indra.

Meru: A legendary mountain of enormous height and sometimes the seat of the gods.

Moodevi: Elder sister and the opposite in everything of Lakshmi, the goddess of wealth and good fortune.

Mridangam: A drum instrument popular in south Indian music.

Mullai: Tamil name for the fragrant jasmine and one of the defining locales of Tamil literature. See also *Tinai*.

Murugan: Tamil god identified with Subramanya or Kartikeya, son of Siva.

Musth: Also spelt 'must'. It is a state of violent, destructive frenzy in male elephants.

Naga: Literally serpent or cobra, but also a group of people with a kingdom of their own, often located beneath the earth.

Nagini: Feminine of Naga.

Nazhikai: A measure of time, roughly equalling twenty-four minutes.

Narasimha: The fourth of the ten incarnations of Vishnu. He appeared in the form of a lion-faced man, to kill the atheist asura called Hiranyakasipu who had obtained a boon from Brahma that he could not be killed by man or beast, during day or night or inside or outside a residence. Hence, this form that was neither wholly man or wholly beast. And the asura was killed on an evening at the doorstep of his palace. The incarnations of Vishnu are: Matsya (fish), Kurma (turtle), Varaha (boar), Narasimha (man-lion), Vamana (dwarf), Parasurama, Rama, Balarama, Krishna and Kalki (the last yet to come).

Palai: Literally, the desert or arid region, another of the five *tinais* or generic locales in Tamil poetry. See also *Tinai*.

Parvati: Wife of Siva, also known by many other names.

Palasa: A tree with red leaves, identified with *gloriosa superba*.

Pancha bhoothas: The five elements that constitute the world: *Prithvi* (earth), *Apa* (water), *Agni* (fire), *Vaayu* (air) and *Aakasa* (ether).

Pancha Mahapapas: Five unforgivable sins: murder, theft, drunkenness, lying and abusing one's teacher.

Panchendriyas: The five senses of sight, smell, hearing, touch, and taste.

Panchasayanam: The acme of luxury in beds. Its five constituents are detailed as swansdown, silk cotton, red cotton, peacockdown and white cotton. The five have also been interpreted as beauty, coolness, thickness, fragrance and brightness. Another version is that it is a bed made of cotton, drawn out five times over, to rid it of any impurity and make it extremely soft and comfortable.

Parasurama: The son of the brahmin sage Jamadagni, a colourful figure in Indian mythology. A paragon of an obedient son, he cut off the head of his mother at his irate father's bidding. (However, by a boon granted by his father, she was brought back to life.) Later, he became a sworn enemy of kshatriyas, the kingly caste, because one of them had killed his father. He then killed innumerable generations of kings in vengeance but was finally humbled by Rama. See also *Karthaveerya*.

Pials: A parapet like space in front of a house.

Pothikai: A mountain in the southern kingdom of the Pandiyas, famed as the seat of Sage Agastya.

Poosam (*Pushya* in Sanskrit): The eight of the twenty-seven asterisms of Hindu astrology in which Bharata was born.

Poovai: A dark flower.

Pralaya: The flood, accompanied by tornadoes, that occurs at the end of every yuga.

Pulaiyan: A member of one of the lowest caste outside the varna system of brahmins (*brahman*), kings (*kshatriya*), traders (*vyasya*), and agriculturists (*shudras*).

Punarpoosam (*Punarvasu* in Sanskrit): The seventh asterism in Hindu astrology in which Rama was born.

Punnai: A kind of tree.

Pushpaka: The aerial car originally belonging to Kubera, the god of wealth. It was seized by Ravana and, after his death, used by Rama to fly to Ayodhya in time to prevent self-immolation by Bharata.

Putra (Puththiran in Tamil): Sanskrit for son. A son is indispensable for a father since without one, he wouldn't be saved from the hell called *Puth* in afterlife.

Putra kameshti yaga: A special sacrifice for obtaining the boon of a son.

Rahu: The malefic planet, often visualized as a serpent, swallowing the sun and the moon and thus causing the eclipses.

Rakshasas: A species of asuras or evil-doers, in eternal conflict with the devas. Though evil by nature, they are capable of acquiring extraordinary powers by propitiating the Trinity of supreme gods—Brahma, Vishnu and Siva, which powers they put to evil use. Ravana, the king of the rakshasas, was a supreme example.

Rambha: One of the many celestial beings held captive by Ravana and employed as maids for his wife, Mandodhari.

Rasa: Literally, juice, is metaphorically the generic name for emotions or sentiments. It constitutes the core of Indian aesthetics. The literary or artistic excellence of any work is determined by the ability of the writer or artist to evoke them. There are usually eight of them but a ninth and even a tenth are sometimes included in the list. These are: *Sringaaraa* (love), *Hasya* (humour), *Karuna* (compassion), *Raudhra* (anger), *Veera* (valour), *Bhaya* (fear), *Bhibasta* (disgust), *Adbhuta* (wonder). Two others, *Shantham* (peace) and *Vatsalya* (love for children), are sometimes included.

Rati: Wife of Manmatha, or Kama, the god of love.

Rishyasringa: The young stag-headed sage who performed the son-bestowing sacrifice on behalf of Dasaratha.

Sagaras: Distant ancestors of Rama. See also *Bhagiratha*.

Sanyasa: The fourth stage in a man's life as prescribed by the ashrama concept. See *Ashrama*.

Saptaswara: The seven basic notes of Indian music, corresponding to the solfa system of Western music symbolically represented by sa, ri, ga, ma, pa, da, ni; sa.

Sarabhanga: Literally, 'an arrow breaker', the arrow in question being that of Kama, the god of love and passion. His spiritual ambition was so great that he spurned the offer of Brahma for a place in his world. He waited for Rama's arrival in order to get total liberation. After seeing Rama and, despite his pleas, he burnt himself to death.

Saraswati: Consort of Brahma and the goddess of learning and the arts.

Shastras: Codified knowledge or prescriptive ritual and ethical manuals.

Sibi: An ancestor of Rama who in his generosity bartered his flesh to save a pigeon claimed by a hunter as his trophy.

Skanda (*Kandan* in Tamil): One of the many names of Subramanya, son of Siva.

Swara: See *Saptaswara*.

Tali: Tamil word for mangalasutra, the sacred thread that Hindu women wear to indicate their married status.

Tapaswi/Tapaswini: He (or she) who performs tapas or severe penance.

Tamrabarani: A river in the far south of India.

Tilottama: One of the celestial nymphs in the court of Indra. See also *Rambha*.

Tinai: The five conventional locales of Tamil literature, comprising *Kurinchi, Mullai, Palai, Marudam,* and *Neytal*. Each has its specific characteristics. See separate entries on each locale.

Thumburu: Man-horse. A master of music, often mentioned alongside sage Narada with his vina.

Tulsi (*Tulasi* in Tamil): The leaf of the basil plant, sacred to Vishnu.

Uma: One of the many names of Siva's wife, daughter of Himavan, the lord of the Himalayas.

Umaththam: A kind of prickly fruit, which, if eaten, is believed to cause insanity.

Uragas: Strange beings with men's bodies and the hoods and tails of serpents.

Vanaprastha: See *Ashrama*.

Vani: Another name for Sarasvati, goddess of learning and the arts.

Varal: A kind of fish.

Vanji (*Vanjula* in Sanskrit): A creeper much loved by Tamil poets as a metaphor for a woman's sinuous grace.

Varuna: God of the ocean and maritime tracts, also of rain.

Vasishta: Son of Brahma and the official preceptor of the royal family of Dasaratha.

Vaikuntham: The abode of Vishnu, like Kailasa, the abode of Siva.

Vengai: A word with many meanings, a kind of tree, a species of tiger and a hill.

Vennainallur Sadaiyan: Kamban's patron, a rich landowner belonging to a large village called Vennainallur.

Vidhyadharas: A class of celestial beings.

Vellam: A troop formation of incredibly large numbers.

Yali: A mythical animal, part-lion, part-elephant.

Yama: God of death.

Yojana: A measure of distance. A yojana measures roughly nine miles.

Yuga: There are four yugas or time-cycles, each lasting several million years. These are: *Satya yuga*, *Treta yuga* (the period of the happenings in the Ramayana), *Dwapara yuga* (the period of the Krishna legends) and *Kali yuga*, the current one. Each succeeding yuga is characterized by the worsening ethical behavio worsening ethical behaviour of mankind.